Watts
Pocket
Handbook

2008

G000088342

The essential guide to property and construction, as used by professionals since 1983

First published in 1983, the Watts Pocket Handbook is an annual publication.

The editors wish to express their indebtedness to previous editors of the handbook, who laid the foundations on which this 24th edition has been built.

The editors would also like to acknowledge with thanks the contributions of individuals in the property market and construction industry who send suggestions and comments. Such contributions are always welcome and should be sent to Duncan Coombs, Production Executive, Watts Group PLC, 1 Great Tower Street, London, EC3R 5AA.

Acknowledgements

Specification data from the BCO Guide, *The British Council for Offices Guide 2005 Best Practice in the Specification of Offices*, is reproduced with permission from the British Council for Offices.

BRE material is reproduced with permission from Building Research Establishment Ltd.

Text from *Constructing for Sustainability – a basic guide for clients and their professional advisors*, is reproduced with permission from the Construction Industry Council.

Crown Copyright material is reproduced with the permission of the Controller of HMSO and the Queen's Printer for Scotland.

An extract from the Joseph Rowntree Foundation's website www.jrf.org.uk/housingandcare/lifetimehomes/questions/answer.asp?ID=21 is reproduced by permission of the Joseph Rowntree Foundation.

ISBN 978 1 84219 350 1

Published by the Royal Institution of Chartered Surveyors (RICS)

Typeset by Cantate Print, Battersea, London

Printed Cromwell Press, Trowbridge, Wiltshire

Cover design work by Art and Industry, Clerkenwell, London

Contents

Contents

Contents

Contents

Introduction

Indelible landmarks are rare in the physical world and even more extraordinary in publishing. This means that, in its 25th year, I can be duly objective in my praise of the Watts Pocket Handbook 2008 – the quintessential guide to property and construction.

Watts Group PLC is no slouch either having, last year, celebrated 40 years of trading, while simultaneously moving from partnership to incorporation. We also took this opportunity to galvanise our values: honest; responsible; progressive – and the Handbook, with its range and articulation, is a small but important part of this ethos.

The current edition of the Handbook has 12 new sections:

- ❖ Code for Sustainable Homes;
- ❖ contractor appointment/tendering;
- ❖ how to appoint consultants;
- ❖ types of tendering route;
- ❖ indicative construction costs 2007 – UK;
- ❖ value engineering;
- ❖ Official Journal of the European Union;
- ❖ Building Regulations and historic building conservation;
- ❖ a basic introduction to structures;
- ❖ geomatics;
- ❖ electromagnetic fields; and
- ❖ green legislation.

Similarly, the scope of other sections has been expanded, such as the newly titled 'ozone depleting substances' and 'floor loadings in buildings'. We have also reorganised the content of the Handbook which, we believe, will greatly assist readers in making the most of this reference tool.

Note, too, that all technical and legal references are believed to be accurate at the time of going to press and, of course, the Handbook is supported by Watts' monthly technical bulletins.

Whether you are an industry professional, a client, student or even a Chairman, I am sure – as I was last year – that you will find the Watts Pocket Handbook a valuable and unswerving work of reference. As always, too, I would be pleased to hear your comments.

Finally, I must record a huge vote of thanks to all contributors and wish all our readers the best of fortune in the current year which, more than in recent ones, can be expected to contain its share of challenges for our industry.

Tony Williams
Chairman (Non-Executive)
Watts Group PLC

Technical due diligence

Property investment and ownership

Best practice in building surveys

Introduction

Conceptually, there is little difference between the inspection and method of reporting upon commercial and industrial property compared with surveys of residential or other property. Many of the principles of setting up, confirming the instruction and report writing are identical, as is of course the process of reflective thought that is a key ingredient in any survey for investment or occupation.

Of course, it is the form of construction and style of building that is often different (although not exclusively so) and surveyors must be familiar with the forms of construction, common defects and things to watch out for before accepting instructions.

Commercial and industrial property

Commercial and industrial buildings take many forms, but just as importantly, purchasers and occupiers have many different requirements. The form of reporting on an identical building for an investor could require a different emphasis to that needed for an occupier or indeed that needed to be included in a vendor's pack. Flexibility and professionalism is the key, both for providing an appropriate level of service and for maintaining the quality of professional advice. All too often we see quality standards dropping in favour of fiercely competitive fee quotations and timescales that are unrealistic.

The RICS guidance note *Building Surveys and Inspections of Commercial and Industrial Property* (hereafter referred to as 'the Commercial/Industrial GN') provides comprehensive guidance and advice for surveyors and engineers involved in building surveys of commercial property. It is written to apply in England and Wales although its content is equally applicable elsewhere. The document is important for RICS members. They are not obliged to follow the advice and recommendations given and are free to make their own mind up when it comes to what to include or how to present the information, and as long as the advice given is properly thought through with the correct level of skill and care there should be no need for concern. However, in cases where professional negligence is being considered, adherence to the guidance note would at least give partial defence by virtue of having followed recognised practice.

Taking instructions

Experience has shown that managing client expectation is the key to ensuring that the client is satisfied with the service and the quality of the report. The instruction stage is often botched or not recorded properly – in many cases this is where a job will start to go wrong. It is very important to take the time to understand the client's exact requirements, the purpose of the survey, the scope and limitations, specialist inspections, etc.

The guidance notes set out in some detail the issues that are recommended to be resolved at this stage including:

- ❖ the identity of the client (this is sometimes unknown until completion);
- ❖ the scope of service;
- ❖ timescales;
- ❖ the fee;
- ❖ terms and conditions of business; and
- ❖ limitations.

One interesting recommendation is to make the client aware of the fact that surveyors are not infallible, although of course one should expect reasonable competence.

At this stage it will be apparent whether or not specialist subconsultants will be required. Commonly this will include mechanical, electrical, public health and lift engineers, cladding consultants, environmental engineers or structural engineers. Are these consultants to be paid direct by the client (preferable) or by the surveyor? In the latter case, make sure that these appointments are tied down – preferably with back to back agreements – and that Professional Indemnity Insurance (PII) levels are matched.

Time pressures are usually acute – particularly with a shortage of good investment stock on the market and purchasers making rash promises in order to secure preferred bidder status. This often places unreasonable pressure on the surveyor. Whereas at one time quick 'walk-around' surveys were frowned upon, the Commercial/Industrial GN acknowledges that it may be necessary to accept this type of instruction, but points out that surveyors must ensure that the client is under no illusion that compromising on time will reduce the quality of the report. Under these circumstances you should take great care to explain the limitations of such an approach. Preferably, demands to compromise should be resisted, but as an alternative spend the same time on site and reduce the time reporting by focusing on key issues only.

Health and safety

'Time spent in reconnaissance is seldom wasted' is a maxim that surveyors should remember. Aside from giving the opportunity to plan resources, assess the fee and determine the need for specialist investigations, it also enables time for a proper risk assessment to be prepared.

Regrettably, too few surveyors treat health and safety as seriously as they should; it is criminal law and penalties for non-compliance are severe. Employers have a duty to protect the safety of their staff – one of the key issues being a proper risk assessment. The risk assessment should be appropriate for the particular circumstances, but it should be recorded in writing. See the RICS publication *Surveying safely* for more details.

Key points are:

❖ risk assessment – can be in any appropriate form but it should be recorded and filed;

❖ employer has a duty not to put surveyor at risk;

❖ surveyor must bring limitations to employer's notice;

❖ wear appropriate dress; and

❖ use appropriate equipment and maintain it in good order.

You must also ensure that:

❖ the places in which you work are safe;

❖ safe working practices are clearly defined;

❖ first aid equipment is available;

❖ you do not endanger yourself or others;

❖ you protect anyone who uses your services;

❖ you protect the people that work for you; and

❖ you protect anyone affected by your work.

Perfect Planning Prevents Poor Performance – make sure that your team is properly briefed as to their roles and responsibilities, the purpose of the survey and the extent of the instruction. Furthermore, it is vital to arrange proper access with the tenant/occupier.

Preparation is vital, it gives the opportunity to seek out relevant documents – as-built drawings, certificates, previous reports and the like. It also establishes any particular working practices on site that could impinge upon the survey and any particular health and safety issues that may be relevant. Arranging for an hydraulic platform to attend site to facilitate a roof inspection is fine, but not if the tenant is not expecting it and has say a 24-hour operation with lorries coming and going all the time. Frequently, working arrangements on large industrial or distribution sites are such that the operators demand full risk assessments before using access equipment – trying to sort these out at 10.00 on the morning of the survey with the team on site is not the most productive use of time.

Equipment and note taking

Unlike the equivalent guidance for residential surveys, the Commercial/Industrial GN is not specific as to the equipment that you must use when conducting a survey – it merely lists a range of basics that a survey kit 'may' include. Clearly, one should expect to take the equipment that would be necessary to undertake the task properly – it would not be very sensible, for example, to turn up without a measuring tape if you had specifically been asked to prepare a fire insurance valuation.

Over the years there has been considerable debate over the use of electronic dictating equipment. Many surveyors prefer to use this equipment to take comprehensive notes – there is no problem with that but:

- ❖ beware of things like wind and background noise;
- ❖ keep checking to make sure that you are actually recording;
- ❖ sometimes you can record things you don't intend; and
- ❖ is it productive to have secretarial staff typing notes all day before you can write the report?

The key issue is to take good, legible notes and to retain these on file. Do not expect to dictate the final version of the report on site – this does not allow time for reflective thought.

The inspection

Different survey types demand different levels of inspection, and this will need to have been agreed with the client at the outset. In the event that physical restrictions are more onerous than expected, this needs to be communicated back to the client as soon as possible and certainly not left to a small line in the completed report.

Making friends with the occupier is a good move; often there will be issues with site security and the need to be accompanied (although this can often be worked around by diplomacy – and weight of numbers). A team of five or six cannot do their job properly if one security guard has been allocated, but patience and compromise can often work well in achieving proper access.

Surveyors will each have their own methodology for dealing with surveys and the guidance notes do not dictate how inspections should be carried out. However, a methodical approach is the key, and this would normally mean that an elemental approach is to be preferred.

Conducting a good building inspection and preparing a good report is not something that should be treated lightly. Taking a graduate with you and then asking him or her to 'do the insides' whilst you examine the exterior – or the interesting parts – is not very good training and certainly runs the risk that small pieces of evidence that relate to a bigger picture may not be assimilated. Technical knowledge is all too often taken for granted – but if you don't know what can go wrong how can you possibly be expected to look for it? It is very easy to look at something and to describe it, but does this necessarily address the real issues?

As RICS guidance notes point out, surveyors are not infallible, but it is imperative that you do not fall into the trap of simply describing what you see without thinking about the job that the element is doing and how it interrelates with other components or elements – think behind the surface – consider the building in its underpants.

The guidance notes set out many of the types of issue that ought to be identified during an inspection; some of the more important are summarised below:

❖ In a large building it is not anticipated that the surveyor will check each and every unit/window or feature where there is a lot of repetition.

❖ You will be expected to comment on fire resistance, compartmentation, thermal and insulation standards.

❖ The effectiveness and condition of a structural frame should be assessed.

❖ Check degree of flatness along with surface defects (particularly important for industrial and storage buildings).

❖ Ceiling and floor voids should be inspected. Check space for services/crossovers as well as fixity of pedestals/suspension systems.

❖ Roof voids should be inspected where they are accessible.

❖ Efforts should be made to inspect ducts and similar enclosed areas where this is possible.

❖ Check staircase width, handrail height, etc. and general compliance with Building Regulations.

❖ Check provision of sanitary facilities for DDA and Workplace Regulations.

❖ Disability considerations should include different textures to wall and floor finishes.

Services installations

In complex buildings, mechanical, electrical and public health (MEP) installations are usually inspected by specialists, often under the direction of the surveyor. However, in certain circumstances this will not occur and a surveyor may be commissioned to provide general advice. The object here is to carry out a general visual inspection and to form a view as to the type of the installation, the materials used and the need for more detailed investigations. RICS cautions against direct appointments and payment of subconsultant's fees for fear of assuming a liability for parts of the report.

One point to watch is the services engineers' tendency to rely upon Chartered Institution of Building Services Engineers (CIBSE) tables of life expectancy. Too frequently we find observations like 'the installation is 25 years old and therefore at the end of its life' without comment upon the standard of maintenance and use of the particular component when in reality a longer life can be anticipated. It is the surveyor's role to challenge such observations and make sure that the advice given is sensible and practicable.

Surveyors will be expected to provide general advice on issues such as compliance with relevant lighting standards under the Workplace Regulations. The position of gas service intakes as well as the condition of appliances and pipe runs should also be identified. Any smell of gas should be reported immediately.

Surveyors are advised to note and report on the nature of the installation including pipework, point of entry, stopcocks, etc. as well as compliance with water bye-laws, visual corrosion and leaks. The guidance note suggests a representative number of taps are turned on.

As far as hot water and heating installations are concerned, these should be checked for operation and general condition.

Underground drainage is often an area that fails to be mentioned properly – either through lack of access for visual inspection (reasonable) or because the surveyor forgot to bring drain cover keys or could not be bothered to lift lightweight covers (unreasonable). Be clear about the extent of the inspection and whether or not covers are to be lifted. Under the guidance note, surveyors are advised to:

- ❖ open all reasonably accessible lightweight inspection chamber covers within the curtilage of the property;
- ❖ record assumed drainage runs; and
- ❖ report their general condition.

CCTV inspections might be commissioned, but beware of the limitations of these – it is not always possible, within the time available to inspect and plot all runs. Furthermore, silting and encrustation may mean that an element of jetting and cleaning is needed before a survey can be undertaken. It is worth being very clear about the scope of work in these circumstances and agreeing this with the client at the outset. For example, if a fixed sum is required, agree that this be limited to what can be achieved with this equipment for a fixed time.

Another point worth checking is the direction that drainage runs take when they leave site – for example, do they cross adjoining land?

External areas

The scope of the external inspection depends upon instructions, but remember to be alert for boundary issues, tree growth, Japanese Knotweed, Giant Hogweed, power lines, etc. as well as any particular topographical points of concern.

Health and safety legislation

A detailed analysis of the property for compliance is not normally undertaken unless of course it has been specifically agreed with the client at the outset. Surveyors should be aware of relevant legislation that might affect health and safety in the building and to advise accordingly. The following are important:

- ❖ protection against falling;
- ❖ sanitary provision;
- ❖ lighting;
- ❖ floors and traffic routes;
- ❖ glazing;
- ❖ working at height; and
- ❖ fire precautions – resistance, means of escape and protection.

For more detail on these aspects, see pages 126 to 143.

Security

With increased terrorist threats, security issues are becoming important and should command some attention to detail in an inspection and report.

One of the points recommended for attention is the existence and condition of window film – a word of caution though – to be effective, the film must transfer explosion loads back to the structure of a building where it is more likely that they can be dissipated safely by the inertia of the building. This can only be achieved with physical connection to glazing beads with silicone at the perimeter. Furthermore, providing film on laminated glass alters the properties of the glass and can give rise to a greater propensity for the glass to rupture around the edge – and so form a large and lethal projectile.

The guidance note recommends reference to guides like *Secured by design* which may help a surveyor comment on security aspects.

DDA

Again, and unless otherwise instructed, a surveyor would not be expected to carry out a detailed audit of the premises. However, the identification of key barriers to access and any other significant points of concern ought to be mentioned, not forgetting that there is much more to DDA than simply the provision of ramps and disabled toilets. See also the DDA section on page 129 onwards.

Environmental issues

Investors are sensitive to environmental issues – particularly funding banks, which often place more store on Phase 1 reports than on the physical condition of the building. More often than not an investment purchase will involve the preparation of a suitable Phase 1 (and sometimes a Phase 2) environmental audit by suitably qualified specialists. In these circumstances (and assuming that the process includes a site visit) it is important to establish exactly where responsibility stops to avoid duplication and more importantly conflicting information.

If an audit is not being undertaken, the surveyor should be alert to the usual environmental risks and comment accordingly. In the UK, there are several valuable sources of information such as the Environment Agency, the Scottish Environment Protection Agency which have accessible postcode-search facilities to allow detailed advice on matters such as flooding risk. However, take care to understand the limitations of the material that is provided and in particular what is meant by the risk assessments themselves.

Knowledge of gas protection measures – membranes and passive venting is also useful. It is sometimes the case that solicitors will turn up a requirement for gas protection in planning documents or past environmental reports – and it will be useful to be able to reply that indeed measures were in place.

The RICS guidance notes state that the impact of orientation (not just the orientation) of the building should be clearly stated.

With the impact of climate change becoming ever more topical it is to be expected that surveyors will need to take a more active role in the analysis of the performance of buildings. At the present time, surveyors are advised to:

- ❖ describe the thermal shell taking into account orientation;
- ❖ consider the nature of the heating and cooling systems;
- ❖ consider the nature of artificial lighting; and
- ❖ provide advice on practical methods of upgrading insulation and measures to reduce associated condensation risk.

However, the *Energy Performance of Buildings Directive* (EPBD) will place additional demands upon surveyors. By the end of 2005, all EU member states were required to have enacted legislation on enhanced minimum energy performance standards in buildings under the EPBD. All buildings, commercial and domestic, will need to have an Energy Performance Certificate. In addition, there will be regular inspections of boiler and air-conditioning systems.

Noise and disturbance are also matters that should command attention:

- ❖ consider the effects of noise from external sources;
- ❖ sound insulation of party structures; and
- ❖ other possible nuisances.

For more detail on the EPBD see page 352.

Deleterious materials

Whilst testing for deleterious materials may be outside the scope of the survey (at least to begin with), surveyors should be aware of the key issues and materials and provide reasoned advice accordingly. Typically, the list of materials normally considered would include:

❖ high alumina cement (HAC);

❖ calcium chloride additive;

❖ asbestos;

❖ lead in plumbing and paint; and

❖ woodwool as permanent shuttering.

Some clients may have particular concerns with, for example, GRC, RAAC planks, MMMF, etc. In Scandanavian countries, the use of mastic containing PCBs has been viewed with concern, and owners can go to great lengths to decontaminate their buildings of this material.

For buildings constructed up until 1974, it is common to consider tests for HAC. Chlorides were effectively banned from 1978, so buildings constructed later than this should be free of those materials in construction (although, of course, chloride contamination can still occur as a result of atmospheric conditions or exposure to de-icing salts).

Asbestos warrants a specific section in the report owing to the special considerations that this material warrants. Ask to see a copy of the asbestos register and consider its adequacy.

For industrial and retail buildings, particularly those constructed in the last ten years or so, the likelihood is that composite cladding materials will have been used. Since 2000, insurers have been wary of panels that contain combustible cores – EPS, PUR and some types of PIR. Of these, EPS is of most concern as this will be found in cold stores and self-supporting panels. There have been reports of insurers making significant increases in premiums or deductibles where there is uncertainty as to the nature of the core and whether or not it is LPS approved. Whilst the industry has taken a slightly more robust view of late, it is important to take steps to try and identify the nature of the core and if it is of an approved type. If it is not, provide advice on the thickness and location and particular fire risks – arson, cardboard storage, battery charging, etc. to facilitate a proper risk assessment.

Warning of the existence of deleterious and hazardous materials is one thing – but their existence needs to be placed in perspective and straightforward advice given. For more information see *Investigating Hazardous and Deleterious Building Materials*, published by RICS Books. See also the *Materials and defects* chapter of this handbook, starting at page 259.

Further enquiries

During the course of the inspection, various technical and legal issues might arise. It is appropriate to draw attention to these points with the client and its legal advisor. However, questions and referrals should be relevant and sensible – not issues that are readily within the ambit of a surveyor to establish – for example, contacting the manufacturer of a composite panel to find out if it is LDA approved.

Recommendations to do something inappropriate – like check the warranty package on a 12-year old building – may cast the surveyor in poor light.

Always make it clear whether or not the enquiries and investigations need to be concluded before proceeding to completion.

The report

However competent and experienced the surveyor, he or she will be let down by a badly presented, ill prepared report, particularly if that report contains errors in presentation and spelling or if it appears 'lightweight' in the quality of the advice. Remember:

> 'The difficulty', said Robert Louis Stevenson, 'is not to write, but to write what you mean, not to affect your reader, but to affect him precisely as you wish.'

Clarity of thought and clarity of advice are vital ingredients – a few hours spent reviewing material from the Plain English Campaign will be worthwhile – even if you think that you know how to do it.

The Commercial/Industrial GN sets out a 'coat hanger' for successful presentation:

- ❖ What is wrong with it?
- ❖ Why it is wrong.
- ❖ What damage has occurred?
- ❖ How serious this is.
- ❖ What is needed to put it right?
- ❖ How much?
- ❖ When?

By the time the client has read the report, he or she should have been informed and influenced in precisely the way in which the surveyor wished.

Some tips for clearer writing

- ❖ Think of your reader, not yourself.
- ❖ Do not try to impress people by using your language and technical knowledge to show off: keep it as straightforward as possible. Use everyday words, avoid Latin or foreign phrases.
- ❖ Use sentences of 15 to 20 words. Use shorter ones for 'punch'. Longer ones should not have more than three items of information; otherwise they become difficult to follow.
- ❖ Be careful with jargon. It is only useful if people are familiar with it. Be prepared to explain your jargon words and acronyms – will your audience know them?
- ❖ Use 'active' verbs mainly, not 'passive' ones. For example, 'John Smith inspected the property' (active) is better than 'The property was inspected by John Smith' (passive).
- ❖ Use lower case bold for emphasis. Don't underline or use block capitals (these are harder to read).
- ❖ Put complex information into bullet points.
- ❖ Plan and draft your writing. Break it into short steps that follow a logical sequence and are easy to understand.
- ❖ In text, write numbers one to ten as words; with 11 and upwards, put the figure. Do not add 'No.' after a figure (for example, '5 toilets', not '5No toilets').
- ❖ Use the 'personal touch'. For example, 'A flood helpline is also operated by Surveys R Us for the convenience of our clients' becomes 'We also operate a flood helpline for your convenience'.

The above points are derived from the Plain English campaign. See also their guide to writing reports: www.plainenglish.co.uk/reportsguide.pdf

Content of the report

The Commercial/Industrial GN suggests that an executive summary be provided – this should include recommendations for further tests, budgets, programme, etc. – main items of concern. A number of possible inclusions are suggested, although unless care is exercised, the summary simply ends up being an abridged version of the main body of the report – keep it to a page or two at most.

The introduction to the report should include a résumé of the instructions, the limitations that apply, the date of inspection and by whom, weather conditions and the names of persons providing information. Make it clear in the introduction that, in view of the complexity of most buildings, the surveyor does not guarantee to have seen each and every defect/deficiency that may exist at the property, but that he or she expects to have seen all the major items relating to the brief and many/most of the lesser ones.

A description of the property and its locality should follow the introduction. If floor areas are included, make it clear who has provided them or if they have been derived from site measurements. The elemental condition of the building is the main section of the report, with each element being described under separate headings.

Given the importance of legislative issues, health and safety, deleterious materials, asbestos and means of escape, these topics demand separate sections in their own right.

Budget costs are a useful way of giving weight to your observations, but make clear the basis upon which they are produced. Similarly, it is worth drawing a distinction between essential repairs and improvements.

Residential surveys

Most of the comments in the preceding section apply equally to surveys of residential buildings. In this case the most appropriate guidance for members of the RICS is *Building Surveys of Residential Property* (2nd edition), published in 2004 (hereafter referred to as 'the Residential GN').

Whilst the essentials of taking instructions, setting up the job, agreeing a fee and limitations are equally as important as with commercial and industrial surveys, in many cases clients will not be experienced in property and the different levels of service that can be provided. It is very important therefore, and the Residential GN confirms this, to explain the differences and limitations of types of survey so that the client is in no doubt as to the scope of the instruction and that the contract between the parties is properly set up and documented.

Prior to visiting site, the surveyor is encouraged to undertake a desk top study wherever possible. The study should include such matters as:

- ❖ property sale particulars;
- ❖ relevant site information;
- ❖ particular exposure to environmental factors;
- ❖ statutory consents for previous work to the building;
- ❖ relevant guarantees, etc.;
- ❖ conservation area or listed building status; and
- ❖ lease details if relevant.

Readers are urged to follow the advice of the Residential GN, which covers taking and giving instructions, preparing for the survey, the inspection, and the report. 'Example Terms and Conditions of Engagement' are also included.

The Residential GN makes numerous specific recommendations regarding the nature of the inspection and the report; they are too numerous to mention here, but among the most important are the following:

❖ Allow time for reflective thought.
❖ Be wary of making recommendations for further investigations to be carried out by persons who have a financial interest in the implementation of their own advice or recommendations.
❖ Provide a clear statement of the limitations posed by the building or its occupation.

Suggested pre-survey checklist for surveyors:

❖ Confirm instructions:
  – nature of the instructions;
  – date and time of the survey;
  – access arrangements, particularly occupied premises;
  – statement of surveyor's intentions; and
  – limitations.
❖ Bear in mind:
  – *Unfair Contract Terms Act* 1977;
  – liability in negligence and contract; and
  – 'requirements of reasonableness'.
❖ Equipment to take – consider the following:
  – powerful, robust torch;
  – claw hammer and bolster;
  – ladder (minimum 3m long);
  – pocket probe;
  – binoculars or telescope (not more than x8);
  – hand mirror (minimum 100mm x 100mm);
  – moisture meter;
  – screwdrivers – assorted;
  – measuring rods or tapes, notebook and writing equipment;
  – plumbline;
  – spirit level;
  – first aid kit; and
  – protective clothing, hard hat and suitable footwear.
❖ Site notes to be recorded:
  – notes of defects;
  – record of weather, persons present, etc.; and
  – answers to queries of vendor/neighbours, etc.

Suggested outline of report

❖ **Introduction**
  – brief;
  – limitations;
  – general description of property and situation; and
  – present accommodation.

❖ **Structural condition and state of repair**

❖ *External:*
  - roofs;
  - other defects at roof level;
  - eaves;
  - flashings;
  - external walls;
  - likelihood of cavity wall tie failure;
  - airbricks (provision and adequacy);
  - damp-proof course;
  - foundations and settlement/subsidence/heave;
  - rainwater goods;
  - soil/waste stacks, gullies;
  - other external comments; and
  - external decorations.

❖ *Internal:*
  - roof spaces;
  - partitions;
  - plasterwork;
  - windows;
  - doors;
  - joinery;
  - ceilings;
  - other internal defects; and
  - internal decorations.

❖ *Services:*
  - plumbing/wiring;
  - heating;
  - electricity/gas;
  - sanitary fittings; and
  - drainage.

❖ *Outside:*
  - boundaries, pavings, fences, gates and outbuildings;
  - noise, contamination and other environmental factors;
  - adjoining properties;
  - garden/trees – risk of ground movements/mining subsidence;
  - garage/car parking; and
  - probability of flooding.

❖ *General:*
  - compliance with statutory regulations;
  - planning situation;
  - energy consumption;

- any responsibilities under a lease;
- limitations of report;
- any appropriate approximate costings;
- presence/condition of toxic materials, e.g. asbestos;
- general condition and conclusion;
- risk and likelihood of fungal decay, insect infestation or conditions that could give rise to these attacks;
- risk of contaminated land;
- risk of radon emissions, power lines, etc.; and
- any other relevant information.

Golden rules

When drafting the report, endeavour to avoid technical jargon and take care to communicate precisely.

Avoid assumptions and ill-thought out statements.

When describing elements answer the following questions:

- ❖ What is it?
- ❖ What is wrong with it?
- ❖ What will need to be done to put it right?
- ❖ What are the consequences of not putting it right?

Health and safety

When surveying a property – especially one that is empty – practitioners ought to conform to the procedures outlined in 'Practical Procedures' under the 'Health and safety at work' section of this handbook.

See also *Surveying Safely* published by the Royal Institution of Chartered Surveyors.

Further information

Building Surveys and Inspections of Commercial and Industrial Property (3rd edition), RICS guidance note, 2005

Building Surveys of Residential Property (2nd edition), RICS guidance note, 2004

Surveying safely, RICS, 2006: www.rics.org/NR/rdonlyres/B3EBF5B7-281A-43AB-9EEE-AFDCAEB9BF7E/0/surveying_safely07.pdf

Real Estate Investment Trusts

Real Estate Investment Trusts, or REITs, are listed entities that may hold, manage and maintain properties for investment. They provide a means for both large and small investors to buy shares in a portfolio of residential/commercial property with tax advantages, income return and protection from inflation. Portfolios may include retail, industrial and office space as well as rental accommodation (i.e. sector specific) although there is only one of these, 'the Local Shopping REIT', or can be general portfolios (the majority). In America, the balance is different, with the majority being specialist.

REITs were first established in the USA in the 1960s and then in the Netherlands and Australia. In the 1990s their popularity started to grow, with 23 countries around the world now having, or proposing to introduce, REIT-type vehicles. REITs are structured differently in each country. America and Australia have the most mature REIT markets, with the American regime being the most liberal. In contrast, REITs in the Netherlands and Belgium are the most restricted. Worldwide, REITs are estimated to account for 48% of listed real estate, valued at more than $500 billion (source: RICS Business). Italy has one of the most recent REITs structures to be permitted.

In the UK, the *Finance Act* 2006 confirmed the introduction of REITs in January 2007. Prior to REITs, investment in commercial property made up only 7% of pension funds' total share holdings (source: RICS Business). It was anticipated that from January 2007, UK REITs would have widespread investor appeal due to the strong performance of the property sector in recent years. However, some would say that the timing has been unfortunate. In the first nine months of 2007, REITs were down 20% collectively and arguably have failed to achieve the government's objective of introducing property to new investors. UK REITs began 2007 trading at premium to net asset value and at the end of 2007 traded at quite significant discounts. Against this backdrop some speculate that UK REITs are ripe for takeover by overseas REITs or private equity finance. Generally, Europe has 4.9% of property listed of a total of €5 trillion of direct commercial property, whereas this percentage is 10.2% in USA, 12.6% in Asia and 44% in Australia (EG Central September 2007).

What are the criteria?

To qualify for conversion to a UK REIT, companies must meet the following criteria:

❖ be UK tax resident;

❖ be listed on a recognised stock exchange;

❖ not be an open-ended investment company, nor a closed-ended company;

❖ not issue more than one class of ordinary share; and

❖ not be funded by a loan that is linked to either the profits or assets of the company, or one with interest or repayment terms that exceed a reasonable commercial return.

A prospective UK REIT must also comply with the following conditions:

❖ it must own at least three properties for property rental purposes;

❖ no one property must exceed 40% of the total value of the portfolio;

❖ it must distribute 90% of profits to shareholders;

❖ it must not hold owner-occupied property;

❖ profits from the tax exempt business must be at least 75% of total profits; and

❖ the value of all assets of the tax exempt business must be at least 75% of total assets held by the REIT.

What are the tax implications?

REITs are tax exempt for both property rental income and for chargeable gains on disposals. However, they will be taxed on other income such as that accrued from property trading and other gains. Tax exemptions also apply to subsidiaries of REITs holding property investments.

When converting to a REIT, a tax charge is payable equivalent to 2% of the market value of the property assets held. This conversion charge can be paid in four instalments: 0.5%, 0.53%, 0.56% and then 0.6% respectively are payable at yearly intervals.

The main purpose of a REIT is tax advantage and the HM Treasury has recently issued a document on the taxation of foreign property. These proposals are broadly to:

❖ allow a tax exempt method of dealing with foreign participation dividends;

❖ introduce new company and interest rules to limit abuse;

❖ explore options for future taxation of portfolio and dividends; and

❖ remove the requirement for treasury consent.

The idea is to remove uncertainty around double taxation and could make UK REITs an interesting proposition for a cross border REIT.

Benefits for investors

From 2007, for the first time, UK investors have been able to diversify their portfolios into a sector that has proved its ability to produce high returns for a small initial stake, although they did not have the best start in 2007.

For investors, UK REITs can provide:

❖ a highly liquid method of investing in property;

❖ asset class diversification;

❖ new investment opportunities for major players and small investors alike, many of whom previously could not easily have included property in their share portfolios; and

❖ the ability to invest in a wide range of property types.

When buying shares in REITS, investors do not only take a stake in the ownership of property via increases and decreases in value, but will also benefit from any income generated by the property.

UK REITs

The following list of UK REITs is accurate at the time of going to press:

❖ Big Yellow Group;

❖ British Land;

❖ Brixton Plc;

❖ Derwent London;

❖ Great Portland Estates;

❖ Hammerson;

❖ Land Securities Group;

❖ Liberty International;

❖ Local Shopping REIT;

❖ McKay Securities;

❖ Mucklow AJ Group;

❖ Primary Health Property;

❖ Segro;

❖ Shaftesbury;

❖ Warner Estates Holdings;

❖ Workspace Group.

Further information

www.hm-treasury.gov.uk

www.hmrc.gov.uk

Property derivatives and options

Derivatives

A derivative is, in very simple terms, a sale or purchase of a promise. A party will agree to buy from another a promise that at an agreed point in the future (usually one month, six months, a year or five years from the agreement date) the purchaser will buy from the seller an agreed quantity of some asset the buyer wants for a price which is agreed at the time the promise is made.

For the buyer a deal of uncertainty is taken out of the transaction. For example, a major user of electrical power may want to purchase a derivative for the unit price of electricity. To operate their business they need certainty and are currently exposed to the risk of electricity unit price fluctuations. They are therefore happy to purchase promises that for the next five years they will not have to pay more than a pre-agreed range for electrical units. If the price of the units goes above the defined range then the seller pays the difference to the purchaser; if the price dips below the defined range the user pays the price difference to the seller.

There are various different combinations and complexities of promises but basically there are three different types of general derivatives:

* the sale of a promise to deliver an asset in the future – a forward contract;
* the sale of a promise either to deliver a quantity of an asset or to pay its market value in the future – a futures contract; and
* the sale of a promise to pay the market value of an asset in future – a contract for differences.

However, the property derivatives market in the UK to date has been dominated by two basic instruments:

* property total return swaps; and
* property structured notes or property index certificates.

A question often asked against this background is: 'Will derivatives make the prices more volatile?' The economics of the arrangements are very detailed but economists have generally concluded that trading in derivatives actually helps to decrease the extremes of market price changes rather than to increase them.

Another attraction is that trading derivatives is arguably more liquid than trading the actual asset, particularly if trading in that asset is likely to be slow. This is exactly what has happened with property. Property was the last major asset investment class without a liquid derivatives market. So in many ways a property derivatives market would seem to be more essential than a similar market in another asset class which is inherently more liquid in its pure form.

Background

Property derivatives actually date back to the early 1990s. This initial launch was poorly timed. Property Index Certificates were developed in 1994 but they were not popular and were relaunched in 2004. Property derivatives did not go away but now the climate is more favourable and after a slow start they are here to stay.

There are three reasons why the time is now right for property derivatives:

- ❖ high demand from buyers and sellers at this stage in a property cycle;
- ❖ clarification of recent tax allowances and treatments; and
- ❖ a change in regulation that allows insurance companies to use derivatives for capital relief.

One of the reasons that property derivatives have not been successful in the past is that, unlike trading some other commodities, all properties are different and the market can be slow moving. For the first time now with a property derivative it is possible to profit by 'betting' on a falling market.

How it all works

A prerequisite to a derivatives market is an independent index correlated to changes of value in the asset class. The United Kingdom has the investment property databank UK property index to fulfil this role and is regarded as a benchmark.

Using the most common swap contract (total return) a buyer of an exposure to property pays what is known as Libor, or London Interbank Offer Rate, used when one bank borrows from another, plus a spread in return for the total annual return (capital and income) on the Investment Property Databank (IPD) All Property Index (other indices are All Retail, All Office and All Industrial). An alternative is to trade individual sector performance against the All Property Index.

Advantages of property derivatives

The advantages of this investment medium are obvious. Property derivatives allow parties to show a view on a market position without having to trade the base asset. Investors can sell (short) a position without having to actually buy it first and go long (buy) an asset or exposure to it without a cash investment. They dramatically reduce the transaction time and the time taken to form a view on the market by allowing a party to sell or buy immediate exposure to the main property return indices. They also crucially avoid the transaction costs associated with actual property transfers, such as Stamp Duty Land Tax (SDLT) and conveyancing costs. Traditionally costs for physical transactions can be 5.75%, whereas for derivatives they are likely to be just 0.5%.

The future and any trends

The trade press have reported that initial take up and overall interest has been quite low, although this picked up through 2007. The commercial sector has taken off more than the residential sector and although initially most of the trades were swaps on the All Property level there is now an increase of sector and even subsector trading, together with interest in France and Germany. During 2007 offices have returned strongest and retail the weakest.

Options

Real property options are opportunities and prior commitments to acquire, develop, refurbish or dispose of property linked real assets at an investment cost determined in the present time with the benefits delivered in the future.

There must be an underlying asset or value in the first place. Real property call options are chances for the owner or holder of the option to benefit from the upside while only suffering the cost of the premium as the downside.

Put options are the reverse, in other words, chances for the holder to benefit from any down side, such as a depressed sale value or depreciation.

Vendor surveys

The traditional approach to selling investment grade property is to release details to the market, consider offers and reach heads of terms which are often subject to survey and legal enquiries. This due diligence process may give the prospective purchaser cause to renegotiate terms with a risk to the vendor in terms of cost and time. If matters proceed smoothly, exchange of contracts and completion can then take place.

The process is time consuming and fraught with risk. To streamline the procedure and manage risks, vendors are increasingly procuring full survey reports prior to sale – the government's 'Home Information Pack' for the residential market is a similar concept albeit the requirement for a Home Condition Report has now been dropped. A vendor survey can be defined as a building and other surveys commissioned by a vendor but primarily for the benefit of a purchaser.

Normally, the vendor's sale pack will include the normal building survey, a Phase 1 environmental report or land quality statement, test reports on deleterious materials (where relevant) and probably a report on the building's services installations.

Whereas a conventional report may often make recommendations for further investigation, a vendor survey must not invite further questions. Thus, it is very important to either make a judgement and express an opinion based upon the evidence, or commission additional tests and inspections where it is relevant to do so. Similarly, questions that would normally be referred to the legal team should be addressed in advance of the production of the final report. In other words, every effort must be made to 'close' particular issues or observations.

Traditionally, building and other surveys include a number of limitations. The third party clause (where the report can only be relied upon by the client) clearly needs variation with vendor surveys. There is always some scope for discussion, but the usual basis is that the client (or vendor) can rely upon vendor survey reports as well as the first purchaser. A duty is often extended to the first purchaser's bankers. Furthermore, there should be no change of use, as this may have impacts on the building that the surveyor cannot foresee. The purchaser must also accept that the building's condition may have changed since the date of the report. Assignment of the report to the first purchaser is traditionally done by exchange of letters but can also be executed as a deed.

Simply readdressing a report to the purchaser is unlikely to be good enough as this does not create a contractual link between the parties.

An advantage of a vendor survey is making information on the condition of the property available to the vendor, which is essential for good asset management. Such surveys also take technical due diligence off the critical path, because they are prepared before the property is marketed. Heads of terms can be entered into without being subject to survey. This approach may also give less scope to prospective purchasers who are not sincere in proceeding on the basis of their original offer.

Home Information Packs

Since 14 December 2007, all homes for sale in England and Wales have needed a Home Information Pack (HIP), which includes a home energy rating. When first proposed, the Packs were to include a Home Condition Report (HCR) but this is no longer mandatory.

The Pack includes an Energy Performance Certificate (EPC), containing advice on how to cut carbon emissions and fuel consumption. Also included are documents such as a sale statement, searches and evidence of title. Each pack must have an index listing all documents included. Certain documents are termed 'required' and must be provided whilst 'authorised' documents are not obligatory.

The production of an EPC or an HCR needs to be undertaken by an individual who has satisfied certain criteria. Mere membership of the RICS is not sufficient, although the RICS does operate an accredited scheme that has been approved by government. See www.rics.org/MyRICS/Accreditationandcertification

A sample Home Information Pack and Energy Performance Certificate may be downloaded from www.homeinformationpack.gov.uk. This site also has a Home Condition Report template.

For more information on HIPs see page 28.

Identifying the age of buildings

This guide cannot pretend to be a comprehensive dissertation on the architectural and construction history of Britain. It is a concise yet wide-ranging guide to clues and explains what to look for when seeking to assess the age of a building. Always remember that, almost without exception, any building, unless of very recent construction, will, at some time in its life, have undergone some form of change, modernisation or conversion that may well hide the age of the original construction.

If you have the time and opportunity, always seek to consult such archival sources as are immediately available. Even if the building is not a historic building, some records of the original date of construction will exist somewhere in the files of the local administration.

If the building is listed as being of Special Architectural or Historic Interest or a Scheduled Ancient Monument, the listing description or entry in the Scheduled Monuments Register will provide some indication of the believed age of the building or monument. A word of caution here is that these believed ages are based in most cases on external inspections only and even the most experienced inspectors of historic buildings and ancient monuments have been known to have been deceived. The problem usually takes the form of putting a more recent age on the structure based on external elevations that are the result of, say, a late Victorian refronting of a Georgian building, or an early 18th century brick refronting of a Tudor or earlier timber framed building. This last is often referred to as a Queen Anne front on a Mary Anne back, therefore, always ensure that you look at the back of the property as well as the front.

Where to go to find records

Every county in Britain has a County Archivist and contact can be established through the local authority of the area in which the building is situated. Alternatively contact can be made via the relevant heritage authority – English Heritage, Scottish Heritage, Welsh Heritage (CADW) or the Northern Ireland Heritage Department of the Department of Environment of Northern Ireland. Alternatively the Local Authority Conservation Officer will be able to put you in touch and indeed the relevant conservation or heritage authority or office could be a useful source in their own right.

Archives, be they county, district or more local, even down to parish level, will include one or more sets of the following which may assist:

❖ maps, especially tithe maps, showing down to considerable detail ownerships and the building in outline on each site or plot;

❖ sale documents, especially auction details that themselves give indications of believed age(s) of the building;

❖ newspaper and other articles indicating the believed age(s) of the building;

❖ deeds registers, which can be particularly useful in establishing exact dates for the original building lease from the lord of the manor or landed estate owner, granting the right to the construction of the building being considered;

❖ local authority building bylaw and drainage permissions or approvals to the construction of the building and subsequent alterations. This last one usually only reaches back to the mid-19th century but the equivalent landed estate or manorial records can reach back much further. If the building is still held in freehold or equivalent by the landed estate or manorial estate then such records may still be held by them. However, some such estate records have been transferred to the county or district archives; and

❖ the National Monuments Records Office in Swindon via their website at www.english-heritage.org.uk will link you into 'Learning & Resources' with various sites via 'Online Resources' including Images of England and Access to Archives the United Kingdom strand of the A2A Archives database – also available currently at www.a2a.org.uk but ultimately to change to www.nationalarchives.gov.uk/a2a which links into 390 record offices. CADW-Welsh Heritage has 'Coflein' and other free to use, no need to register, databases on www.rcahmw.gov.uk. For Scotland try www.rcahms.gov.uk/search.html and register and use the various databases, particularly the free Canmore database. For Northern Ireland try www.ehsni.gov.uk

Published and unpublished archival research

The Victoria County Histories, which should be available in the county or district central reference library may contain a reference to your building.

London has the Survey of London volumes now produced by the Survey of London branch of English Heritage. Those started in the late 19th century only cover a part of the historic areas of London and are available in principal reference libraries and gradually online at www.british-history.ac.uk then link to 'Survey of London'. The British History site has numerous additional online sources covering London and the United Kingdom.

Other public and private publications may exist for your particular building. The Dr Nikolaus Pevsner *Buildings of England/Britain* series may assist. Local history librarians are a mine of information in such a search. They and the county or district archivists may also be able to assist in pointing you towards unpublished works either held by them or produced by local historians.

Research in specialist public archives can also be extremely positive in producing plans and documentation. For any building that is or has been in government or Crown ownership, including the Crown Estates, the Public Record Office at Kew can be invaluable, with large parts of their catalogues available online. See www.nationalarchives.gov.uk and enquiry@nationalarchives.gov.uk

For a building by an important architect, the *V&A/RIBA Drawings Collection* at the Victoria and Albert Museum can produce drawings back to the 17th century.

For London, the Metropolitan Archives (T: 020 7332 3820) hold papers dating back to the 16th century.

For any building that has at any point in its life been in the direct ownership of (or occupation by) the Monarchy, the Royal Archives at Windsor Castle can produce vital details unobtainable elsewhere.

The building

Once you have understood the types and forms and materials of construction used in particular periods, as you inspect or survey a building the less altered areas of the building can be very revealing. This is particularly true of roof spaces, basements, rear elevations, back or rear additions or anywhere else that has escaped the 'improver of antiquity', i.e. the previous owner(s) who modernised the property. As you crawl around the building look out for such unaltered places. Above ground archaeology is the increasingly common term for such on-the-property investigations.

Development monitoring

The need for development monitoring

Development monitors are appointed to oversee a third party's interest in a development. Development monitoring involves identifying, advising on and monitoring construction related risks, which are not under the client's direct control. There is a need for the monitor to actively protect the client's interest during the lifetime of the development. This is particularly important where the client takes a more risk-averse approach to the project than the developer.

A key element of the role is that advice is provided to the client from a party that is independent and not associated with the development or the development team.

The need for development monitoring is diverse and each instruction will reflect the requirements of the client and their relationship to a particular development. Development monitoring is typically undertaken on behalf of investment funds, banks and future occupiers, as summarised in the following table.

Development monitors are also commonly referred to as project monitors, fund surveyors and construction monitors.

Typical clients

Type of organisation	Examples of organisation	Interest in development
Fund	Property investment fund, pension fund, private equity fund, joint venture partner	Will purchase the scheme as an investment on completion, or will acquire the land and fund the development during construction as an investment
Funder/lender	Clearing banks, investment banks	Will earn interest on a loan for the land purchase and/or the building during construction, as well as a pre-agreed arrangement fee and possibly an exit fee
Prospective occupier	Various tenants	Will acquire a leasehold interest in the completed development, which may include full repairing and insuring obligations

The monitoring service

The development monitoring service will depend on the nature of the client's interest in the development and the risks associated with this interest. Therefore, there is no standard service. The client and the monitor must work closely together to ensure the monitor's brief fully meets the specific project requirements.

Where a funder is providing debt finance, the principal focus is likely to relate to the value of the works undertaken and the completion of the works within the agreed budget. Progress of the works during construction will also be an important aspect to monitor. However, where the loan is secured against the property, it is prudent for the funder to ensure that the quality of the works is also considered.

In situations where the client has, or has agreed to, purchase the development, a quality focus is more prevalent. The client will want to ensure that the completed development is of a quality suitable as an investment asset. Where the fund is financing the works, it is common for development and purchase agreements between funds and developers to include maximum cost limits for the fund, or developer profit erosion provisions, which protect the fund from cost overruns.

Progress of the works may be critical if there is an agreement for lease with a future tenant, or tenants. In this instance, close monitoring of the likelihood of achieving the access date(s) for the tenant's fit out works will be required. This can be undertaken on behalf of the fund, funder or future occupier.

In general terms the monitor will comment on the cost, programme and quality of the proposed development, from the initial concept to full design, and throughout the construction period, and into the defects liability period.

The key skills and competencies that should be sought in a development monitor are:

- ❖ diverse technical knowledge of construction;
- ❖ thorough understanding of the client's interest in the development, including the development/purchase/finance agreement and the conditions precedent;
- ❖ project management and procurement expertise;
- ❖ cost management knowledge;
- ❖ risk awareness;
- ❖ independence from the development team;
- ❖ reporting and appraisal skills; and
- ❖ proactive and a good communicator.

Development monitoring is usually carried out in four stages. Each stage is listed below and is discussed in the following sections.

- ❖ appraisal and risk assessment;
- ❖ construction and finance monitoring during the works; and
- ❖ advice at practical completion and at end of the defects liability period.

Appraisal and risk assessment

The development monitor will request and then review a wide range of information on the proposed development, including the programme, construction cost, design quality, future maintenance requirements, procurement route, selection of consultants and contractors, building contract, provision of warranties, insurances, statutory requirements, neighbourly matters, and land contamination issues. This review is summarised in an appraisal report, which will highlight any potential risks associated with the project.

The focus of the appraisal will reflect the needs of the client and its interest in the particular development. This should be defined in the legal documentation, such as the development/purchase/finance agreement or the agreement for lease. Where possible it is advantageous for the development monitor to provide technical advice to the client on the construction related matters at the pre-agreement stage. Such advice would relate to any potential significant risks associated with undertaking the development that may have an adverse effect on value.

Construction and finance monitoring

Following the appraisal stage and agreement to proceed with the development, monitoring is undertaken during the construction works. This involves periodic site inspections and attendance at site progress meetings, typically on a monthly basis. A formal report will be prepared that comments on a variety of construction issues, including:

- ❖ construction costs, cash flow and expenditure against budget;
- ❖ progress of the works against programme;
- ❖ quality of workmanship on site;
- ❖ development of the design;
- ❖ status of any statutory approvals;
- ❖ status of appointment documents and warranties; and
- ❖ status of insurances.

The monitor may also be required to monitor expenditure of all development costs against the agreed budget. This can include expenditure such as legal fees, marketing costs and professional fees.

Practical completion and the end of the defects liability period

The role of the development monitor at practical completion and at the end of the defects liability period is usually set out in the development/purchase/finance agreement or in the agreement for lease. A robust role may be specified involving inspection of the completed development and advising the client on whether they should accept the development as complete, or that the end of the defects liability period has been achieved.

Practical completion is particularly critical where a prospective tenant is in place, as practical completion is likely to trigger rent commencement. Furthermore, practical completion is likely to result in payment for the building to the developer (projects which are not interim funded), or payment of the developer's profit.

The monitor can help to ensure that all the necessary handover documentation is in place, such as the health and safety file, as built drawings, the operation and maintenance manuals and warranties.

Housing and residential property

Property investment and ownership

Home Information Packs

The introduction of Home Information Packs (HIPs) as a requirement for buying and selling homes in England and Wales has now taken place. The primary legislation was originally detailed in the *Housing Act* 2004 although the current regulations differ in many ways.

After a staged introduction, from 14 December 2007 every home marketed for sale in England and Wales will require a HIP.

Content

The contents of the Home Information Pack include:

- ❖ terms of sale;
- ❖ evidence of title;
- ❖ replies to standard preliminary enquiries;
- ❖ copies of planning and building regulation consents;
- ❖ copies of warranties, guarantees for work carried out to the property (not compulsory);
- ❖ replies to local searches; and
- ❖ an Energy Performance Certificate (EPC);

and, additionally, for leasehold property:

- ❖ a copy of the lease, recent service charge accounts (last 36 months);
- ❖ buildings insurance policy details;
- ❖ any regulations, memorandum and articles of the landlord or management company may be required; and
- ❖ a summary of any current or proposed works to the demise of the building in which it is situated.

What is an Energy Performance Certificate (EPC)?

The certificates will give homebuyers and sellers A to G ratings for their home's energy efficiency and carbon emissions. They will tell them current average costs for heating, hot water and lighting in their home, as well as how to cut costs with energy efficiency measures.

Part of the energy performance review will advise consumers on which energy measures – ranging from thicker loft insulation right through to solar panels – could cut carbon emissions from their home and improve their energy rating.

The government have stated that the introduction is due to 'the growing challenge from climate change and rising energy costs ... to improve energy efficiency ... and to help sellers and buyers to cut carbon emissions and fuel bills'. Also, the European Energy Directive requires that from 2009 all homes for sale should have energy certificates.

What is the Home Condition Report?

On 18 July 2006, the government announced that a major component of the HIP, namely the Home Condition Report (HCR), would not be mandatory, only voluntary. It was felt by many experienced commentators that the main thrust of HIPs, to speed up the buying process, would not be helped by HCRs. It has been commonly accepted that there were not enough trained inspectors and that this was also a reason why HCRs became voluntary. The government have indicated that HCRs will only become mandatory if the voluntary take-up is a success.

Why HIPs?

The aim of HIPs is to remove uncertainty in the house buying and selling process and, in theory, reduce the transaction time. Despite the withdrawal of HCRs, opportunities for gazundering should still be reduced but perhaps less so. Currently, information required by buyers and sellers appears some time after an offer has been made and accepted, increasing the potential for abortive expenditure on surveys, legal fees, searches, etc.

How will HIPs work?

The legislation will require home owners or their selling agents to have an HIP prepared before putting a home on the market and to make a copy of that pack available to prospective buyers on request.

What will it cost?

Estimated prices for the HIP will be determined by the market but £250–£500 plus VAT, excluding the HCR, is being quoted by leading providers.

Who will carry out the work?

Energy Assessor qualifications are currently awarded by three organisations: the Awarding Body for the Built Environment, City and Guilds and the National Association of Estate Agents. After training, Energy Assessors need to join an accreditation scheme in order to practise.

Home Inspectors need to undertake an assessment process that will lead to a Level 4 qualification (degree level) in Home Inspection. Qualifications are offered by two awarding bodies – the Awarding Body for the Built Environment (ABBE) and City and Guilds. The Secretary of State has approved three Home Inspector certification schemes run by BRE (Buildings Research Establishment), RICS (Royal Institution of Chartered Surveyors) and SAVA (Surveyors and Valuers Accreditation Ltd).

Penalties

If an HIP is not provided, it is anticipated that the enforcement regime will be based on civil sanctions.

Trading Standards Officers would be given discretion to determine appropriate action in each case – whether to provide information and assistance, issue a warning or a civil fixed penalty notice (initially envisaged by the then ODPM to be around £200). Trading Standards Officers would also be able to notify the Office of Fair Trading (OFT) of any breach by persons acting as estate agents, which could also trigger action by the OFT under the *Estate Agents Act* 1979. Trading Standards Officers would have a duty to do this where a fixed penalty notice had been issued. In addition, a person who breached the HIP obligations would be liable to be sued by prospective buyers for recovery of the costs of obtaining documents which should have been provided in the pack.

Further information

Department for Communities and Local Government (CLG): www.communities.gov.uk

Royal Institution of Chartered Surveyors (RICS): www.rics.org

Home Information Pack website: www.homeinformationpacks.gov.uk/home.aspx

Housing Health and Safety Rating System

Background

The Housing Health and Safety Rating System (HHSRS) replaced the former Housing Fitness Regime in England and Wales in 2006. HHSRS, which has been introduced under the *Housing Act* 2004, has also superseded the Fitness Standard as an element of the Decent Homes Standard. Surveyors and other construction professionals, particularly those working in the social housing sector, should be aware of these changes and understand the basic principles of the new system.

The department for Communities and Local Government (CLG) states that '... the government's aim is that this reform will enable local authorities to address more effectively the hazards to health and safety present in the home'.

Local authorities' obligations

Under the *Housing Act* 2004, a local authority is obliged to keep housing conditions under review and take any enforcement action needed to ensure that housing conditions meet the requirements of the HHSRS.

Local authorities are also obliged to investigate any official complaints regarding the condition of any residential premises. This includes home owners and private sector landlords.

The regulations are designed to ensure that any residential premises and their environs provide a safe and healthy environment for occupiers and their visitors. The HHSRS works by assessing the risk associated with particular hazards that may be encountered in the home. If there is a significant chance that they could cause harm, a local authority may take action to ensure that the risk is removed or reduced.

Unlike the former Fitness Standard, the HHSRS assessment is not designed to set a standard but to provide objective information which will determine and inform enforcement decisions made by local authorities. The new assessment sets out 29 categories of housing hazard, including factors not covered (or considered to be covered inadequately) by the former Housing Fitness Standard.

The hazards

Under the new system the hazards given priority are:

1. Damp and mould growth
2. Excess cold
3. Excess heat
4. Asbestos and MMF
5. Biocides
6. Carbon monoxide and fuel combustion products
7. Lead
8. Radiation
9. Uncombusted fuel gas
10. Volatile organic compounds
11. Crowding and space
12. Entry by intruders
13. Lighting
14. Noise
15. Domestic hygiene, pests and refuse
16. Food safety

17. Personal hygiene, sanitation and drainage
18. Water supply
19. Falls associated with baths, etc.
20. Falling on level surfaces, etc.
21. Falling on stairs, etc.
22. Falling between levels
23. Electrical hazards
24. Fire
25. Flames, hot surfaces, etc.
26. Collision and entrapment
27. Explosions
28. Position and operability of amenities, etc.
29. Structural collapse and falling elements

The list of hazards can be found in Schedule 1 of the Housing Health and Safety Rating System (England) Regulations 2005 (SI 2005/3208). © Crown copyright material is reproduced with the permission of the Controller of HMSO and Queen's Printer for Scotland.

Scoring the hazards

Each of the 29 hazards is provided with a risk rating for an average property. This risk rating is based upon statistics, gathered by the government, on the likelihood of that hazard occurring to an occupant and the level of harm that will occur as a result of the hazard occurring.

Likelihood x harm = risk

In undertaking an HHSRS inspection of a property it is the inspector's role to establish whether the likelihood and the level of harm associated with each hazard is above the national average provided by the government guidance. Alterations to the likelihood and harm will result in a change in the hazard band rating.

A rating is given for each hazard, rather than for the dwelling as a whole or, in the case of dwellings in multiple occupation, for the building as a whole. Hazard ratings use a numerical score which falls within one of ten bands. Scores in Bands A to C are Category 1 hazards. Scores in Bands D to J are Category 2 hazards.

According to CLG guidance, 'the HHSRS assessment is based on the risk to the potential occupant who is most vulnerable to that hazard'. For example, when using stairs, these 'constitute a greater risk to the elderly, so for assessing hazards relating to stairs they are considered the most vulnerable'. A dwelling that is safe for those most vulnerable to a hazard is safe for all, says the CLG.

Enforcement

Any action taken by the local authority as a result of an HHSRS assessment will be based on a three-stage test:

❖ the hazard rating given;
❖ whether the authority has a duty or power to act; and
❖ that authority's judgement as to the most appropriate course of action to be taken.

New enforcement options are now available to local authorities, taking into account the statutory enforcement guidance.

Authorities can:

❖ serve an improvement notice requiring remedial works;
❖ make a prohibition order, which closes the whole or part of a dwelling or restricts the number of permitted occupants;
❖ suspend these types of notice;

- ❖ take emergency action;
- ❖ serve a hazard awareness notice;
- ❖ make a demolition order*; and
- ❖ declare a clearance area*.

(* not available for Category 2 hazards)

Further information

More information can be obtained from www.communities.gov.uk/hhsrs

Code for Sustainable Homes

The *Code for Sustainable Homes* (CSH) replaces previous Eco Homes requirements to become the single national standard to measure sustainability of new homes. Driven by the wider requirements of the Energy Performance Directive, the Code complements the introduction of Energy Performance Certificates, bringing more focus and awareness of the sustainability of homes delivered.

The CSH has been adopted by the Housing Corporation who require, under their National Affordable Housing Programme 2008/11, that all homes delivered meet at least a three star rating under the Code.

The Code assesses sustainability across nine categories and awards points in each area. These points are then calculated and converted into a star rating. Not all of the categories have the same rating – minimum standards must be met for materials, surface water run off and waste just to achieve the minimum entry level. Minimum standards do not apply to pollution, health and well-being, management and ecology.

The nine categories are detailed in the table below.

It is hoped that the Code will offer a range of benefits both in terms of the reduced environmental impact of new homes provided, but also to consumers through lower fuel costs and to house builders as a mark of quality assurance.

Category	Minimum standard	Additional points
1) and 2) Energy and water efficiency	The baseline is the minimum requirements of Part L of the Building Regulations 2006. Improvements are expressed in percentages, e.g. for energy and carbon dioxide an improvement over the Target Emission Rate (TER) in Part L is required of: • 10% for one star; • 25% for three stars; and • 100% for five stars.	
3) Materials	To achieve a one star rating at least three of the following five elements must be specified to achieve a BRE Green Guide 2006 rating of at least D:	

Category	Minimum standard	Additional points
3) Materials *continued*	<ul><li>roof structure and finishes;</li><li>external walls;</li><li>upper floor;</li><li>internal walls; and</li><li>windows and doors.</li></ul>	
4) Waste	The minimum standard for waste is based on both:<ul><li>site waste management; and</li><li>household storage.</li></ul>A site waste management plan must be adopted and must include monitoring of waste on site and target setting to promote efficient use of resources. The management of household waste storage requires the containment of waste for each dwelling – the greater (by volume) is required of either:<ul><li>accommodation of external containers provided under the local authority's refuse collection and recycling scheme; or</li><li>at least 0.8m³ per dwelling for waste management as required by BS 5906 – *Code of Practice for Storage and On-site Treatment of Solid Waste from Buildings.*</li></ul>	
5) Surface water run-off	For a one star rating, peak run-off rates and annual volumes or run-off will be no greater than the site's previous conditions.	Extra points can be gained by:<ul><li>the provision of rainwater holding facilities (e.g. water butts) and the attenuation of run-off either to natural water courses or to municipal systems; or</li></ul>

Category	Minimum standard	Additional points
5) Surface water run-off *continued*		• where houses are sited in areas of flood risk, constructing the ground level of buildings above flood level, or through house design, limiting the damage caused by flooding.
6) Pollution	n/a	Extra points can be gained by: • using insulants with little or no global warming potential or ozone depleting potential in either manufacture/ composition (includes insulation materials used in walls, lofts, roofs, and around hot water cylinders); or • using boilers with low nitrous oxide emissions (NOx) emissions as defined in BS EN 297: 1994.
7) Health and well-being	n/a	This category includes daylight, sound insulation and the design of private external areas that are accessible by people with disabilities. Extra points can be gained by: • applying the standards of the Lifetime Homes scheme (design principles for homes designed to cater for people of all ages and age-related disabilities);

Category	Minimum standard	Additional points
7) Health and well-being *continued*		• applying higher standards of sound insulation than required by Part E of the Building Regulations (NB this will either require post-completion testing, or proof of the application of robust details); or • achieving specific daylight factors in kitchens, living rooms and studies.
8) Management	n/a	This category covers both construction and post-construction. Extra points can be gained by: • abiding by the Considerate Constructors Scheme; • delivering a strategy to reduce the harmful effects of construction on the site; or • providing Home User Guides for the operation, and environmental performance of the home.
9) Ecology	n/a	This category includes the ecological value of the site, ecological enhancement, protection of ecological features and the total building footprint. Extra points can be gained by: • adopting the requirements in the BRE Ecological Value Checklist;

Category	Minimum standard	Additional points
9) Ecology *continued*		• limiting the effects of house construction on the local flora and fauna; • demonstrating that anything of ecological value is protected during construction works and able to thrive after completion; or • commissioning a report from a qualified ecologist (the Code is not explicit about acting on its findings).

Further information

For access to the Code, Technical Guidance and other useful information go to:
www.communities.gov.uk/planningandbuilding/building regulations/legislation/englandwales/codesustainable/
or to: www. planningportal.gov.uk/england/professionals/en/ 1115314116927.html

Contracts and procurement

Development and procurement

Public procurement, Public Private Partnerships and the Private Finance Initiative

Public Private Partnerships (PPP) are, broadly speaking, contractual arrangements where the public and private sectors work together to deliver a project or service. This can include many types of arrangement such as transfer of public undertakings to the private sector and private sector investment in public services.

The Private Finance Initiative (PFI) is a type of PPP where the private sector provides an asset-based service under contract to the public sector. The key features of PFI are that there is an underlying asset, often a building or a series of buildings, and that private finance is used to provide the facility and service. In return, the private sector receives a regular payment from the public sector over the life of the concession, typically 25–30 years. PFI is one of HM Treasury's preferred forms of procurement.

This chapter describes some of the key features and mechanisms of PFI and public procurement. Due to the complexity of this field, together with differences in interpretation and practice between contracting authorities, it should be regarded as a guide only and specific advice sought in appropriate cases.

Features of PFI/PPP

- ❖ The private sector contracts not only for the provision of the building or other asset, but for maintenance and services over the life of the concession. This encourages the integration of construction and services provision and investment decisions based on whole life cost, rather than capital cost only.

- ❖ The public sector requirements are expressed as outputs (requirements to be met) rather than inputs (standards to be achieved). This allows the private sector to meet requirements by the most cost effective route and encourages innovation.

- ❖ The private sector is incentivised to deliver the services by a penalty structure which reduces or suspends the regular payment (called the Unitary Payment). Payment reductions may arise from parts of the asset no longer being available (unavailability) or performance failures (e.g. failure to rectify a defect within a prescribed period of time).

- ❖ The public sector remains responsible for the core public service (teaching, healthcare, administration, etc.).

- ❖ The PFI is funded entirely by the private sector in return for the Unitary Payment. In some cases, the public sector may offer long stop guarantees to improve Value for Money (see below).

- ❖ The design, construction, operating and maintenance risks are largely transferred to the private sector. For example, if the project costs more or takes longer than agreed at the outset, the private sector is responsible for the overrun. The assessment, allocation and management of risks is one of the key disciplines in PFI/PPP.

- ❖ The transfer of risk enables public sector authorities to benefit from accounting treatment of the Unitary Payment as revenue expenditure, which does not count against their capital allocations.

❖ The PFI proposal must demonstrate Value for Money (VfM), meaning broadly that PFI has to offer a more cost effective solution to requirements than conventional public procurement. This comparison is made via the construction of a Public Sector Comparator (PSC) financial model for the public sector alternative. A 'shadow bid' is often compiled by the public sector to test the overall value at bid stage.

Key advantages and disadvantages

Advantages

❖ Public service improvements are brought forward by using private capital to offset the shortage of public capital.

❖ Development and operational risk is transferred to the private sector, freeing the public sector to concentrate on the core service.

❖ The private sector is incentivised to provide good quality buildings and services and VfM.

Disadvantages

❖ The cost of private finance is greater than that of public capital, meaning that the PFI must achieve efficiency improvements to offset this.

❖ Major changes in public sector requirements during the concession period may be difficult or expensive to accommodate within PFI.

Projects and clients

The largest single category by value is transport, due in part to the inclusion of the London Underground modernisation programme. Other major sectors include health, education and defence.

Types of projects using PFI include headquarters offices, office roll-out programmes, environmental and waste recycling, transport (road, rail and light railway), education, healthcare, prisons, courts, defence, housing and regional projects. Public sector clients include government departments, local authorities, NHS Trusts and government agencies such as the Inland Revenue.

Because of the long-term nature of the transaction and the cost of the tendering process, PFI is rarely used for projects with a value of less than £20 million. A feature of more recent PFI transactions is the grouping of smaller projects into a single PFI to achieve the appropriate minimum size.

The PFI procurement model has also been adopted by some large private or semi-private clients for their building and facilities provision. This is known as 'corporate', or 'private' PFI.

Project inception

The first formal step in the PFI process is the production of an Outline Business Case by or on behalf of the public sector client. This sets out the project brief and business case for the proposal, and forms the basis for applications for PFI credits from central government where applicable. It is followed up with the output specification which sets out the requirements for the project in performance terms, and in due course this forms a key part of the tender documentation.

A key feature of the output specification is that it is expressed in terms of required outputs, rather than prescribed inputs. Within any constraints set by the public sector, the private sector is free to meet these requirements by means of its own choosing. Sometimes these depart significantly from those envisaged by the client at the outset.

Transaction structure

The parties to a PFI transaction typically comprise the following:

- ❖ Public sector client: The government department, local authority or other public sector authority contracting for the project.
- ❖ Private sector partner: Usually a consortium comprising a contractor or developer, a facilities manager or operator, and a bank or other financial institution.
- ❖ Funders: In addition to the consortium partners, external organisations will normally be involved in the provision of funding. These can include banks or other financial institutions, bond issuers, rating agencies and insurers.

A number of companies with an interest in the PFI market have formed specialist subsidiaries or consortia to participate in contracting, funding or operation, particularly in the field of health care.

The above parties to the PFI will normally be advised separately and a typical consultant team would include a financial adviser, legal adviser and one or more technical advisers.

The organisational structure of a typical PFI transaction is shown in Table 1 on page 43.

Procurement

Public procurement is subject to EU rules which are intended to promote fair competition across the EU and a transparent procurement process. Some differences in practice will nonetheless be encountered between contracting authorities and member states.

For public works and services above certain cost thresholds, a notice must be placed by the public sector contracting authority in the Supplement to the Official Journal of the European Communities (OJ). Most PFI transactions will exceed the cost thresholds. The cost thresholds are reviewed every two years and those applying from 1 January 2008 are shown in Table 2 on page 44.

The Supplement to the OJ is published daily in electronic form and may be viewed on the internet (see useful information sources page 393). Tender information services are available on subscription, and a selection of OJ notices are published from time to time in the construction press.

Tendering procedures

There are three types of tender procedure:

- ❖ **Restricted:** Expressions of interest are invited and the most suitably qualified are invited to submit a tender.
- ❖ **Open:** A notice is published and anyone can submit a tender.
- ❖ **Negotiated:** The contract is negotiated with at least three tenderers, or with the maximum number available. Use of this procedure is subject to justification.

The choice of tendering procedure is made by the contracting authority having regard to the nature of the works or services, and the circumstances under which they are to be delivered. For example, the nature of the service may mean that a specification cannot be drawn up with sufficient precision to allow the use of the Open or Restricted procedure.

An accelerated procedure can be used where justified in conjunction with the Open or Restricted procedure.

Types of notice

Prior Information Notice (PIN): optional notice of intent to invite tenders or expressions of interest later. When placed in accordance with the mandatory timescales, it allows the period for submission of tenders or expressions of interest to be reduced. (The mandatory timescales for the tender process are shown in Table 3 on page 44.)

Contract Notice: main notice providing full information and informing parties how to bid or pre-qualify for the project.

Content of notices

Notices are in a form prescribed by the EU and group information into the following sections:

    I.   Contracting authority
    II.   Object of the contract
    III. Legal, economic, financial and technical information
    IV. Procedure
    V.   [Spare number]
    VI. Other information.

Within these sections, certain information is mandatory. However notices contain more than the minimum information, to encourage a good quality and level of response from bidders.

Certain conventions are used in notices, including CPV (Common Procurement Vocabulary) and NUTS (Territorial Designation). For an explanation of these and other conventions, refer to the SIMAP website: www.simap.eu.int

The official forms for placing of notices in the OJ can be downloaded from the SIMAP website.

Project processes

The post tender processes can vary widely depending on the project nature and external factors. Typically an Invitation to Negotiate (ITN) will be issued to a shortlist of bidders, and this may be followed by a further bidding round (Best and Final Offer or BAFO). In order to reduce bid periods and associated costs, current practice is to encourage the provision of full information by both parties at the outset, and the use of standard contract terms as far as possible.

At the conclusion of bidding and post bid negotiations, a Preferred Bidder is selected, together with a reserve bidder. The parties then negotiate the remaining details of the project and confirm funding, legal and third party issues. During this period, development of the design and construction proposals continues, and planning permission may be sought. Once the terms are fully agreed and funding secured, contract award (or 'Financial Close') takes place, and the project can proceed.

Funding

PFI transactions are mainly debt financed, and senior debt is normally provided independently of the consortium partners. The main sources of PFI funds are:

    ❖   Equity – normally provided only in limited amounts by the private sector consortium partners.
    ❖   Subordinated or mezzanine debt – provided by consortium partners or other funding institutions.
    ❖   Senior debt – normally the bulk of the funding, provided by bank lending and/or via the capital markets.

The choice between bank and capital market options will depend on the nature and size of the project, and the market conditions at the time of placement. Bank debt is suitable for smaller, shorter life or higher risk projects, and the finance cost is generally higher than the capital markets option.

The capital markets option is particularly suitable for larger, lower risk projects for central government, where the covenant is perceived as strongest. This option requires the issue of an index linked or fixed rate bond which is typically taken up by other financial institutions and pension funds. Although the process of issuing a bond is more expensive than arranging bank debt, this will be recovered over the life of the bond in lower finance costs.

The bond issue is underwritten by a financial institution and may be credit rated by an agency such as Standard and Poor's to improve marketability. As an alternative, or in addition, bonds may be enhanced by private or public sector guarantees, or by the use of credit risk insurance (called monoline insurance). A bond enhanced in this way is known as a wrapped bond.

PFI transactions may be re-financed during the concession period, typically by the renegotiation of debt finance once the development period is over and the project risk profile is reduced. Some PFI contractors have also begun to sell on their equity stakes, creating a secondary transaction market.

Success factors

Some PFI transactions are more successful than others, and some success or failure criteria are subjective. While it is difficult to draw general conclusions, research has identified the six most significant value for money drivers in PFI as: the level of risk transfer; linking the output specification requirements to payment; the length of the contract needed to recoup investment; appropriate performance measures and incentives; a competitive bidding process; and excellent management skills in the private sector.

PFI – an assessment

Since it was inaugurated in 1992, PFI has enabled significant investment in public facilities and services which might not otherwise have taken place. Studies by the National Audit Office have indicated that under PFI, the proportion of projects being delivered late or over budget has fallen from roughly three quarters to a quarter, and that four-fifths of public bodies involved with PFI believe they are achieving satisfactory or better value for money from PFI contracts.

There has been criticism of some early grouped PFI projects on grounds of poor design quality, which has led to a series of design quality initiatives led by the government-sponsored Commission for Architecture and the Built Environment (CABE). Others have criticised PFI on the grounds of doubtful value for money, reduction in safety standards, and dilution of the public service ethos. As the number of PFI projects grows and the process matures, the focus is likely to move from the initial transaction to the quality of facilities management (FM) services and operational management over the life of the concession.

The PFI model, which originated in the UK, has been taken up in several other countries, both in Europe and beyond; and so long as there is a demand for better public services and a continuing shortage of public capital, it seems set to continue and even grow in popularity.

PFI: strengthening long-term partnerships

Published by HM Treasury in March 2006, this report confirms that the government sees PFI continuing to play an important role in the overall objective of delivering modernised public services. In percentage terms, PFI is likely to be used for between 10–15% of total investment in public services, with around 200 projects worth £26 billion in capital value anticipated over the period 2006–2011.

The report also highlights survey-based evidence that PFI is now meeting public service needs across more than 500 operational projects with the following particular conclusions:

❖ 'users are satisfied with the services provided by PFI projects, with 79% of projects reporting that service standards are delivered always or almost always;

❖ public authorities are reporting good overall performance and high levels of satisfaction against the contracted levels of service. Authorities report that the overall performance of 96% of projects is at least satisfactory, and that in 89% of projects, services are being provided in line with the contract or better;

❖ the services contracted for are appropriate with 83% of projects reporting that their contracts always or almost always accurately specify the services required, with this result getting better the more recent the contract; and

❖ the incentivisation within PFI contracts is working. While payment deductions have been low reflecting the general levels of high performance, almost all projects report satisfactory levels of service after a deduction has been applied, and 72% report good or very good performance.'

The quote above is Crown copyright and is reproduced from the report *PFI: strengthening long-term partnerships*, 2006, published by HM Treasury.

Table 1 – PFI Transaction Structure

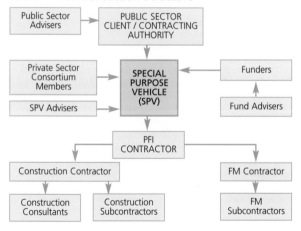

Table 2 – EU thresholds for public procurement

Details of the thresholds from 1 January 2008 are given below. Thresholds are net of VAT.

	Supplies and services	Works
Public Contracts Regulations		
Central government bodies	£90,319[1] (€133,000)	£3,497,313 (€5,150,000)
Other public sector	£139,893 (€206,000)	£3,497,313 (€5,150,000)
Indicative notices	£509,317 (€750,000)	£3,497,313 (€5,150,000)
Small notices	£54,327 (€80,000)	£679,090 (€1,000,000)
Utilities Contract Regulations		
All sectors	£279,785 (€412,000)	£3,497,313 (€5,150,000)
Indicative notices	£509,317 (€750,000)	£3,497,313 (€5,150,000)
Small notices	£54,327 (€80,000)	£679,090 (€1,000,000)

[1] With the exception of the following services, which have a threshold of £139,893 (€206,000):

- ❖ Part B (residual) services;
- ❖ Research and Development Services (Category 8);
- ❖ The following Telecommunications services in Category 5;
  - – CPC 7524 – Television and Radio Broadcast services;
  - – CPC 7525 – Interconnection services;
  - – CPC 7526 – Integrated telecommunications services;
- ❖ Subsidised services contracts under regulation 34.

Note: this is a summary of procurement thresholds only. Reference should be made to the current EU Regulations, which contain exceptions and additional categories.

Table 3 – EU Procurement Process

Key timescales for publication in OJ and return of tenders (based on Restricted procedure)

Prior Information Notice (PIN)	Between 52 days and 12 months before Contract Notice.
Contract Notice	Period for expressions of interest 37 days (see Note 1).
Tenders	Period for return of tenders 40 days (26 days if PIN issued as above) (see Note 1).
Contract Award Notice	Within 48 days of award of contract.

Note 1: Accelerated procedure can be used where justified and will allow periods for expressions of interest and return of tenders to be reduced.

Table 4 – Glossary of Common PFI Terms

BAFO	Best and Final Offer final stage in negotiation prior to selection of Preferred Bidder.
Contract Notice	Main notice placed in OJ Supplement to advertise a public contract.
Financial Close	Stage when all contractual and financial terms have been agreed and private sector funding is in place; formal execution of the PFI agreement.
Gateway Reviews	Project stage reviews by the public sector to review and confirm proposals and acceptability of risk profile.
ITN	Invitation to Negotiate: invitation to the private sector to provide detailed proposals leading to negotiations and a decision on the Preferred Bidder.
KPI	Key Performance Indicator: definition of performance requirement(s), failure events and penalties (deductions from the Unitary Payment).
OBC	Outline Business Case: the PFI project brief and business case, produced by or on behalf of the public sector contracting authority.
OJ	Official Journal of the European Communities (also OJEC or OJEU). The OJ Supplement carries notices of public contracts.
Output Specification	Specification of requirements for the PFI project and service, produced by or on behalf of the public sector contracting authority.
PFI	Private Finance Initiative
PIN	Prior Information Notice: a preliminary notice placed in OJ to advertise a public contract.
PPP	Public Private Partnership
Preferred Bidder	Stage in negotiation where a Preferred Bidder (and usually a reserve bidder) are selected to negotiate the detailed terms leading to Financial Close.
PSC	Public Sector Comparator: a benchmark of the cost of the PFI against the publicly financed alternative.
SPV	Special Purpose Vehicle: the company created and owned by the private sector consortium and which contracts for the PFI project.
Unavailability	Service failure against KPI availability criteria, resulting in a financial penalty to the private sector.
Unitary Payment	The regular user payment made by the public sector client to the private sector SPV.
VfM	Value For Money: the objective of best value, or meeting user requirements at the lowest whole life cost.

Procurement methods

All construction projects involve risk and the primary function of construction contracts is to assign risks to the respective participants to the building contract.

Risk is an inherent element of any construction project and therefore risk management is an essential part of contract strategy. The primary risks should be identified, and their likelihood and potential impact assessed.

This information should then be used, together with an understanding of the employer's priorities in terms of time, cost and quality to decide upon the procurement method to be followed. The tendering procedure to obtain prices for the procurement route to be followed can be either single stage, two stage or negotiated.

There are currently three main procurement options used within the industry (other alternatives are Term Contracts and Partnering), which reflect various ways by which risk is balanced between the participants to the contract.

Traditional procurement (general contracting)

Under this method the contractor agrees to build the design that it is provided by the employer.

The contractor has no responsibility for design. This method is appropriate for projects where the employer's objectives have been clearly and comprehensively determined.

The financial outcome, responsibility and risk usually resides with the employer.

Advantages

- ❖ Most employers and contractors familiar with this route;
- ❖ high degree of design and product control/selection;
- ❖ robust variation control; and
- ❖ direct employer relationship with designers.

Disadvantages

- ❖ Split responsibility between construction and design;
- ❖ limited risk transfer and increased economic uncertainty;
- ❖ limited opportunities to refine design and improve cost efficiency;
- ❖ potentially more likely to lead to disputes; and
- ❖ longer project delivery.

Design and build procurement

Design and build procurement can come in many forms, but the underlying basis is that the contractor takes both design and construction responsibility. This allows the contractor to have more flexibility on design and allows the employer to place the financial outcome responsibility risk with the contractor.

Advantages

- ❖ Single point responsibility;
- ❖ time – potential to fast track projects by overlapping design and construction phases;
- ❖ contractor involvement in design and resolution of 'buildability' issues; and
- ❖ cost certainty.

Disadvantages

❖ Loss of design control;

❖ restricted scope for change post contract (without paying a premium);

❖ possibility of increased cost – risk premium;

❖ quality – careful drafting of the employer's requirements is needed to ensure the required quality standards; and

❖ specification may be cost driven rather than quality driven.

Management procurement

The key feature of any management contract is that a 'manager' is appointed with the responsibility to manage a project on behalf of the employer. These contracts require the 'manager' to manage, procure and oversee the construction operations.

Under this procurement method there are two distinct routes that can be followed, either Management Contracting or Construction Management.

In Management Contracting the works contractors have direct contractual relationship with the Management Contractor, whereas in Construction Management the works contractors have direct contractual relationships with the employer.

Advantages

❖ Less confrontational;

❖ contractor involvement to advise on buildability issues;

❖ time – can allow earlier start of physical works on site; and

❖ can provide flexibility to develop design whilst inviting tenders and letting packages.

Disadvantages

❖ Increased risk to employer – little contractual risk carried by the construction manager;

❖ out-turn cost is not defined until all packages are let – cost risk lies with the employer; and

❖ greater employer involvement may be required.

Standard form contracts

Standard form contracts have always been a feature of the construction industry. Although there are many types of contract, The following table lists the more commonly used commercial construction contracts relevant to the three main procurement options namely; traditional, design and build, and management.

It is important to note that there are a number of contracts used in the construction industry for both commercial and residential developments and therefore careful selection is required.

Commonly used forms of contract	Procurement types		
	Traditional	Design and build	Management
Large scale			
JCT Major Project Construction Contract, 2005 edition	●		
JCT Standard Building Contract 2005	●		
NEC Engineering and Construction Contract, 3rd edition	●		
GC/Works/1 With Quantities (1998)	●		
Simple content			
JCT Intermediate Building Contract 2005	●		
JCT Intermediate Building Contract with Contractor Design 2005	●		
JCT Minor Building Works Building Contract 2005	●		
NEC3 Engineering and Construction Short Contract	●		
ACA Form of Building Agreement 1982, 3rd edition 1998 (2003 revision)	●		
ICE Conditions of Contract for Minor Works, 3rd edition (2001)	●		
GC/Works/2 (1998)	●		
GC/Works/4 (1998)	●		
Measurement			
JCT Standard Building Contract without Quantities 2005	●		
JCT Measured Term Contract 2005	●		
ICE Conditions of Contract Measurement Version, 7th edition	●		
Design and build			
JCT Design and Build Contract 2005		●	
ICE Design and Construct Conditions of Contract, 2nd edition		●	
GC/Works/1 Single Stage Design and Build (1998)		●	
GC/Works/1 Two Stage Design and Build (1998)		●	

Commonly used forms of contract	Procurement types		
	Traditional	Design and build	Management
Management forms			
JCT Management Building Contract 2005			●
JCT Construction Management Agreement 2005			●

Further information

For further information on a range of construction contracts and supplementary guides please go to the following websites:

- ❖ www.jctcontracts.com/JCT/contracts/index.jsp
- ❖ www.ppc2000.co.uk
- ❖ www.cic.org.uk/services/publications.shtml

The contract administrator's role

It is a feature of most construction contracts that a person is appointed by the employer to administer the terms of the contract on the employer's behalf.

Although contracted by the employer, the contract administrator owes a duty of care to the contractor. Under the terms of the contract he or she must undertake a number of administrative functions including the following:

- ❖ managing the client/contractor;
- ❖ coordinating the pre-project, project and post-project phases;
- ❖ instigating client variations;
- ❖ agreeing interim payments; and
- ❖ issuing certificates including payment certificates and practical completion.

The contract administrator has an important role in giving advice and information and also monitoring the work. However, he or she must also remain unbiased in matters such as certification of payments and ensuring that the contract terms are adhered to.

The mandatory nature of these duties is reflected in the contract between the contract administrator and the employer and in contract between the employer and the contractor. As such, there is often considerable scope for disagreement between the contracting parties, both in contract and tort, on whether these duties have been satisfactorily performed.

It is with this background that those fulfilling the contract administrator's role should be clear on what is required of them.

As a contract administrator the following pre- and post-contract services should be considered important.

Pre-contract

- ❖ Agree detailed brief with client. Agree procedures for modifying the brief as commission proceeds and recording variations.
- ❖ Set budget and project time constraints and establish reporting procedures.
- ❖ Establish clear routes of responsibility for design, drawings and specification and ensure client approval as scheme develops.
- ❖ Prepare tender documents and approve tendering processes with client, including the selection process.

Post-contract

- ❖ Administer the terms of the building contract during operations on site.
- ❖ Inspect the progress and quality of the work on a regular basis.
- ❖ Prepare interim financial reports to client including the effects of any variations.
- ❖ Agree interim valuations with the contractor and issue interim certificates in accordance with the contract allowing for the submission of interim applications for payment.
- ❖ Convene and chair site progress meetings on a regular basis to principally discuss progress, cost and quality issues. Record all principal matters in minutes distributed to all project team members.
- ❖ Prepare regular progress reports for client, including details of any applications for extensions of time or disputes.
- ❖ Agree practical completion of the works under the contract terms. This may include the preparation of 'snagging' lists detailing the non-completion of minor work items remaining outstanding at practical completion.
- ❖ Administer the contract conditions during the defects liability period ensuring that all items of disrepair are rectified before the issue of the making good defects certificate and release of retention monies.

Collateral warranties and reliance letters

Collateral warranties

Introduction

The doctrine of 'privity of contract' has for many years prevented someone who is not a party to a contract from enforcing that contract. As a consequence, third party reliance documents have been a feature of the property and construction industry for over 20 years and there is little sign of them dying out. Such documents commonly take the form of collateral warranties. These documents are also sometimes called 'duty of care deeds'.

What do they do?

Collateral warranties create a contract between two parties. The main purpose of the contract is to allow the recipient ('**beneficiary**') of the collateral warranty to rely on the proper and competent performance of services by the giver ('**warrantor**') of the collateral warranty when the services concerned have actually been provided originally to another party and not to the recipient.

Should the beneficiary discover that the services have not been provided properly and competently by the warrantor, the beneficiary has a contractual route of redress through the collateral warranty.

Who gives collateral warranties?

There is no general restriction in the UK property and construction industry on who can give collateral warranties. Literally any person providing professional services or supplying goods can give collateral warranties, but they are used more particularly by those responsible for design services, or responsible for construction activities, such as:

- ❖ project managers;
- ❖ architects (building, landscape);
- ❖ engineers (mechanical, electrical, structural, acoustic, geotechnical);
- ❖ cost consultants or quantity surveyors;
- ❖ main contractors; and
- ❖ specialist contractors with design obligations (lifts, cladding, steelwork, roofing).

The diagram below identifies, in simple form, how collateral warranties might come about.

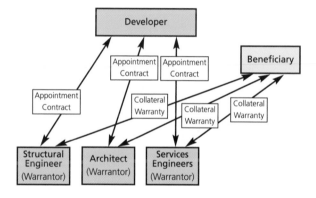

Who receives collateral warranties?

In the property and construction industry there are four basic parties who seek collateral warranties, namely:

- ❖ purchasers of freehold property (whether for investment of occupation);
- ❖ tenants of leasehold property (whether for investment of occupation);
- ❖ funders advancing loans for property acquisition and development; and
- ❖ employers under building contracts.

Are all warranties the same?

There is no single form of warranty wording adopted by the industry as a whole. Solicitors will have their own precedents as might property owners and developers. Certain industry bodies have developed their own precedents for use, for example:

- ❖ British Property Federation;
- ❖ Joint Contracts Tribunal (new suite from 2005) published by Sweet & Maxwell; and
- ❖ Construction Industry Council.

What are their common features?

Apart from identifying the beneficiary and the warrantor, warranties will normally contain clauses dealing with the warrantor's **primary obligation** to the beneficiary and **limits to the warrantor's liability**.

Primary obligation: This will normally be expressed in terms of use of reasonable skill and care and the warrantor will acknowledge that it owes the beneficiary the same obligations as are owed to the warrantor's client/employer in return for consideration on the part of the beneficiary. The payment is nearly always a nominal sum (such as £1 or £10), but there is no reason why the sum should not be more substantial.

Limits on liability: Potential liabilities arising under the collateral warranty may be limited in terms of:

- ❖ type of loss for which the warrantor is to be liable;
- ❖ net contribution when other parties also giving warranties are considered equally or jointly liable for the loss;
- ❖ equivalent rights to defence allowing the warrantor to raise in defence rights equivalent to those available in respect of claims from the client or employer;
- ❖ prohibited (deleterious) materials;
- ❖ professional indemnity insurance required;
- ❖ copyright and use of documents by the beneficiary;
- ❖ assignment rights and restrictions;
- ❖ limitation periods for the bringing of an action; or
- ❖ exclusion of *Contracts (Rights of Third Parties) Act* 1999.

Collateral warranties given to purchasers and tenants are normally almost identical.

Collateral warranties given to funders contain many of the same provisions as purchaser or tenant warranties but they might also include 'step-in rights'. These are rights permitting a funder to replace the warrantor's client or employer, in order to ensure that a scheme or transaction being funded is completed in the event that the client or employer becomes insolvent or otherwise fails to properly discharge their obligations to the warrantor.

Collateral warranties will normally be completed as deeds rather than as simple contracts. This means that the limitation period (the period within which legal proceedings for breach of the terms of the warranty must be commenced) is 12 years. A warranty completed as a simple contract would impose a limitation period of 6 years only on the beneficiary (*Limitation Act* 1980).

What do collateral warranties cost?

It is common for warranties to be provided at little or no cost. However, there is no reason why a more substantial fee should not be charged for a warranty by the warrantor, if the circumstances merit the levying of such a charge. The beneficiary will normally be expected to pay the fee for the warranty. There is no industry-recognised scale for fees associated with the provision of a warranty. Reasonableness, the perceived commercial value of the warranty, and the bargaining positions of the parties are the drivers in respect of the fee sought and paid.

What about the *Contracts (Rights of Third Parties) Act 1999*?

In the late 1990s, in a move to offer an alternative to collateral warranties, parliament enacted the *Contracts (Rights of Third Parties) Act* 1999. This Act came into full force and effect on 11 May 2000. It allows one party entering into an agreement with another party to contract on behalf of a third party, which might be a specific person or a class of person. The Act has not abolished the doctrine of privity of contract – it still exists – but the 1999 Act provides parties with a means to modify the doctrine, for the purposes of individual contracts, if they so decide.

With the arrival of the *Contracts (Rights of Third Parties) Act* 1999, collateral warranties were expected to decline in importance and wither away. Collateral warranties were (and perhaps still are) viewed as difficult and costly to procure. The provisions of the 1999 Act have not fallen into common usage however, and remain largely untested in law. Collateral warranties still have the upper hand when it comes to extending the benefit of contractual obligations and rights to third parties and the operation of the *Contracts (Rights of Third Parties) Act* 1999 is usually expressly excluded from agreements, including collateral warranties.

Reliance letters

Introduction

These are generally simpler documents than collateral warranties and, as the name suggests, they take the form of letters rather than more formal deeds or agreements. They are a recent appearance on the property and construction scene and tend to be encountered more frequently in relation to professional advisers' reports on properties as opposed to construction works.

Reliance letters tend to arise more commonly in relation to property transactions, as opposed to development work.

What do they do?

Reliance letters enable a third party to rely, for some purposes, on professional advice and opinion expressed in a report produced (normally) by a consultant for another party at an earlier point in time. This is particularly beneficial, for example, if the third party is seeking to purchase a property and wishes to rely on a report (or reports) produced in the recent past for the vendor.

Reliance letters can, but do not normally, result in the formation of a contractual relationship between the relying party and the party issuing the letter. The relying parties redress is in the law of tort, specifically negligent misrepresentation following the House of Lords decision of *Hedley Byrne & Co Ltd v Heller and Partners Ltd* 1964.

❖ Hedley were advertising agents who had provided substantial amounts of advertising on credit for Easipower. If Easipower did not pay for the advertising then Hedley would be responsible for such amounts. Hedley became concerned that Easipower would not be in a financial position to pay the debt and sought assurances from Easipower's bank (Heller and Partners Ltd) that Easipower could pay for the additional advertising which Hedley was proposing to give them on credit.

❖ Heller, gave a favourable report of Easipower's financial position, but stipulated that the report was given 'without responsibility'. On the strength of the report given by Heller, Hedley placed additional orders for Easipower. Easipower went into liquidation. Hedley lost £17,000 and commenced an action against Heller for damages under the tort of negligence.

❖ The House of Lords held that a negligent, although honest, misrepresentation, may give rise to an action for damages for financial loss, even if there was **no contract** between the advisor and the advisee, and no fiduciary relationship. The law would imply a duty of care when the advisee seeks information from an advisor who has special skill and where the advisee trusts the advisor to exercise due care, and that the advisor knew or ought to have known that reliance was being placed upon his or her skill and judgement.

❖ Fortunately for Heller, in this case, they expressly disclaimed responsibility and there was therefore no liability, as this effectively barred the claim. However, the decision established the doctrine of negligent misrepresentation.

Who gives reliance letters?

There is no general restriction in the UK property and construction industry on who can issue reliance letters. Literally, any professional person providing advice in the form of a report can allow a third party to rely on the report that he or she produces. There is no obligation in law on a professional to extend their liability in this manner: it is a commercial decision for the professional concerned and might well attract a fee.

Who seeks reliance letters?

Reliance letters are most commonly given to:

❖ purchasers of freehold property (whether for investment of occupation); or

❖ funders such as the banks.

There is no reason why a prospective tenant of property (whether for investment or occupation) could not seek a reliance letter, but this is less common.

It is for the party seeking reliance to determine whether they properly understand the context of the report and the circumstances surrounding its preparation. This might necessitate confirmation of the terms of reference and brief given to the professional originally in order to be sure that the advice and opinions in the report itself are not taken out of context. The professional will not warrant that the report concerned is fit for the purposes of the relying party.

Are all reliance letters the same?

No – reliance letters vary widely in content. There is no single form of wording for such letters adopted by the industry as a whole. Solicitors will have their own precedents as might professionals who issue reliance letters regularly.

What are the common features of a reliance letter?

Reliance letters are generally shorter than collateral warranties. For a reliance letter to be effectual, it is not necessary for it to record or evince the payment of a sum of money by the relying party to the professional. Reliance letters are addressed to the party seeking reliance. The letter should:

❖ state the reason why reliance is being sought – this will often, but not always, be linked to the purchase of a property, or funding of such a purchase;

❖ identify the document(s) on which reliance is being placed and expressly acknowledge that the relying party is entitled to and will rely on the documents;

❖ identify the specific instructions and brief pursuant to which the documents were originally produced; and

❖ set out any restrictions placed on the reliance including:

- the financial limit of any liability that the professional is willing to assume;
- a limit on the period of time over which the professional is willing to extend their liability (typically 6 or 12 years but sometimes less or more depending on the circumstances);
- whether or not the benefit of the reliance can be assigned to any third party; and
- confirmation that the advice in the document(s) concerned has not been updated.

What do reliance letters cost?

There are no recognised scales or rates in the property or construction industry relating to the provision of reliance letters.

It is more common to charge for reliance letters than for collateral warranties, as why should a professional extend their liability to others for nothing. A fee for each report relied upon is a reasonable starting point, as each report could give rise to liability. The number of different parties to whom the letter is addressed is also a relevant consideration.

Reasonableness, the perceived commercial value of the letter, and the bargaining positions of the parties are factors to consider in the final agreement of a fee.

Conclusion

Depending on the precise manner of drafting, it can be possible for a reliance letter to comprise a collateral warranty. For this to be the case the letter needs to contain evidence of a payment by the relying party to the vendor and it needs to be signed and delivered as a deed rather than simply signed like a letter.

Contract management

Development and procurement

Employer's agent

Employer's agent duties

Clients routinely wish to procure projects in the pursuit of certainty of cost. Design and build forms of procurement are now in frequent use and these transfer the 'risk' in any development to the contractor, while giving him or her greater flexibility to deliver the product. As an agent acting on behalf of the employer, it is essential that the following pre-contract and post-contract services are provided:

Pre-contract service

* Define the responsibilities of the employer, employer's agent and contractor.
* Appraise and quantify the risks.
* Formulate the employer's brief and identify specific requirements.
* Assess the contractor's proposals and ensure compliance with the employer's requirements.
* Undertake design audit of the contractor's proposals for compliance with the employer's requirements.
* Evaluate the offer, the contract sum analysis and stage payments and assess value for money.

Post-contract service

* Set up quality control procedure and report on works carried out on site.
* Provide site visits and chair meetings.
* Implement changes to the employer's requirements only on written approval of the client.
* Agree stage payments and recommendations for payments.
* Prepare monthly project control statements and cash flow forecasts to client.
* Advise on practical completion, preparation of snagging schedules and component literature.

General exclusions

* Checking and verifying contractor's design in terms of adequacy and efficiency.
* Checking and verifying contractor's design in terms of fitness for purpose.

In undertaking duties as the employer's agent, it is important to recognise the contractor's freedom to design, while respecting the client's brief and auditing the quality of the end product.

The quantity surveyor's role

Capital project advice

The quantity surveyor is tasked with controlling construction cost by accurate measurement of the works required and the application of expert knowledge of costs of labour, materials and plant required. An understanding of the implications of design decisions at an early stage ensure that good value is obtained for the money to be expended.

Several capabilities are required to fulfil this role:

- ❖ An ability to predict future costs from limited information and in dynamic market conditions.
- ❖ An ability to manage the procurement process to ensure that predictions of cost, time and quality are delivered.
- ❖ An awareness of risk with a capability to assess and manage that risk.
- ❖ An ability to demonstrate value for money.

Current trends in the industry lean towards cost reductions, with pressure coming from major purchasers; the importance of value for money is undoubtedly here to stay. Fixed out-turn costs are a necessity.

This is against a backdrop of upward cost pressure on suppliers of construction resources. Skills shortages are emerging and price rises are sticking.

The challenge to the construction industry and the quantity surveyor is sizeable. Changes in working practices and culture are inevitable and there needs to be a significant change in emphasis towards:

- ❖ value rather than cost;
- ❖ more professionalism in the early stages of project delivery;
- ❖ effective team work between the construction professions and contractors – adversarial relationships are no longer appropriate and will not survive;
- ❖ an understanding of the clients' business, and with that, the ongoing costs of the finished project;
- ❖ an awareness of financial incentives and opportunities available to the client (VAT relief and capital allowances – for details, see relevant sections in the cost management chapter beginning on page 77); and
- ❖ an awareness on the part of purchasers that effective management of the construction process is a valuable service and does not come cheap.

Partnering

The traditional approach to construction procurement is driven by the terms of a contract. Relationships are imposed rather than developed; cost is focused at the expense of value; problems are packaged into liabilities rather than accepted as joint responsibilities; risk is off-loaded rather than managed. Partnering offers an alternative.

Partnering unites the sponsoring, design and construction teams and it endeavours to drive them forward with a common purpose.

The important characteristics are involvement, ownership and trust. This becomes obvious when one considers the facts:

- ❖ The parties' objectives are not mutually exclusive.
- ❖ A construction project should not comprise a discrete stage of design followed by construction.

❖ Generally, parties to a venture perform better if given a measure of control and a share in the action. This is all about ownership and being a stakeholder.

There are several levels of partnering. The simple indicators include the following:

❖ Early involvement of contractors and subcontractors; viewing a construction team rather than a design team and a contractor.

❖ Flexibility – for example, being prepared to accept higher short-term costs in the interests of longer-term value; reducing cost rather than simply transferring it to others.

❖ A willingness to look beyond contractual responsibilities and provide more than is called for. 'The gold service' – going the extra mile.

❖ Concentration upon relationships rather than contractual positions. Actions driven by a common purpose rather than a book of rules.

More formal arrangements are implied in:

❖ project partnering; and

❖ strategic partnering.

The tools implied in partnering usually involve the following:

❖ Two stage tendering – getting the contractor on board early.

❖ Negotiation – allowing the contractor to contribute to the design process rather than having to react to it; gaining a clear understanding of the project's objectives before committing to contract and ultimately being able to reduce the contractor's costs and, in that process, the client's costs. Perhaps more importantly, however, if the process of negotiation is conducted correctly the contractor is afforded the opportunity of understanding the client's definition of value.

❖ Open book – everything competitively tendered but with the leader in the procurement process, the contractor, fully acquainted with the project's decision-making rationale.

❖ A charter – as distinct from the rigidity of a contract, the parties set out what they want to achieve rather than what they are obliged to do.

❖ Performance related reward – allowing the contractor to become a stakeholder in the project budget rather than a conduit through which it flows.

Ultimately of course, partnering is all about attitude. The logic of partnering is inescapable; the extent to which it works will depend on the ability of the parties to shake free from traditional attitudes but also on the ability of the management team to deliver a project in unison and without (necessarily) conventional contract protection.

Development

61

Construction management

Under this form of procurement, the client appoints a construction manager who is paid a fee for managing and overseeing pre- and post-contract project activities. Site overheads may be included or paid direct by the client. Separate direct appointments will exist for the design team members. Building can begin as soon as the design is sufficiently advanced to allow the initial stages of construction to proceed and to prepare and agree a cost estimate for the entire scheme.

Construction is divided into works packages and the client enters into direct contracts with each of the individual package contractors. This differs from management contracting where the contracts are between the management contractor and each package contractor. The individual packages are tendered at appropriate times throughout the construction period under the direction and management of the construction manager.

Whether a given project is suited to construction management (CM) will depend on a number of factors, as identified in the following table.

Factors	Considerations
Size	CM is an involved form of procurement and can seldom be justified for small projects of less than £5 million.
Complexity	CM is suited to complex projects with a substantial proportion of specialist package contractor involvement.
Uncertainty	Where the project is being conducted in an uncertain environment, CM affords clients a higher degree of flexibility to make changes during the process while minimising the consequent time and cost penalties.
Time	CM permits overlap between design and construction because tendering of packages can take place on a staggered basis rather than all at once as per traditional arrangements. This can save time and suit a 'fast track' approach. Greater involvement of the client with the CM and package contractors may also improve efficiency and introduce opportunities to reduce the overall programme. It should be noted however that time savings may be at the expense of cost risk as the scope is not fixed until much later in the process.
Cost	Cost certainty is not known until all of the packages have been let. To overcome this difficulty robust cost planning is required from the outset of the project. However, procuring the works from trade contractors and not main contractors (in common with management contracting) should result in the lowest cost at the end of the day because the best price is chosen for each package contract without a main contractor's profit. Clients have more options to alter or adapt the design throughout the construction period without leaving themselves at a negotiating disadvantage with a main contractor. There is also greater potential to 'value engineer' the project under these arrangements.
Design	Often clients wish to retain control of the design process and this is facilitated under CM. Changes to design during construction carry less cost and time risk than under other procurement methods.

Achieving excellence in construction

'Through the Achieving Excellence initiative, central government clients commit to maximise, by continuous improvement, the efficiency, effectiveness and value for money of their procurement of new works, maintenance and refurbishment.'

With this statement, the Office of Government Commerce (OGC) launched 'Achieving Excellence' in 1999 – a programme which aims to incorporate the recommendations of the Latham (*Constructing the Team* 1994) and Egan (*Rethinking Construction* 1998) reports into new ways of working for a construction industry that is notoriously resistant to change.

The initiative prescribes best practice for construction procurement in the public sector. Principal themes that run through the guidance are:

- ❖ long-term relationships, encouraging shared learning as a route to improving performance;
- ❖ crisper decision-making;
- ❖ investment in people through skills development then empowering them to take ownership and make decisions;
- ❖ development of 'metrics' so that performance can be measured and compared; and
- ❖ active management of value and risk across the whole life of a built asset – from construction to operation.

Certain factors are seen as critical to success

Leadership and commitment – the successful project starts at the top with 'ownership' by a senior competent individual and the correct commitment of his or her time. This is seen as absolutely crucial but frequently neglected.

Stakeholder involvement throughout – 'stakeholders' are all those parties with an interest in the project and who will influence its outcome. This may range from bosses to staff to neighbours to the general public. These parties will each have a different perspective on the project. These perspectives need to be understood and reconciled as far as is possible. The successful project aims to exceed the expectations of all these parties.

Roles and responsibilities – each player should know its place in the team and what is expected of it.

Integrated teams – the 'design team' or 'construction team' should be subsumed within the greater group of client, designers, constructors, specialist suppliers and even facilities managers, operating as a single development team with common overriding goals and objectives. This means investment in bringing the parties together and building the team ethos.

Integrated processes – in which design, construction, operation and maintenance are considered as parts of a whole rather than separate activities.

Design quality – that which achieves whole-life value by combining functionality with serviceability while respecting the environment. Design Quality Indicators (DQIs) have been developed as tools to give measurability to this multi-faceted dimension of individual projects.

Health and safety – a commitment to excellence, because it is ethical, shows respect to the team and community and makes business sense.

Procurement strategies – adopting those that ensure an integrated team and process approach. The Private Finance Initiative, Prime Contracting and Design and Build are those preferred by the government for this reason. Traditional routes of procurement should only be used if they can be fully justified by business case.

Risk and value management – These are interrelated activities that should involve the integrated team in constructive collaboration to deliver best value throughout the project. The independent key stage, or 'gateway' review process has an important role to play here.

Whole-life business perspective – business decisions should be made based on the balanced long term costs of site acquisition, design, development and operation, rather than short term costs only. This is consistent with the integrated process approach.

Continuous improvement – this requires a genuine commitment allied to schemes of measurement, key performance indicators (KPIs) and benchmarks so that levels of performance can be established and trends tracked.

Sustainability – Construction has a major impact on the environment and project teams have an important responsibility in this respect in areas such as quality of life, flexibility, creating desirable environments and ensuring the efficient use of resources.

The Achieving Excellence initiative is supported by a suite of publications and a web-based toolkit. They jointly comprise perhaps the most comprehensive best practice 'manual' in the history of the industry. They are all available on the OGC website at www.ogc.gov.uk.

How successful is the initiative proving? Consistent with the emphasis on measurable performance, a strategic target was set for the period 2003–05 that 70% (by volume) of public sector construction projects should be delivered on time, within budget, exceeding consumer and stakeholder expectations and with zero defects.

OGC information note 1/2007 reports continued success in results recorded for April to September 2006 and compared to the original strategic targets set.

Compared to the 70% target set for 2005, 74% of projects were delivered on time, 70% delivered within budget, 83% exceeded customer expectations and 68% were delivered with zero defects for the 2006 period. The total amount of waste avoidance since April 2003 is now £235 million.

Project management

Project management can be defined as the direction of any complex of activities that have a defined beginning and an end. This process has a direct application to all industries and particularly to the construction process. The application of project management techniques in construction has developed rapidly over the past 30 years in response to the growing complexity of projects and the need to coordinate an increasingly fragmented and specialised industry.

The first task of a project manager is to define precisely the scope of the project, including the gaining of an understanding of the fundamentals of the client's business plan for the anticipated scheme.

The second is to gain an understanding of the client's objectives in terms of time, cost, quality and perceived risk. These objectives should be specified by means of a precise brief and schedule of target dates, a master budget, a risk register and specification standards. The relative priority that the client gives to each of these measures should also be understood. For example, a client may have an overriding need to complete by a certain date, so requiring the expenditure of additional funds to make this event a greater certainty. The project manager needs to reflect these factors in a strategy and plan for the project, usually termed the Project Execution Plan (PEP).

The third task is to assemble a competent team to deliver the project. The team needs to be briefed on the client's objectives and their precise role in such delivery. Coordination and reporting routines should be clearly defined at this point.

An effective project manager will be skilled in leading and directing a team drawn together specifically for the duration of the project. This requires personal, managerial, presentational and, above all, communication techniques. Stimulation of coordination in the project team and control of time, cost and quality requires the establishment of master control documents, such as the PEP, information flow tracking tools, risk registers, project master budgets and programmes. These are invaluable tools to enable the project manager to promote coordination, monitor progress, evaluate status and manage delivery.

Successful construction project management entails:

- ❖ strong balanced leadership;
- ❖ an empowered client project sponsor;
- ❖ project team focus on client's objectives;
- ❖ strong team relationships and motivation;
- ❖ a strong business case;
- ❖ a clear and developed brief and schedule;
- ❖ identification of measurable time, cost and quality objectives;
- ❖ defining roles and communicating objectives throughout the team;
- ❖ establishment of strategic as well as detailed controls;
- ❖ recognition that only the remaining time, cost and performance can be managed;
- ❖ management apportionment of risk;
- ❖ awareness of opportunity;
- ❖ robust project management practice – alive to risks and opportunities;
- ❖ an appropriate procurement and delivery methodology;
- ❖ an appropriate project contractual matrix;
- ❖ balanced risk apportionment;
- ❖ early established use of project control documentation;
- ❖ dynamic programme management;
- ❖ use of gateway review techniques;
- ❖ open, truthful and transparent lines of communication;
- ❖ continual challenge to ensure best quality, long-term value and programme;
- ❖ active management; and
- ❖ regular review to ensure long-term value.

Quality management and professional construction services

Quality management is a continual process that does not just happen but evolves over time and through experience. As clients' needs change and their expectations grow, it is essential that businesses continually improve so that they can carry on providing high quality products and services that continue to meet changing requirements. Organisations can help secure their future in an effective and efficient way by introducing a quality management system (QMS), which includes a commitment to continual improvement.

The ISO 9000 family of standards listed below provide the basis for many organisations to develop, implement, operate and maintain an effective QMS:

- ❖ ISO 9000:2005 *Quality management systems – Fundamentals and vocabulary*
- ❖ ISO 9001:2000 *Quality management systems – Requirements*
- ❖ ISO 9004:2000 *Quality management systems – Guidelines for performance improvement*
- ❖ ISO 19011:2002 *Guidelines for quality and/or environmental management systems auditing.*

All standards are subject to routine reviews and ISO 9001 is currently under review; the British Standards Institute (BSI) expects this process to be completed in June 2009.

The ISO 9000 documents were developed around the following quality management principles:

- ❖ customer focus;
- ❖ leadership;
- ❖ involvement of people;
- ❖ process approach;
- ❖ system approach to management;
- ❖ continual improvement;
- ❖ factual approach to decision making; and
- ❖ mutually beneficial supplier relationships.

ISO 9001 is the only auditable standard within the series and, although there is no legal requirement to adopt it, many client organisations make third party ISO 9001 certification a prerequisite for their suppliers. This is especially true for clients operating in the public sector.

The standard itself promotes a 'process approach' and looks to integrate quality management with business management. The content has been arranged into five main sections as follows:

- ❖ quality management system;
- ❖ management responsibility;
- ❖ resource management;
- ❖ product realisation; and
- ❖ measurement, analysis and improvement.

In addition, ISO 9001 supports the methodology known as *Plan-Do-Check-Act* (PDCA), which can briefly be described as follows:

- ❖ **Plan** – establish the objectives and processes necessary to deliver results in accordance with client requirements and the organisation's policies.
- ❖ **Do** – implement the processes.
- ❖ **Check** – monitor and measure processes and product/services against policies, objectives and requirements for the product/services and report the results.
- ❖ **Act** – continually improve process performance.

ISO 9004 is designed to complement ISO 9001 but can also be used independently. It provides guidelines on a wider range of objectives associated with a QMS that go beyond the requirements set out in ISO 9001. In fact ISO 9004 clearly states that 'It is not intended for certification, regulatory or contractual use, nor as a guide to the implementation of ISO 9001'.

With the development and introduction of BS EN ISO 14001:2004 (*Environmental management systems – Requirements with guidance for use*) and BS OHSAS 18001:2007 (*Occupational health and safety management systems – Requirements*), organisations are increasingly looking to develop more integrated management systems that build on the common elements shared with ISO 9001. Once again, there is no legal requirement to adopt ISO 14001 or OHSAS 18001. However, some clients and organisations at the head of supply chains are looking to make third party certification to these standards a measure of competence for their providers.

Latent defects insurance

Latent defects insurance is commonly required on construction projects by developers, purchasers, tenants and funders. The objective of the policy is to provide cover for latent defects that existed prior to practical completion, but remained undiscovered at that time, and became apparent during the period of the policy (usually 10–12 years). These policies include defects in design, materials and/or workmanship.

Latent defects insurance is also known as decennial insurance (ten years cover), wrap up insurance and BUILD (building users' insurance against latent defects).

The basic policy covers physical damage to the structure of the building, or damage that resulted from the latent defect in the structure. Weatherproofing (e.g. roof coverings) and waterproofing cover is usually incorporated, however the policy wording should be verified. Cover for non-structural elements and mechanical and electrical services can usually be purchased as an addition. The policy will not cover works that were outstanding at practical completion, therefore these outstanding works should be kept to a minimum. In addition, cover is not included for defects that occur after practical completion. Policy exclusions, such as business interruption and loss of profit, should also be carefully reviewed.

The cost of a policy is generally between 0.65% and 1% of the contract value for the basic cover. Adding cover for the non-structural elements and the mechanical and electrical services would increase the premium to between 1% and 2%, which is relatively expensive.

The developer usually takes out the policy, however its benefits can be assignable to future owners, tenants or funders.

For a successful claim, insurers will usually pay for the repair costs, emergency works, professional fees, site clearance and compliance with statutory requirements. The insurance will provide almost immediate funds for repairs which minimises disruption. The developer does not need to rely on proving a claim against the designers' or contractor's professional indemnity insurance for inherent defects. Furthermore, the insurance helps to provide a no-blame approach that aids the resolution of the defects in a less confrontational environment.

The insurer will want to make an independent assessment of the design and construction of the project. They will generally appoint a technical monitoring surveyor to act on their behalf throughout the duration of the project.

Contract insurance

Construction contracts, by their very nature, give rise to risks of injury to persons and damage to property. On a large construction project the financial implications can be enormous. It is critical that the right insurance provisions are in place.

Contract insurance is one of the principal features of a construction contract and ensures that certain risks are clearly covered by one or other of the parties. However, it is also one of the most complex elements and great care should be exercised when advising on the correct insurance requirements.

On 14 January 2005, the Financial Services Authority (FSA) introduced the *Insurance Mediation Directive Regulations*, requiring anyone who carries out certain regulated activities (such as advising on choice of contract insurance) to be authorised by the FSA. Providing advice when not authorised by the FSA, is in breach of the regulations and is a criminal offence. Consequently specialist assistance is often required.

Within the construction industry there are two main types of insurance; a liability insurance policy and a loss insurance policy.

Liability insurance policies

A liability insurance policy provides protection against claims, arising from negligence or inappropriate action, resulting in injury to persons or property damage.

Liability of contractor

Under the JCT traditional forms of contract, the contractor is required to take out and maintain a liability policy in respect of:

- ❖ personal injury or death of any persons, which is caused by the carrying out of the works, unless that is due to act or neglect of the employer or its agents; and

- ❖ injury or damage to property (with the exception of the works) that is due to negligence, omission or default of the contractor, subcontractor or its agents.

Liability of employer *(non-negligence cover)*

This type of policy covers liability of the employer if damage is caused to any property, other than the works, by the carrying out of the works. The provision is usually optional and operates when damage that occurs is not due to negligence on the part of either the employer or contractor.

In the case of *Gold v Patman & Fotheringham Ltd* [1958] 2 ALL ER 497, the employer was found liable in nuisance to the neighbouring property for subsidence damage caused by the works. It was found that the contractor had not been negligent in carrying out the works and therefore the employer was liable for third party costs. Hence the need for insurance.

When deciding on whether to select this type of policy, it is important to consider the surrounding environment and location of adjoining properties, together with the nature of the works.

Loss insurance policy

The general principle of construction contracts is that they place a commitment on the contractor to complete the works. If the contract works become damaged or destroyed then the contractor is obliged to repair or reinstate the works at its own cost. Under a loss insurance policy the insured party is able to recover its losses from the insurers.

Insurance of the works

Typically under the JCT traditional forms of contract, insurance of the works is split between 'new buildings' or 'existing structures'.

For new building works, either the contractor or the employer may take out a joint names policy covering 'all risks' insurance. This is insurance against physical loss or damage to work and site materials, including theft and vandalism, however it excludes a list of industry standard exclusions such as war or nuclear contamination.

When works are undertaken to existing buildings, it is usual for the employer to take out a joint names policy covering 'specified perils' in respect of existing structures, as well as an 'all risks' joint names policy for the works. Specified perils includes a finite list of events such as fire, explosion, storm, flood, civil commotion, riot, etc. and is narrower than that of an all risks policy.

Joint names policy

Construction contracts often require that a 'loss' insurance policy is taken out in the joint names of the employer and contractor. The purpose of a joint names policy is to protect both parties whereby the insurers have no right of subrogation against one or other of the parties if damage occurs due to the other party. Subrogation is an important legal principle relating to insurance and is the right of the insurers to stand in the shoes of the insured party and recover the loss.

In practice, it is not always possible for a policy to be taken out in the joint names of both parties. In this instance, a 'subrogation waiver' may be obtained to prevent the insurers seeking compensation from the defaulting party.

Further information

Financial Services Authority (FSA) website: www.fsa.gov.uk

Contractor appointment/tendering

There are a number of factors affecting the selection of contractors and their possible inclusion on a project shortlist.

Pre-tender/pre-qualification

Validation of a tender list will typically involve internal market intelligence from the project management and design team, based on previous performance in delivering key objectives matching those of the subject project.

Evaluation of any contractor shortlist should be based on agreement of the measurement criteria and thus the suitability of the selected group. The nature of the project will determine the most important criteria and thus assessment.

In most cases pre-tender interviews should take place to confirm the selected contractors' resources during the project period.

Typical pre-qualification submissions

❖ Company details including structure, financial standing and management systems, references from similar projects and Health and Safety policy.

❖ Specific details of the proposed project team – authority, experience, qualifications and resource, including design integration, control and coordination.

❖ Recent track record based on proposed project and procedure route.

❖ Project execution – programming approach, site logistics and snagging/completion strategy.

On the basis of the information received, a scoring system should be used to formulate a shortlist of contractors to include on the tender list.

Quality and price assessment

❖ The objective of assessments is to select the one firm providing best value for money based on both quality and cost. A scoring format should be applied on both quality and cost – agreed prior to issuing tenders. Weighting of marks against criteria needs to be adjusted depending on project type.

❖ The design team should agree on a quality threshold (regardless of competitiveness) at which point any tenders below this level are discounted.

❖ Low tenders should be thoroughly reviewed to ensure the full scope of the scheme is understood. Written explanations from contractors should be sought to test the robustness of any submitted bid.

Other factors

❖ Contractors should be aware of any specific provision in terms of appointment – i.e. variation to standard appointment contracts which they agree to as part of tender submission.

❖ Where contract amendments apply, it is worth ensuring that these are resolved and agreed as soon as possible. Protracted contract negotiations can stall the progress of a project if priority and time limitations to resolve are not imposed as a condition to the appointment of the selected contractor.

❖ Each project will have different drivers, be it time, cost or quality. Assessment of contractor shortlists and tender evaluation must be bespoke to ensure key drivers are met.

How to appoint consultants

In order to appoint consultants, as with contractors, it is preferable that a transparent and competitive process is undertaken to ensure best practice and to demonstrate best value for the client and the client's project.

There are three steps undertaken in any appointment process of a consultant, be it either on a competitive or a negotiated basis:

❖ a request for fee proposal commonly known as the RFP process or the provision of a fee bid;

❖ the selection of successful consultant; and

❖ a formal appointment of the consultant.

Once the need for consultancy advice has been identified, the first step is to draw up a list of consultants who are known to be competent, and may be available, to provide the required services.

Invitation for consultant to present a fee proposal

In order for the consultant to provide a fee proposal, on which their appointment will be based, the following matters need to be **clearly defined**.

Brief

The brief should be as specific as possible. In some cases it may be useful to make informal approaches to a number of consultants to discuss the project before finalising the brief.

The following items will be relevant in most cases:

❖ the required end product (plan, contract drawings, report, etc.) – this is crucial and needs to be identified as clearly and explicitly as possible;

❖ the context for the proposed work;

❖ a list and copies of the basic information already available;

❖ the parameters: financial limitations, previous commitments, physical limits, area of influence, established plans and policies, etc. Indicate which parts of the brief are fixed and which are open to proposals by the tendering consultants on methodology, timetable or sequence;

❖ an indication of the likely project budget if available;

❖ proposed key members of the client team, including the project manager and the steering group;

❖ the anticipated number of meetings with the project manager and/or the steering group;

❖ any confidentiality requirements;

❖ the evaluation criteria, especially the price/quality relationship;

❖ unique aspects of the project must be covered (so as to avoid surprises, e.g. requirements for warranties, specific levels of required PI insurance, requirement for Novation of consultants, i.e. something that might make a consultant change the proposal; and

❖ additional conditions relating to the particular project and the specific requirements of the client should accompany each appointment.

Programme

The programme should include:

❖ the timescale for the work, with a target start date and completion dates and a programme for any intermediate stages; and

❖ the timetable for the selection process and the work.

Scopes of service

In order to enable consistency between the same type of consultants and also different consultant disciplines to be engaged on the same project, it is preferable to generate a bespoke set of scopes of service to be used in conjunction with a matrix of responsibilities. This:

❖ allows the demonstration of clear definitions of where each of the consultants' responsibilities start and finish; and

❖ ensures there are no gaps between the consultants' services.

The consultant should be asked to provide:

❖ the background experience of the firm;

❖ any special experience relevant to the project;

❖ the proposed technical approach and methodology – this should comprise an itemised account of the tasks to be undertaken and factors to be examined in carrying out the work;

❖ details of the consultancy staff to be assigned to the work, including their individual responsibilities and past experience;

❖ a proposed work schedule – this could, for instance, be in the form of a bar chart, indicating the timescale and completion date for each part of the work;

> ❖ details of how the consultant proposes to organise and manage the work – this should cover any planned head office involvement, back-up support, and use of subcontractors for, say, survey work; and
> ❖ a financial proposal, covering the basis of charging fees, reimbursable expenses, etc.

Criteria for selection of consultants

The selection of a consultant is based on a number of factors including the consultant's expertise and specialist knowledge of particular issues and projects, fee costs and past performance.

In order to do this the following should be carried out:

> ❖ Assess consultants' bids on a level playing field of consistent terms (this is established by the first step in the process described above – the brief) to ensure the bids are comparable and can be assessed fairly.
> ❖ Ensure multiple bids from the same type of consultants and ensure bids and other elements of the consultant team are aligned with each other.

Analysis of the consultants' bids should also consider:

> ❖ The bids should be assessed in context of quality, cost and value. The intangible aspects (such as quality of services, unique ideas that the consultant is able to bring to the project, ability of consultant to work within a team) need to also be assessed.
> ❖ Bids should demonstrate sufficient flexibility to accommodate modifications to the bid. Payment regimes should reflect the client's cash flow forecast requirements or motivational milestones on the project.
> ❖ It is important to take account of factors such as the consultant's experience of comparable work, the seniority and experience of individual staff, and the extent to which the consultant has understood the nature of the project and the client's priorities.

In addition, the following points should be taken into consideration:

> ❖ Has the consultant demonstrated a real insight into the needs of the client, or does the proposal read like a routine effort?
> ❖ Does the quality of presentation of the proposal indicate hasty and careless preparation, or does it give the confidence that the end product will be of a high professional standard?

Effectively, a judgement will need to be made on the consultant's ability to deliver a high quality and cost effective service within an agreed financial and performance framework.

Fees and expenses

The fee basis should be agreed in writing between the consultant and the client prior to the commencement of work. It may reflect:

> ❖ the importance of the project to the client;
> ❖ the cost or value of the project;
> ❖ the skills required; and
> ❖ special circumstances such as the need for urgent action or the novelty of the matters raised.

Fees should preferably be determined on a lump sum basis, in which the consultant agrees a fixed price to cover all the time likely to be spent on the work and all expenses likely to be incurred. This mitigates the financial exposure to the client and contributes to providing a better level of cost certainty on the project.

The fee basis should also include:

- ❖ rates for principals and assistants involved in the work, calculated on an hourly basis, including where applicable a definition of what is deemed to be a day;
- ❖ prospective changes in hourly rates (e.g. reviewed annually in line with inflation);
- ❖ details of the method of payment. This may include payments on account, interim payments or stage payments. The consultant may stipulate that if such payments are called for and not met within the specified time, the consultant may suspend work on the project;
- ❖ estimates of:
  - the total fee (subject to assumptions or exclusions);
  - the amount of billable time anticipated to be required to complete the project (subject to limitations);
- ❖ where appropriate, the rate of interest to be charged on outstanding accounts;
- ❖ specific administration costs;
- ❖ travelling time, and how this is to be charged;
- ❖ disbursements;
- ❖ indemnity insurance and any increase to provide cover for a specific project;
- ❖ the appointment and payment of subconsultants; and
- ❖ the method of charging for, and arrangements for distribution of income from, any report or other publication (including plans).

When fees are based on time costs, the time spent on a project (including travelling time) is chargeable at the daily or hourly rate of the person doing the work.

Activities that are included in the time charge include:

- ❖ technical work as defined in the contract or by agreement with the client;
- ❖ survey work or data processing;
- ❖ meetings with the client, with any other consultants or advisers associated with the work, and with relevant external organisations;
- ❖ site visits;
- ❖ travelling in connection with the work;
- ❖ preparation and production of project drawings and other graphic material;
- ❖ writing, editing and processing reports;
- ❖ community involvement and consultation procedures; and
- ❖ presentation of reports and follow-up work.

Expenses which are incurred directly as a result of an assignment and which are properly recoverable from the client are charged separately from time costs, usually in the form of an itemised invoice. Such expenses may include travel, accommodation and subsistence, data processing, and the purchase of maps and other documentation. They will normally be subject to VAT.

Appointment of the consultant

In most instances, a simple exchange of letters will be sufficient to confirm the appointment of a consultant. However, a client may prefer to have a formal contract agreed, especially on larger value projects. This should be prepared in draft by the legal advisors of the client, preferably in advance of selection, and a copy forwarded to the consultant for comment prior to formal agreement.

The items that should be specified in any contract with a consultant should include:

- ❖ the services to be provided by the consultant;
- ❖ the timing, phasing and stages of the work;
- ❖ report schedules, including the submission of progress reports;
- ❖ the keeping of project accounts and records by the consultants;
- ❖ costs and payments;
- ❖ ownership of reports, copyright of documents and plans;
- ❖ levels of required professional indemnity Insurance (PII) – this will vary depending on the value of the project and services offered; and
- ❖ requirements for consultant warranties. (Please refer to Collateral warranties and reliance letters on page 50.)

In drawing up either a formal contract or a simpler document of appointment, other specific points may need to be considered:

- ❖ the terms of appointment and the fee basis
  - – Avoid terms of conditions that come from other consultants. It is preferable to create a bespoke appointment document that provides consistent terms for all consultant agreements on a project.
  - – It is also good practice to avoid industry standard agreements when appointing consultants, but this is not always possible. In these cases the overlap or underlap between these types of agreements needs to be managed.
  - – If there is no readily available format, use or adapt the nearest equivalent in preference to trying to devise one from scratch;
- ❖ if any office is to act 'in association', the financial arrangements for this should be determined;
- ❖ the individual to whom the consultant will be directly accountable;
- ❖ provision for any additional work which may prove necessary for the satisfactory completion of the project, or which the client may wish to commission for some other reason;
- ❖ default or release clauses to cover the eventuality of the work not proceeding to completion; and
- ❖ provision for handing over survey and analysis information in a useable form for updating and review, and compatibility of computer-based data.

For industry standard agreement documents for consultant appointments please refer to the following:

- ❖ Architects: RIBA Standard Agreement for the Appointment of an Architect (S-Con-07-A) which replaces SFA/99 and CE/99.

- ❖ Engineers: ACE conditions of engagement 2002 (revised 2004). A suite of conditions to accommodate particular engineering services, including also a short form agreement and subconsultancy agreement.

- ❖ Consultancy Agreement: BPF May 2005.

- ❖ Quantity/building surveyors: RICS form with guidance notes, 1999, for quantity surveying services and RICS form with guidance notes, 2nd edition, 2000, for building surveying services.

- ❖ CDM co-ordinators: The RIBA, RICS and ACE standard form appointments make provision for CDM co-ordinator services. It is common for the architect, quantity surveyor or engineer to also undertake the role of CDM co-ordinator. Sometimes an independent consultant is appointed to undertake the CDM co-ordinator role.

- ❖ Project managers: RICS Project Management Memorandum of Agreement and Conditions of Engagement, 3rd edition, September 1999 and RIBA Form of appointment for Project Manager PM99 (revised 2004).

- ❖ General: The ICE Professional Services Contract, and Adjudicator's Contract, 3rd edition, 2005. This is part of the New Engineering Contract.

Cost management

Urban regeneration

What is urban regeneration?

As cities and urban conurbations grow they constantly change to respond to demand and supply according to prevailing economic, social and environmental factors. Many thriving communities lose their regenerative capacity over time and fall into decline. We know many examples from our own history such as the economic decline of the London Docklands and the pit communities in the north, or social decline in the major cities such as Manchester's Hulme district.

Sustainable urban regeneration requires a balanced mix of social, economic and environmental factors to enable each area to establish its own continuous regenerative capacity.

Urban regeneration projects tend to be large scale and multi-faceted; successful schemes incorporate mixed uses such as commerce, retail, industrial and of course residential. They also have a mixture of tenures including freehold and leasehold in both the public and private sectors. Projects often involve many different organisations such as local authorities, government bodies, private developers or house builders and social housing providers and more.

Key players

The key players in urban regeneration can be divided into the following groups:

- ❖ Government departments and agencies: English Partnerships is the national regeneration agency and reports to the department for Communities and Local Government (CLG). Regional and local agencies include the likes of SEEDA, EEDA, London Development Agency, Sheffield One, etc.
- ❖ Local and regional authorities are often key landowners and major drivers of urban regeneration in deprived areas. They also have land assembly powers.
- ❖ Housing associations are key to the provision of social and public sector housing and management.
- ❖ Private house builders are often essential to realising the economic value of many urban areas and providing initial capital investment.
- ❖ Private developers: many schemes require commercial, industrial, retail and other property essential to the initial and continuing regenerative capacity of an area.
- ❖ Private business and occupiers are essential to local economic welfare.
- ❖ Investors and funders are essential for raising the requisite capital.
- ❖ Infrastructure companies, including transport, statutory supplies and services.

Types of regeneration

Urban regeneration can be classified into three main types:

- ❖ Urban centre renewal – town centre regeneration schemes like Lewisham High Street.
- ❖ Estate regeneration – generally housing based schemes in deprived and declining areas.
- ❖ Urban renewal and new urban villages – schemes like the Greenwich Millennium Village.

Key areas for growth

The CLG has identified four key areas for growth to meet a massive predicted shortfall in housing provision in the South East. These include:

- ❖ Thames Gateway;
- ❖ Cambridge – Stanstead – London Link;
- ❖ Milton Keynes (and East Midlands); and
- ❖ Ashford.

The predominant focus in these areas will be to bring developers together with the central government agencies tasked to deliver government housing policy.

Procurement strategy

The projects associated with urban regeneration are large and activity is set to continue over the long term. Various forms of Public Private Partnership are essential in bringing together necessary resources and skills to undertake:

- ❖ land assembly and contamination issues;
- ❖ infrastructure development for transport and statutory services;
- ❖ social infrastructure development for essential schools, hospitals, affordable housing, etc.;
- ❖ planning and urban design for sustainable communities and buildings;
- ❖ construction industry supply chain management, standardisation and innovation in techniques; and
- ❖ funding and capital development routes.

New skills will be required in integrating development management with project management in the context of regeneration.

Each regeneration project will have its own unique and challenging dimensions across the economic, social and environmental factors that make for sustainable placemaking for the benefit of people today and future generations.

VAT in the construction industry – zero rating

VAT and construction works

VAT in relation to buildings and construction is a complex area but below are some of the fundamental issues to consider when building new or carrying out works on an existing property.

Building new property

All goods and services supplied for use in the construction of a building are standard rated (at 17.5% generally and 5% in specific situations) except in the following circumstances, when they would be zero rated.

Where the new building is a dwelling and it is:

- ❖ self contained;
- ❖ able to be sold as a single dwelling;

❖ has been granted planning consent; and

❖ entitled to be used as a dwelling throughout the year.

NB: Certain elements within a dwelling will always be standard rated (see note on DIY projects later in this section). This zero rating only applies to goods and services supplied in the course of construction of a new building and to the first grant of a major interest, by the developer.

Relevant residential building fulfilling the following criteria:

❖ facilities shared by residents, for example, children's homes, old people's homes, hospices, living quarters for school pupils or armed forces; and

❖ an institution which is the sole or main residence for 90% of its residents.

NB: Flats and sheltered housing schemes made up of individual flats will be zero rated as dwellings rather than relevant residential buildings.

NB: Prisons, hospitals and hotels are specifically excluded from zero rating. This applies to goods and services and the first grant of a major interest.

Relevant charitable building is:

❖ a building used solely by a charity for the **non-business use** of the charity or as a village hall.

NB: The supply must be made to the person who intends to use the building for such purposes before the supply is made, then the person receiving it must give to the person making the supply a certificate that the intended use is for relevant residential or charitable purposes.

Works to an existing property

All goods and services supplied will be standard rated except in the following circumstances.

Relevant Housing Association (HA) converting a building from non-residential to residential use, to alllow zero rating the HA must:

❖ be a Registered Social Landlord within the meaning of Part 1 of the *Housing Act* 1996; and

❖ be a registered HA within the meaning of the *Housing Associations Act* 1985 (or Part II of the *Housing (Northern Ireland) Order* 1992).

NB: This applies to goods and services only.

Approved alterations to existing protected buildings – basic principles to allow zero rating are as follows:

❖ the work must be to a qualifying protected building as defined in VAT law and to the fabric of that building (for example, a listed building or scheduled monument);

❖ the work must require and be granted listed building consent;

❖ the works must not be of a repair or maintenance nature; and

❖ the works must be apportioned if there is an element of both repair and maintenance and approved alteration.

NB: Unlisted buildings in conservation areas do not qualify as protected buildings for the purposes of VAT relief. This applies to goods and services only.

Substantial reconstruction to existing protected buildings – basic principles to allow zero rating are as follows:

- ❖ definition of protected buildings as above;
- ❖ the work must require and be granted listed building consent;
- ❖ at least 60% of the cost is attributable to 'approved alterations'; or
- ❖ only the wall(s) remain along with the other features of architectural or historic interest.
- NB: This applies to the first grant of a major interest to the person carrying out the substantial reconstruction.

Conversion of buildings from non-residential use to dwellings or relevant residential use:

- ❖ from 1 March 1995 if you are the person converting a building the first grant of a major interest can be zero rated provided the building was neither designed nor adapted as a dwelling (or relevant residential purpose), or if it was designed as a dwelling and/or subsequently adapted, it has not been used as a dwelling for the whole of the previous ten years.

Residential conversions

From 12 May 2001 a lower rate of 5% applies to the following supplies of building services and related goods:

- ❖ a 'changed number of dwellings conversion', i.e. a conversion of a building (or part of a building) so that after conversion it has a different number of single-household dwellings (SHD) from the number before the conversion;
- ❖ a 'house in multiple occupation conversion', i.e. a conversion of a building (or part of a building) containing one or more single-household dwellings so that it contains only one or more multiple-occupancy dwellings; and
- ❖ a 'special residential conversion', i.e. a conversion of premises containing dwellings (single-household or multiple occupancy) for use solely for a relevant residential purpose or converting a care home into a single-household dwelling.

Renovation and alteration of dwellings

The lower rate of 5% also applies to supplies of:

- ❖ building services; and
- ❖ related goods.

In the course of the alteration (including extension) or renovation of a single-household dwelling that has been empty for three years. 'Empty' means unlived in, so use for another purpose, such as storage, is acceptable. The dwelling can remain a single household.

Specific conditions apply to both of these lower rate situations.

The reduced rate of VAT

The reduced rate of 5% VAT has applied since 1 June 2002. The reduced rate is extended to the costs of:

- ❖ converting a non-residential property into a care home or multiple occupancy dwellings, e.g. bedsits;
- ❖ converting a building used for 'relevant residential' purpose into a multiple occupancy dwelling;
- ❖ renovating or altering a care home or other qualifying building that has not been lived in for three years or more; and
- ❖ constructing, renovating or converting a building into a garage as part of the renovation of property that qualifies for the reduced rate.

Charity annexes

Prior to 1 June 2002 all of an annexe had to be used or intended for use for a relevant charitable purpose in order to zero rate its construction. Since 1 June 2002, there has been a concession whereby minor non-qualifying use for example, use where the annexe or part of an annexe is not used solely for a relevant charitable purpose, can be ignored with there being no requirement to apportion these between relevant charitable purpose and alternative usage.

Supplies to handicapped people

Certain goods and services supplied to a handicapped person, or to a charity for making them available to handicapped people for their domestic or personal use, may be zero-rated.

DIY projects

For claims made on or after 29 April 1996, HM Revenue and Customs will refund any VAT chargeable on the supply, acquisition or importation of any goods used in connection with construction or conversion work where the following criteria are met: the work is not part of a business project; the work comprises the construction of a dwelling, relevant residential or charitable building; or is the conversion of a non-residential building into a dwelling.

All works, which fulfil the criteria set out above, can be zero-rated. However there are some items, within these categories, which will always be standard-rated:

- ❖ site investigations;
- ❖ temporary site fencing;
- ❖ concrete testing;
- ❖ site security;
- ❖ catering;
- ❖ cleaning to site offices;
- ❖ temporary lighting;
- ❖ transport and haulage to and from site;
- ❖ plant hire (without operator);
- ❖ professional services (architects, engineers, surveyors, solicitors, etc.);
- ❖ landscaping;
- ❖ furniture (other than fitted kitchens) – material only;
- ❖ some electrical or gas appliances – material only; and
- ❖ carpet and carpeting materials (including underlay and carpet tiles) – material only.

See the following notices issued by HM Revenue and Customs for further expanded information and definitions:

- ❖ Notice 708 VAT Buildings and construction;
- ❖ Notice 742 Land and property;
- ❖ Notice 719 VAT refunds for 'do it yourself' builders and converters;
- ❖ Notice 701/1 Charities;
- ❖ Notice 701/7 VAT reliefs for people with disabilities;
- ❖ Notice 701/19 Fuel and power; and
- ❖ Notice 708/5 Registered social landlords (housing associations, etc.).

The primary legislation relating to this subject includes:

- ❖ Group 5 of Schedule 8 to the *VAT Act* 1994 as amended by SI 1995/280 and SI 1997/50 – buildings under construction;
- ❖ Group 6 of Schedule 8 to the *VAT Act* 1994 as amended by SI 1995/283 – approved alterations to protected buildings;
- ❖ Group 12 of Schedule 8 of the *VAT Act* 1994 – supplies to the handicapped;
- ❖ Section 35 of the *VAT Act* 1994 – DIY scheme;
- ❖ The *VAT (Input Tax) Order* 1992 as amended by SI 1995/281; and
- ❖ Schedule 10 to the *VAT Act* 1994.

Capital allowances

The following provides a brief summary of the capital allowances that are available to UK property owners, occupiers and investors. It is intended as an overview at the time of print and the authors would direct readers who require more detailed or specific advice to contact a capital allowances expert.

The UK taxation system has no general provision for tax relief for capital expenditure or for the depreciation in value of capital assets with the passage of time. Although there are numerous accounting standards detailing how the depreciation of capital assets must be dealt with for accounts purposes, there is no allowable deduction for tax purposes. Accounting depreciation is therefore added back to the accounting profits when computing the tax charge.

Capital allowances provide tax relief for at least some of this accounting and tax mismatch. Qualifying capital expenditure incurred on certain buildings, fixtures and chattels will attract specific rates or amounts of tax relief, which are available for offset against taxable profits.

This valuable form of tax relief is, in most cases, either under-claimed or not claimed at all due to a lack of understanding or application of the legislation and case law governing the availability of the relief.

General scheme of allowances

There are certain hurdles that must be cleared before capital allowances can be claimed. The entity incurring the expenditure must be within the charge to UK tax, therefore local authorities, government departments, charities, pension funds, etc. will not be in a position to use the relief (although they may be able to pass the benefit on for consideration).

The expenditure must be capital in nature, i.e. there must be an enduring benefit to the trade of the entity incurring it, e.g. the initial acquisition of an asset, or the subsequent improvement of it. Expenditure on the maintenance or general upkeep of an asset or on the development of an asset held as trading stock is likely to be revenue in nature. Revenue expenditure will not qualify for capital allowances, but could still potentially be tax deductible in its entirety in the year it is incurred if it is written off through the profit and loss account. It should be noted that the revenue deduction is dependent on the accounting treatment of the expenditure. Revenue expenditure that is capitalised for accounts purposes, e.g. to improve the balance sheet, will not qualify for the 100% deduction in the year it is incurred.

The capital expenditure must be incurred for the purpose of a qualifying activity, e.g. a trade, profession, vocation, etc. In some situations, the asset that is acquired or created must also be 'in use' for the purpose of the qualifying activity.

Finally, the capital asset that is acquired or created must be qualifying for capital allowances purposes, and in this regard many tests have evolved through statute and case law.

Types and rates of allowances

Plant and Machinery Allowances (P&MAs)

These are currently given at a rate of 25% per annum on a reducing balance basis, i.e. 25% of the balance of the qualifying expenditure carried forward year on year. There is generally little help from the tax legislation on what constitutes qualifying P&M and therefore there has been much litigation in this area. Specialist advice should be taken, but typical examples will include IT equipment, heating and ventilation systems and specialist mechanical and electrical installations.

The rate at which this relief is given will reduce to 20% per annum from April 2008. The 2007 Budget announced a separate classification of fixtures that are integral to a building, and their inclusion within a 10% capital allowances pool.

Qualifying P&M that has a useful economic life, when new, of exceeding 25 years is deemed to be a Long Life Asset (LLA) by the capital allowances legislation. The test applies from when the P&M is first used, therefore a second hand asset with a useful economic life of less than 25 years at the date of purchase may still be a LLA in the new owner's business. LLAs attract allowances at a rate of 6% per annum on a reducing balance basis and therefore are less attractive than non-LLAs. Excluded from this is expenditure incurred on a dwelling house, hotel, office, retail shop and showroom.

From April 2008 the rate of tax relief will increase from 6% per annum to 10% per annum.

Expenditure incurred on new (unused) qualifying P&M by a small or medium sized enterprise (SME) currently attracts a first year allowance of 50%. This first year allowance will be replaced from April 2008 by an Annual Investment Allowance (AIA) of £50,000 for all businesses. Up to the first £50,000 of qualifying capital expenditure incurred may therefore attract relief at 100%. Any balance of qualifying expenditure will be relieved on the 20% or 10% reducing balance basis, depending on the nature of the expenditure.

Specific legislation exists to give a 100% first year allowance for expenditure incurred on new P&M that satisfies defined energy saving or environmentally friendly criteria.

Hotel Building Allowances (HBAs), Industrial Buildings Allowances (IBAs) and Agricultural Buildings Allowances (ABAs)

These categories of buildings have been grouped together as they all attract allowances at the rate of 4% per annum on a straight-line basis, i.e. the qualifying expenditure is written off over a period of 25 years from when the building is first used.

The properties must satisfy certain criteria specified in the capital allowances legislation in order to be 'qualifying'. For HBAs, the property must be open for four months or more between April and October, have a minimum of ten letting bedrooms and provide guest services of at least breakfast, dinner and room cleaning. For IBAs and ABAs the test relates to the use to which the building is put, therefore there has to be qualifying industrial or agricultural use for the relief to be forthcoming.

This form of tax relief is being phased out from April 2008 with complete withdrawal by April 2011.

Research and Development Allowances (R&DAs)

Expenditure incurred on facilities used for qualifying R&D attracts allowances at 100% in the first year. Again, the accounting treatment of the expenditure is key and this is supplemented by published guidelines providing more clarity. The underlying test is innovation.

Business Premises Renovation Allowances (BPRAs)

A new form of capital allowance was introduced from 11 April 2007 giving 100% tax relief for expenditure incurred on qualifying conversion, renovation or repairs to a building that is in a disadvantaged area and which has remained unused for a period of at least a year up to the date that the work commenced.

The building must have previously been a business premises in use for a trade, profession or vocation, or as offices. It must not have last been used as a dwelling. The completed building must be used or available for use in a trade, profession or vocation, or as an office. The premises must not be available for use as a dwelling.

Expenditure is not qualifying if it is incurred on the acquisition of rights over land, the extension of the qualifying building, the development of land adjoining the qualifying building, or on the provision of plant and machinery (except where this is an integral fixture).

Where there is both qualifying and non-qualifying expenditure incurred, then the relief must be apportioned on a just and reasonable basis. For example, if the premises are being extended, the extension work will not qualify for BPRA. There are also various anti-avoidance provisions to prevent any abuse of this form of tax relief.

Capital allowances issues for property transactions

Except where it has already been identified that qualifying expenditure must be on 'new' P&M, capital allowances are available on the purchase of second hand assets. There are many tests and restrictions that apply to property transactions to ensure that a subsequent owner is restricted in its claim to the original cost of the asset. Where no previous capital allowances claim has been made, there may be an opportunity to 'step up' the new owner's claim to reflect the price that it has paid for the asset, where this is greater than the original cost.

The vendor and the purchaser must apportion the purchase price, on a just and reasonable basis, between the components of the sale, i.e. the interest in the land, the building and the qualifying P&M. These figures are then compared to the original cost to establish what restriction may apply to the subsequent claim and conversely what disposal proceeds the vendor must account for on sale. In some situations, it is possible for the parties to the transaction to agree and formally elect for a specified value to be attributable to fixtures qualifying for P&MAs. The effect of the election is that all, part or none of the allowances can be passed between the transacting parties. Tax aware parties may be able to negotiate an adjustment to the purchase price to reflect the agreed capital allowances position.

It is important to establish the capital allowances history of a property during the pre-acquisition due diligence. The information that will be relevant to the claim is generally more readily made available at this time than post-transaction and the opportunity to obtain any additional benefit through joint elections may not arise once the deal is concluded.

The following table provides a guide to the expected levels of qualifying P&M that may be available on an unrestricted basis for differing property and transaction types. It should be noted that depending on the type of property, ABAs, HBAs or IBAs might also be available in addition to the expected P&MAs identified.

Property type	Acquisition/ disposal Qualifying %	New build Qualifying %
Office	14% – 25%	15% – 45%
Office refurb/fit-out	–	40% – 100%
Retail	2% – 20%	5% – 35%
Retail refurb/fit-out	–	40% – 90%
Industrial	2% – 15%	5% – 20%
Hotel	10% – 40%	15% – 50%
Hotel refurb/fit-out	–	40% – 80%

Summary

The above is intended as an overview of the current availability of capital allowances. Specialist advice should be sought to maximise the availability and quantum of capital allowances.

Further sources of information

Capital Allowances Act 2001

Income and Corporation Taxes Act 1988

Finance Act 2004

www.eca.gov.org

Land remediation tax relief

Various tax incentives have been introduced following the recommendations of the Urban Task Force set up by the government in 1998 to investigate causes of urban decline. Land Remediation Tax Relief is one such generous incentive that provides up to 150% of tax relief for expenditure incurred in remediating contaminated land or, where a company is loss making, a tax credit (payment from the Exchequer) of 24% of the qualifying cost.

Availability of the tax relief

The qualifying expenditure must be incurred after 11 May 2001 on qualifying remediation works to land situated in the UK that was acquired for the purpose of a trade in a contaminated state. Land includes interests over land and buildings on the land.

The relief is available for companies but not for individuals or partnerships. A company in limited partnership can claim the relief in respect of its share in the partnership's expenditure on remediation. The relief is not available where the land is contaminated due to the actions of the acquiring company or someone connected with that company, or where the company has failed to prevent contamination.

Land is in a contaminated state if there are substances in, on or under the land that are likely to cause harm to people, property or ecological systems or are likely to pollute controlled waters. Nuclear sites are specifically excluded from the definition of contaminated land.

Qualifying expenditure

Expenditure must be incurred on the prevention, remediation or mitigation of the effects of the pollutant or on the restoration of the land to its former state. The expenditure must be directly linked to the remediation and as such, general site clearance will not qualify. Where in-house employees undertake the work, all of these costs are qualifying provided at least 80% of the time is spent on remediation tasks. Where employee time is less than 80%, some pro-rata adjustment will be necessary.

Preparatory works such as site investigations and incidental professional fees can be included in the claim for the relief. Where remediation work is subcontracted, then this cost will form the basis of the claim.

Claiming the relief

This relief is available to property owners, investors and developers. Any claim for the relief must be made within two years of the end of the accounting period in which the qualifying expenditure was incurred.

Interaction with landfill tax and aggregates levy

There are tax-planning opportunities to structure projects such that the waste from qualifying remediation works is exempt from landfill tax or the aggregates levy.

Summary

The above is intended as an overview of the principles and the current availability of land remediation tax relief. Specialist advice should be sought on the availability and to maximise the quantum of the tax relief.

Further sources of information

Income and Corporation Taxes Act 1988
Finance Act 2001
www.hmrc.gov.uk

Types of tendering route

Regardless of the form of contract, the method of tendering can impact on the successful outcome of a project. When appointing a main contractor, reference should be made to the CIB *Code of Practice for the Selection of Main Contractors*, first published in 1997. Below we identify the three most commonly used methods and analyse their merits.

Single stage selective tendering

Single stage selective tendering occurs when the client wishes to obtain the most competitive price for the project. This method will only be successful where the design is substantially complete for the type of contract being proposed, i.e. design and build or traditional, as any incomplete elements of the design will lead to post contract variations and additional costs.

In using this method, the client seeks tenders usually from three to six pre-selected competent contractors issuing detailed tender information, whether it be performance specifications for a design and build route or full detailed bill of quantities for a traditional route. Tenders are returned and assessed under competition, with a contractor being selected on the basis of who bests meets the evaluation criteria.

The advantages include:

- ❖ most competitive price achieved;
- ❖ the client retains greater control of design; and
- ❖ increased cost certainty at signing of contract.

The disadvantages include:

- ❖ the contractor is not able to share its construction expertise at the design stage;
- ❖ increased programme requirements to produce the full design in advance of tender; and
- ❖ possible cost increases and variations are likely where the design is incomplete or errors have been made in design.

Two stage selective tendering

Two stage tendering is best suited where the client requires a competitive price but in particular requires early contractor involvement. The client will issue tenders with limited preliminary information (usually preliminaries, provisional sums, demolitions, earthworks) and a schedule of rates for the areas where the design is incomplete. Tenders are returned and assessed under competition, with the contractor being selected on the basis of who bests meets the evaluation criteria. As the works progress, the schedule of rates is used to complete the pricing of the design.

The advantages include:

- ❖ facilitates an earlier commencement on site;
- ❖ allows contractor input on specialist design areas during the construction phase; and
- ❖ allows for a degree of flexibility in design.

The disadvantages include:

- ❖ greater cost risk as the contract is signed before the final cost is known;

and, if a large number of provisional items exist,

- ❖ risk to the programme, as design information needs to be complete during construction and in line with the contractor's programme.

Negotiated tendering

Negotiated tendering forms a hybrid of both the single and two stage routes. It allows the client to identify a contractor best suited for the project through tendering on limited information. The contractor then enters exclusively into negotiations with the client prior to agreeing a contract sum. This allows the design team to either:

- ❖ complete the design during the tender period and therefore, upon conclusion of the negotiations, the client has achieved a contract sum based on a full design: or
- ❖ provide the contractor with sufficient information at key stages to commence work earlier.

This method is often used where the number of contractors tendering is small or where the client has one or a small number of preferred partnering contractors for repeat projects.

The advantages are:

- ❖ allows early site start;
- ❖ allows the contractor to have input into design and construction techniques;
- ❖ greater programme certainty as risks are identified early; and
- ❖ can build trust between client and contractor.

The disadvantages are:

- ❖ possible increase in construction costs due to lack of competition on tendering;
- ❖ a risk to the programme if negotiations fail to meet targets; and
- ❖ less cost certainty if early site start is preferred.

Tender prices and building cost indices

Tender Prices and Building Cost Indices

Index (Base 1985 = 100)

BCIS All-in Tender Price Index

BCIS General Building Cost Index

= Firm   = Forecast

Date

For further information on the breakdown of the indices, please contact the Building Cost Information Service.

89

The BCIS tender price indices and general building cost indices monitor the movement of tender prices and building costs. They can be used to forecast cost movement for the years to come by using the forecast indices based upon cost trends. The Tender Price Index measures the trend of contractors' pricing levels in accepted tenders for new work (cost to client), whereas the General Building Cost Index measures changes in costs of labour, materials and plant (cost to contractor).

Indicative construction costs 2007 – UK

Introduction

This is the first edition of the Watts Group *Indicative cost table (construction) for the UK*. The scope of buildings covered is limited but has included the majority of building types. The table is a quick guide to construction costs in the UK as a precursor to a detailed cost analysis.

Economic comment

Following from the period of high inflation in the construction industry in the late 1990s and early 2000s, the industry settled to a steady pace and inflation was running at circa 3% per annum. However, tender levels in 2006/2007 rose by around 5.2% reflecting the rising cost of materials such as structural steel and plaster, due to increased demand. Forecast for 2007/2008 is slightly higher at 6.0%.

Location and site factors

Clearly, no two sites are the same. Factors such as geographic location, availability of utilities supplies, existing development, access, topography and planning all contribute towards the cost necessary to complete developments. Our indicative costs are factored to reflect the cost spread throughout the UK. A broad range of building types are covered, however, construction professionals and users of the guide are recommended to obtain detailed advice from Watts Group when assessing specific sites or developments.

Professional and statutory fees, and VAT

Professional fees (which are subject to negotiation and in some cases open tender), local authority fees, contributions and charges, and VAT (which are subject to legislation), have not been included in the guide costs. Indicative allowances for these and other additional costs have been outlined in the notes.

No guarantee is given by Watts Group, or any of its employees, as to this cost table's accuracy. More detailed advice must be obtained before relying on costs indicated.

Location factor		Benchmark	Greater London	North	Yorks & Hum	East Midlands	East Anglia	South East	South West	West Midlands	North West	Wales	Scotland	Northern Ireland
		100	112	104	99	93	98	105	95	96	94	95	103	65
		£/m²	£/m²	£/m²	£/m²	£/m²	£/m²	£/m²	£/m²	£/m²	£/m²	£/m²	£/m²	£/m²
		£/sq ft	£/sq ft	£/sq ft	£/sq ft	£/sq ft	£/sq ft	£/sq ft	£/sq ft	£/sq ft	£/sq ft	£/sq ft	£/sq ft	£/sq ft
Building type														
Houses	Local authority	600–850	672–952	624–884	594–842	558–842	588–833	630–893	570–808	576–816	564–799	570–808	618–876	390–553
		55–80	62–90	57–83	54–79	51–79	54–78	58–84	52–76	53–77	52–75	52–76	57–82	36–52
	Private estate, 2/3 bed	650–860	728–963	676–894	644–851	605–851	637–843	683–903	618–817	624–826	611–808	618–817	670–886	423–559
		60–80	67–90	62–83	59–79	56–79	59–78	63–84	57–76	58–77	56–75	57–76	62–82	39–52
	Private detached, 4/5 bed	690–930	773–1042	718–967	683–921	642–921	676–911	725–977	656–884	662–893	649–874	656–884	711–958	449–605
		65–85	73–95	68–88	64–84	60–84	64–83	68–89	62–81	62–82	61–80	62–81	67–88	42–55
	Luxury detached developments	900–1500	1008–1680	936–1560	891–1485	837–1485	882–1470	945–1575	855–1425	864–1440	846–1410	855–1425	927–1545	585–975
		85–140	95–157	88–146	84–139	79–139	83–137	89–147	81–133	82–134	80–132	81–133	88–144	55–91
Apartments	Social and affordable	670–920	750–1030	697–957	663–911	623–911	657–902	704–966	637–874	643–883	630–865	637–874	690–948	436–598
		60–85	67–95	62–88	59–84	56–84	59–83	63–89	57–81	58–82	56–80	57–81	62–88	39–55
	Private	760–1100	851–1232	790–1144	752–1089	707–1089	745–1078	798–1155	722–1045	730–1056	714–1034	722–1045	783–1133	494–715
		70–100	78–112	73–104	69–99	65–99	69–98	74–105	67–95	67–96	66–94	67–95	72–103	46–65
	Private luxury	1000–1800	1120–2016	1040–1872	990–1782	930–1782	980–1764	1050–1890	950–1710	960–1728	940–1692	950–1710	1030–1854	650–1170
		95–165	106–185	99–172	94–163	88–163	93–162	100–173	90–157	91–158	89–155	90–157	98–170	62–107

		Benchmark	Greater London	North	Yorks & Hum	East Midlands	East Anglia	South East	South West	West Midlands	North West	Wales	Scotland	Northern Ireland
Location factor		100	112	104	99	93	98	105	95	96	94	95	103	65
		£/m²	£/m²	£/m²	£/m²	£/m²	£/m²	£/m²	£/m²	£/m²	£/m²	£/m²	£/m²	£/m²
		£/sq ft	£/sq ft	£/sq ft	£/sq ft	£/sq ft	£/sq ft	£/sq ft	£/sq ft	£/sq ft	£/sq ft	£/sq ft	£/sq ft	£/sq ft
Building type *continued*														
Investment	Student residence	940–1500	1053–1680	978–1560	931–1485	874–1485	921–1470	987–1575	893–1425	902–1440	884–1410	893–1425	968–1545	611–975
		85–140	95–157	88–146	84–139	79–139	83–137	89–147	81–133	82–134	80–132	81–133	88–144	55–91
	Private apartments	760–1100	851–1232	790–1144	752–1089	707–1089	745–1078	798–1155	722–1045	730–1056	714–1034	722–1045	783–1133	494–715
		70–100	78–112	73–104	69–99	65–99	69–98	74–105	67–95	67–96	66–94	67–95	72–103	46–65

Notes: Residential developments may or may not be located within existing foul drainage schemes and may require construction of an individual treatment plant or connection to a local scheme. Costs for such installations will depend on site location and ground conditions, scheme layout, etc. Allowance, say, £3,000/unit for typical system. External works and drainage 10–15%. Professional fees 9–12%.

		Benchmark	Greater London	North	Yorks & Hum	East Midlands	East Anglia	South East	South West	West Midlands	North West	Wales	Scotland	Northern Ireland
Offices	Medium rise, standard fit-out, no a/c	1050–1510	1176–1691	1092–1570	1040–1495	977–1495	1029–1480	1103–1586	998–1435	1008–1450	987–1419	998–1435	1082–1555	683–982
		100–140	112–157	104–146	99–139	93–139	98–137	105–147	95–133	96–134	94–132	95–133	103–144	65–91
	Medium rise, standard fit-out, incl. a/c	1300–1800	1456–2016	1352–1872	1287–1782	1209–1782	1274–1764	1365–1890	1235–1710	1248–1728	1222–1692	1235–1710	1339–1854	845–1170
		120–170	134–190	125–177	119–168	112–168	118–167	126–179	114–162	115–163	113–160	114–162	124–175	78–111
	High rise, standard fit-out, incl. a/c	1650–2450	1848–2744	1716–2548	1634–2426	1535–2426	1617–2401	1733–2573	1568–2328	1584–2352	1551–2303	1568–2328	1700–2524	1073–1593
		155–230	174–258	161–239	153–228	144–228	152–225	163–242	147–219	149–221	146–216	147–219	160–237	101–150
	Headquarters, high quality fit-out, incl. a/c	2000–3000	2240–3360	2080–3120	1980–2970	1860–2970	1960–2940	2100–3150	1900–2850	1920–2880	1880–2820	1900–2850	2060–3090	1300–1950
		185–280	207–314	192–291	183–277	172–277	181–274	194–294	176–266	178–269	174–263	176–266	191–288	120–182

		Benchmark	Greater London	North	Yorks & Hum	East Midlands	East Anglia	South East	South West	West Midlands	North West	Wales	Scotland	Northern Ireland
Location factor		100	112	104	99	93	98	105	95	96	94	95	103	65
		£/m²	£/m²	£/m²	£/m²	£/m²	£/m²	£/m²	£/m²	£/m²	£/m²	£/m²	£/m²	£/m²
		£/sq ft	£/sq ft	£/sq ft	£/sq ft	£/sq ft	£/sq ft	£/sq ft	£/sq ft	£/sq ft	£/sq ft	£/sq ft	£/sq ft	£/sq ft

Building type *continued*

		Benchmark	Greater London	North	Yorks & Hum	East Midlands	East Anglia	South East	South West	West Midlands	North West	Wales	Scotland	Northern Ireland
Offices *continued*	Business park, standard fit-out, no a/c	950–1300	1064–1456	988–1352	941–1287	884–1287	931–1274	998–1365	903–1235	912–1248	893–1222	903–1235	979–1339	618–845
		90–120	101–134	94–125	89–119	84–119	88–118	95–126	86–114	86–115	85–113	86–114	93–124	59–78
	Business park, standard fit-out, incl. a/c	1200–1600	1344–1792	1248–1664	1188–1584	1116–1568	1176–1568	1260–1680	1140–1520	1152–1536	1128–1504	1140–1520	1236–1648	780–1040
		110–150	123–168	114–156	109–149	102–149	108–147	116–158	105–143	106–144	103–141	105–143	113–155	72–98
	Call centre standard fit-out, incl. a/c	1500–2300	1680–2576	1560–2392	1485–2277	1395–2277	1470–2254	1575–2415	1425–2185	1440–2208	1410–2162	1425–2185	1545–2369	975–1495
		140–215	157–241	146–224	139–213	130–213	137–211	147–226	133–204	134–206	132–202	133–204	144–221	91–140
	Car parking, underground per space	17500–22500	19600–25200	18200–23400	17325–22275	16275–22275	17150–22050	18375–23625	16625–21375	16800–21600	16450–21150	16625–21375	18025–23175	11375–14625
	Car parking, multi-storey per space	8000–12000	8960–13440	8320–12480	7920–11880	7440–11880	7840–11760	8400–12600	7600–11400	7680–11520	7520–11280	7600–11400	8240–12360	5200–7800

Notes: Indicative costs for commercial buildings shown are for functional designs to current design norms. Specialised design features, such as external feature detailing, security systems, building management systems (BMS), back-up power supplies (UPS), etc. will add substantially to indicative costs. External works and drainage 12–15%. Professional fees 10–14%.

Location factor	Benchmark 100		Greater London 112		North 104		Yorks & Hum 99		East Midlands 93		East Anglia 98		South East 105		South West 95		West Midlands 96		North West 94		Wales 95		Scotland 103		Northern Ireland 65	
	£/m²	£/sq ft	£/m²	£/sq ft	£/m²	£/sq ft	£/m²	£/sq ft	£/m²	£/sq ft	£/m²	£/sq ft	£/m²	£/sq ft	£/m²	£/sq ft	£/m²	£/sq ft	£/m²	£/sq ft	£/m²	£/sq ft	£/m²	£/sq ft	£/m²	£/sq ft Local
Building type																										
Industrial — Units (shell only)	380–640	35–60	426–717	39–67	395–666	36–62	376–634	35–59	353–595	33–56	372–627	34–59	399–672	37–63	361–608	33–57	365–614	34–58	357–602	33–56	361–608	33–57	391–659	36–62	247–416	23–39
Industrial — Purpose built – base services	550–900	50–85	616–1008	56–95	572–936	52–88	545–891	50–84	512–837	47–79	539–882	49–83	578–945	53–89	523–855	48–81	528–864	48–82	517–846	47–80	523–855	48–81	567–927	52–88	358–585	33–55
Industrial — Distribution warehouse	650–900	60–85	728–1008	67–95	676–936	62–88	644–891	59–84	605–837	56–79	637–882	59–83	683–945	63–89	618–855	57–81	624–864	58–82	611–846	56–80	618–855	57–81	670–927	62–88	423–585	39–55
Industrial — Chilled distribution warehouse	750–1200	70–110	840–1344	78–123	780–1248	73–114	743–1188	69–109	698–1116	65–102	735–1176	69–108	788–1260	74–116	713–1140	67–105	720–1152	67–106	705–1128	66–103	713–1140	67–105	773–1236	72–113	488–780	46–72
Retail (excl. fit-out) — Convenience store	550–930	50–85	616–1042	56–95	572–967	52–88	545–921	50–84	512–865	47–79	539–911	49–83	578–977	53–89	523–884	48–81	528–893	48–82	517–874	47–80	523–884	48–81	567–958	52–88	358–605	33–55
Retail (excl. fit-out) — Supermarket	600–990	55–90	672–1109	62–101	624–1030	57–94	594–980	54–89	558–921	51–84	588–970	54–88	630–1040	58–95	570–941	52–86	576–950	53–86	564–931	52–85	570–941	52–86	618–1020	57–93	390–644	36–59
Retail (excl. fit-out) — Stand-alone (out of town)	420–700	40–65	470–784	45–73	437–728	42–68	416–693	40–64	391–651	37–60	412–686	39–64	441–735	42–68	399–665	38–62	403–672	38–62	395–658	38–61	399–665	38–62	433–721	41–67	273–455	26–42

Building type *continued*

Location factor			Benchmark 100	Greater London 112	North 104	Yorks & Hum 99	East Midlands 93	East Anglia 98	South East 105	South West 95	West Midlands 96	North West 94	Wales 95	Scotland 103	Northern Ireland 65
Retail (excl. fit-out) *continued*	Retail warehouse	£/m²	400–650	448–728	416–676	396–644	372–605	392–637	420–683	380–618	384–624	376–611	380–618	412–670	260–423
		£/sq ft	35–60	39–67	36–62	35–59	33–56	34–59	37–63	33–57	34–58	33–56	33–57	36–62	23–39
	Shopping centres – retail units	£/m²	620–800	694–896	645–832	614–792	577–744	608–784	651–840	589–760	595–768	583–752	589–760	639–824	403–520
		£/sq ft	60–75	67–84	62–78	59–74	56–70	59–74	63–79	57–71	58–72	56–71	57–71	62–77	39–49
	Shopping centres – service areas	£/m²	850–1050	952–1176	884–1092	842–1040	791–977	833–1029	893–1103	808–998	816–1008	799–987	808–998	876–1082	553–683
		£/sq ft	80–100	90–112	83–104	79–99	74–93	78–98	84–105	76–95	77–96	75–94	76–95	82–103	52–65
	Shopping centres – concourses	£/m²	950–1500	1064–1680	988–1560	941–1485	884–1395	931–1470	998–1575	903–1425	912–1440	893–1410	903–1425	979–1545	618–975
		£/sq ft	90–140	101–157	94–146	89–139	84–130	88–137	95–147	86–133	86–134	85–132	86–133	93–144	59–91
Retail fit-out	Superstore	£/m²	1350–1800	1512–2016	1404–1872	1337–1782	1256–1674	1323–1764	1418–1890	1283–1710	1296–1728	1269–1692	1283–1710	1391–1854	878–1170
		£/sq ft	125–165	140–185	130–172	124–163	116–153	123–162	131–173	119–157	120–158	118–155	119–157	129–170	81–107
	Financial/high quality	£/m²	1400–1750	1568–1960	1456–1820	1386–1733	1302–1628	1372–1715	1470–1838	1330–1663	1344–1680	1316–1645	1330–1663	1442–1803	910–1138
		£/sq ft	130–165	146–185	135–172	129–163	121–153	127–162	137–173	124–157	125–158	122–155	124–157	134–170	85–107
Hotels	Three star	£/m²	850–1400	952–1568	884–1456	842–1386	791–1302	833–1372	893–1470	808–1330	816–1344	799–1316	808–1330	876–1442	553–910
		£/sq ft	80–130	90–146	83–135	79–129	74–121	78–127	84–137	76–124	77–125	75–122	76–124	82–134	52–85

Location factor		Benchmark 100	Greater London 112	North 104	Yorks & Hum 99	East Midlands 93	East Anglia 98	South East 105	South West 95	West Midlands 96	North West 94	Wales 95	Scotland 103	Northern Ireland 65
		£/m²	£/m²	£/m²	£/m²	£/m²	£/m²	£/m²	£/m²	£/m²	£/m²	£/m²	£/m²	£/m²
		£/sq ft	£/sq ft	£/sq ft	£/sq ft	£/sq ft	£/sq ft	£/sq ft	£/sq ft	£/sq ft	£/sq ft	£/sq ft	£/sq ft	£/sq ft
Building type continued														
Hotels continued	Four star	900–1500	1008–1680	936–1560	891–1485	837–1395	882–1470	945–1575	855–1425	864–1440	846–1410	855–1425	927–1545	585–975
		85–140	95–157	88–146	84–139	79–130	83–137	89–147	81–133	82–134	80–132	81–133	88–144	55–91
	Five star	950–2000	1064–2240	988–2080	941–1980	884–1860	931–1960	998–2100	903–1900	912–1920	893–1880	903–1900	979–2060	618–1300
		90–185	101–207	94–192	89–183	84–172	88–181	95–194	86–176	86–178	85–174	86–176	93–191	59–120
Education/ health	Primary school	940–1350	1053–1512	978–1404	931–1337	874–1256	921–1323	987–1418	893–1283	902–1296	884–1269	893–1283	968–1391	611–878
		90–125	101–140	94–130	89–124	84–116	88–123	95–131	86–119	86–120	85–118	86–119	93–129	59–81
	Secondary school	860–1250	963–1400	894–1300	851–1238	800–1163	843–1225	903–1313	817–1188	826–1200	808–1175	817–1188	886–1288	559–813
		80–115	90–129	83–120	79–114	74–107	78–113	84–121	76–109	77–110	75–108	76–109	82–118	52–75
	School gymnasium	770–1200	862–1344	801–1248	762–1188	716–1116	755–1176	809–1260	732–1140	739–1152	724–1128	732–1140	793–1236	501–780
		70–110	78–123	73–114	69–109	65–102	69–108	74–116	67–105	67–106	66–103	67–105	72–113	46–72
	Nursing home/ hospice	1100–1550	1232–1736	1144–1612	1089–1535	1023–1442	1078–1519	1155–1628	1045–1473	1056–1488	1034–1457	1045–1473	1133–1597	715–1008
		100–145	112–162	104–151	99–144	93–135	98–142	105–152	95–138	96–139	94–136	95–138	103–149	65–94
Leisure	Restaurants (shell only)	850–1200	952–1344	884–1248	842–1188	791–1116	833–1176	893–1260	808–1140	816–1152	799–1128	808–1140	876–1236	553–780
		80–110	90–123	83–114	79–109	74–102	78–108	84–116	76–105	77–106	75–103	76–105	82–113	52–72

	Benchmark	Greater London	North	Yorks & Hum	East Midlands	East Anglia	South East	South West	West Midlands	North West	Wales	Scotland	Northern Ireland
Location factor	100	112	104	99	93	98	105	95	96	94	95	103	65
	£/m²	£/m²	£/m²	£/m²	£/m²	£/m²	£/m²	£/m²	£/m²	£/m²	£/m²	£/m²	£/m²
	£/sq ft	£/sq ft	£/sq ft	£/sq ft	£/sq ft	£/sq ft	£/sq ft	£/sq ft	£/sq ft	£/sq ft	£/sq ft	£/sq ft	£/sq ft

Building type *continued*

Leisure *continued*	Benchmark	Greater London	North	Yorks & Hum	East Midlands	East Anglia	South East	South West	West Midlands	North West	Wales	Scotland	Northern Ireland
Public house (typical fit-out)	1100–1700	1232–1904	1144–1768	1089–1683	1023–1581	1078–1666	1155–1785	1045–1615	1056–1632	1034–1598	1045–1615	1133–1751	715–1105
	100–160	112–179	104–166	99–158	93–149	98–157	105–168	95–152	96–154	94–150	95–152	103–165	65–104
Leisure centres	850–1500	952–1680	884–1560	842–1485	791–1395	833–1470	893–1575	808–1425	816–1440	799–1410	808–1425	876–1545	553–975
	80–140	90–157	83–146	79–139	74–130	78–137	84–147	76–133	77–134	75–132	76–133	82–144	52–91

Notes: Indicative costs for industrial units are typical shell and basic services. Mezzanine flooring and storage racking not included. Hotels, shop units, restaurants and public houses may have expensive fitting-out costs in excess of those shown due to corporate image requirements or individual architectural or conservation requirements. Retail and industrial external works allowance 7–12%. Professional fees 10–15%.

No guarantee is given by Watts Group, or any of its employees, as to this cost table's accuracy. More detailed advice must be obtained before relying on costs indicated.

Rating revaluation 2005

Introduction

Since the introduction of the *Local Government Finance Act* 1988, rating assessments on business premises have been subject to five yearly revaluations. The new 2005 Rating List came into effect on 1 April 2005. This covers England and Wales only and Rateable Values can be accessed at www.voa.gov.uk. Rateable Values for Scotland can now be accessed from the Scottish assessors at www.saa.gov.uk.

Basis of valuation

The 2005 Rateable Values are based on rental values on 1 April 2003, which is known as the Antecedent Valuation Date (AVD). The rating hypothesis as set out in the *Local Government Finance Act* 1988 forms the basis of valuation.

Right first time

The Valuation Office Agency (VOA) has approached the 2005 revaluation under a new modernised agenda to be 'right first time'. The government felt that past revaluations encouraged too many appeals and wanted to create a more efficient system to more accurately forecast budgets and to ensure that the Uniform Business Rate (UBR) is set at an appropriate level.

'Notice Requesting Supply of Information...'

In order to be 'right first time' the VOA have required the return of Information Notices setting out rental information on any given property. The proportion of forms returned is historically low and the VOA can issue a fine of £100 if the form is not completed and returned within 56 days of its issue, to be increased by £20 per day thereafter.

Uniform Business Rate

The uniform business rate (sometimes known as the multiplier) is an amount set by the government each year. There is a UBR for England and one for Wales. It is set to ensure that the overall amount collected in rates only ever increases by the rate of inflation.

England:
- ❖ The standard UBR for 2007/08 in England is 44.4p
- ❖ The small business UBR for 2007/08 in England is 44.1p

Transitional relief

Transitional relief is a government scheme which ensures that large increases or decreases in rates bills that are due to the revaluation are phased in gradually over a number of years.

The transitional arrangements spread the burden of increases and the benefit of reductions over the five year period of the list to avoid sharp increases over the first few years. Downward phasing of the transitional relief continues to apply to recoup the losses incurred by the government.

Small-business relief

This is a new relief that came into effect on 1 April 2005. Eligible businesses with rateable values of below £5,000 get 50% rate relief on their liability. This relief decreases on a sliding scale by an estimated 1% for every £100 of rateable value over £5,000 up to £10,000. Your local billing authority will calculate the exact decrease.

The relief is available to ratepayers with either:
- ❖ one property; or
- ❖ one main property and other additional properties, providing the additional properties do not have individual rateable

values of more than £2,200 and the combined rateable value of all the properties is under £15,000 (or £21,500 in London). The threshold for the combined rateable value is dependent on the location of the main property. The main property is the only one that has the relief applied to it. The additional properties have their charges calculated using the standard multiplier.

For further information on rating valuation please refer to the following websites:

www.voa.gov.uk

www.mybusinessrates.gov.uk

Cost management

Predicting costs

Be mindful:

- ❖ of the level of information;
- ❖ of the perceived requirements for budget, time and quality;
- ❖ that the brief will inevitably change;
- ❖ that not all of your assumptions will be right; and
- ❖ that the initial assessment will stick in the client's mind.

Always:

- ❖ undertake a detailed assessment;
- ❖ set down clearly all assumptions and exclusions; and
- ❖ make provision for risk – in the market, in design development and in the client changing his or her mind.

Never:

- ❖ rely solely on blanket unit rates; or
- ❖ expect the client to remember anything other than your first assessment.

The procurement process

Be mindful:

- ❖ that the process of project delivery is dynamic; and
- ❖ of the inevitability of the design (in part at least) developing apace with construction and that if this design development is not managed, cost and time over-runs will result.

Always:

- ❖ assess the programme as part of the cost planning process;
- ❖ clearly describe the brief that you have assumed and are working to;
- ❖ select an appropriate form of contract and consider not just the value but the nature of the work;
- ❖ understand the budget and know where the uncertainties are;
- ❖ maintain projections of cost on an 'open book' basis;
- ❖ make the projections 'real time' and as soon as issues are suspected, make provision; and
- ❖ assess and reassess risk.

Never:

- ❖ avoid routine financial appraisals;
- ❖ proceed on the basis that things will turn out all right if left to their own devices – they never will; or
- ❖ proceed without adequate contingency.

Value for money

Be mindful that:

- ❖ value for money is not just the lowest price;
- ❖ it must balance time, cost and quality; and
- ❖ simply applying competitive tender procedures does not itself demonstrate value for money.

Value engineering

Value engineering (VE) is a means of evaluating the function, cost and objectives of a design and construction project with a view to increasing the margin between cost and revenue. Value engineering is not simply cost cutting and VE might well lead to costs increasing – providing of course that value increases by a greater amount. Separate considerations apply to 'not for profit' projects but the essential process is common.

Value engineering is best undertaken in a workshop forum, ideally facilitated by a senior individual having some knowledge of the project but who is not part of the delivery team. Typically, a VE workshop will observe the following simple protocol:

- ❖ Representatives of the design team, the client and the construction team are present.
- ❖ The tone of the meeting should be constructive and the facilitator must encourage the notion of 'free enquiry'. No historic decisions should escape review.
- ❖ A member(s) of the team will present the project and will highlight key aspects of design, brief and cost.
- ❖ A process of functional analysis of the major components follows the general briefing. This process allows the team to fully appreciate the need for and role of each major component. An example of this would be a flat slab framing solution 'essential' to the avoidance of drop beams. Context is added by the consideration of cost, programme and sequence. The key is to concentrate upon the core components only.
- ❖ The definition of 'core components' will involve consideration of their cost, their effect upstream and/or downstream and their sensitivity, such as a client's personally favoured solution.
- ❖ Analysis is followed by speculation and is the creative stage. Nothing (within reason) is off limits. The role of the facilitator is crucial here and he or she must keep the emerging alternatives to a manageable number.
- ❖ To arrive at a set of proposals, the alternatives must be evaluated against a set of criteria and the criteria must start with the basic test – what adds most value? This might be the alternative that also adds most cost.
- ❖ The end game is a list of alternatives, openly debated and validated by the team and worthy of more detailed consideration prior to presentation of recommendations to the client. This usually involves the assembly of a closure report.

Some golden rules for the facilitator:

- ❖ A group of eight is probably optimum.
- ❖ All must be encouraged to participate, including the weakest.
- ❖ All ground that is covered must be documented.
- ❖ The synthesis of ideas and concepts must be encouraged.
- ❖ Be flexible, but firm.

Life cycle costing

The life cycle cost of an asset may be defined as the total cost of that asset over its operating life including initial capital/acquisition cost, occupation costs, operating costs, and the cost or benefit of the eventual disposal of the asset at the end of its life.

Use

Life cycle costing is essential to effective decision-making in four main ways:

❖ It identifies the total cost commitment undertaken in the acquisition of any asset.

❖ It facilitates an effective choice between alternative methods of achieving a stated objective, recognising different patterns of capital and running costs.

❖ It is a management tool that details the current operating costs of assets.

❖ It identifies those areas in which operating costs might be reduced.

The use of life cycle costing techniques has seen considerable growth in recent years, driven predominantly by shifts in public sector procurement policy towards 'best value' rather than lowest cost. This policy change is demonstrated in publications such as *Construction Procurement Guidance, No 7 Whole Life Costs* (Office of Government Commerce) which states that 'all procurement must be made solely on the basis of value for money in terms of the optimum combination of whole life costs and quality to meet the user's requirements'. The increasing reliance upon PFI / PPP for the procurement of major capital projects has also contributed to the need to consider the whole life cost of an asset rather than simply the 'up front' capital outlay.

The benefits of life cycle costing should not be construed as being effective for the public sector alone – long term investment returns on property can be influenced significantly by future maintenance/operational obligations which were not considered at the outset of a project. Energy efficiency of buildings in particular, is considered to be a prime candidate for life cycle cost evaluation. In an era dominated by European directives, the Climate Change Levy, etc. the higher capital cost of energy efficient installations can often be more than offset by longer term savings. Adding the benefit of potential tax advantages, the value of effective whole life cost techniques becomes apparent.

As a result, life cycle cost planning should, wherever possible, form an integral part of the design development process, being implemented from project outset to achieve maximum benefit.

Implementation

Implementation of appropriate life cycle costing techniques must reflect not only the nature of the clients' needs but also their property specific objectives. The objectives of an owner-occupier client, retaining a long term interest, will be significantly different from an investor seeking to transfer maintenance risk to a prospective tenant.

The following major elements should therefore be considered:

❖ the overall time period;

❖ all costs and revenues attributable to the project, including initial investment, recurring costs and revenues, proceeds from ultimate sale or other disposal and tax benefits;

❖ only those costs and revenues directly attributable to the project;

> ❖ the effects of time, including allowance for the impact of inflation; and
> ❖ the fact that pounds spent or received in the future are worth less than pounds spent or received today.

Stages of life cycle costing

Life cycle costing techniques can be split into the following stages.

Life cycle cost planning (LCCP)

Objectives:

> ❖ to identify the total costs of the acquisition of a building or building element; and
> ❖ to facilitate the effective choice between various methods of achieving a given objective.

LCCP can be broken into seven basic steps:

Step 1 – Establish the objective.

Step 2 – Choose alternative options for achieving the objective (consider all realistic possibilities).

Step 3 – Formulate assumptions (e.g. discount rate, construction duration, asset replacement cycle, building life, basis of residual value).

Step 4 – Calculate all capital and recurrent costs over a defined period.

Step 5 – Compare costs and rank the alternatives.

Step 6 – Carry out a sensitivity analysis (i.e. when the results of step 5 are not demonstrably in favour of one choice).

Step 7 – Investigate capital cost constraints.

Applying the foregoing approach for each option under consideration will generate a life cycle cost plan, reflecting all costs and revenues over the selected time period. Recognising that monies spent in the future will be worth less than the same money spent today, the cash flows are discounted to a present day value. The total of all present day values over the life of the LCCP represent the net present value (NPV). Compared against alternative options, the NPV facilitates identification of the option which offers best value for money.

Life cycle cost management (LCCM)

Objectives:

> ❖ to identify areas where running costs might be reduced;
> ❖ to establish where performance differs from the LCCP projection;
> ❖ to make recommendations on more efficient utilisation of the building;
> ❖ to provide information on asset lives and reliability factors for accounting purposes;
> ❖ to assist in the establishment of a maintenance policy for the building; and
> ❖ to give taxation advice on building related items.

LCCM therefore applies throughout the operational phase of a building's life, focused upon maintaining and/or improving the asset's efficiency. LCCM should be read in conjunction with maintenance management.

Life cycle cost analysis (LCCA)

Objectives:

> ❖ to provide a management tool which identifies actual operating costs incurred; and
> ❖ to relate cost and performance data to advisers about the running costs of occupied buildings.

LCCA is an ongoing operation, contributing to both LCCP and LCCM – in practice, one cannot take place without the other.

While each component can be viewed as a separate activity in its own right, there is a logical sequence that links them together. The sequence is demonstrated in the figure on the following pages, where a life cycle cost plan for a proposed project is based upon three similar buildings for which life cycle cost analyses are available.

Main components

Components to consider when implementing life cycle cost techniques:

❖ Capital costs
- Land (including cost of acquisition)
- Demolitions
- Construction costs
- Fit-out expenditure
- Decanting charges (including rental of temporary accommodation)
- Relocation expenses
- Professional fees
- Statutory fees
- VAT (and other taxes)

❖ Financing charges
- Cost of finance for land/site acquisition
- Cost of finance during occupational period

❖ Operation costs
- Heating, electricity and other energy
- Cleaning and caretaking
- Rates
- Insurance
- Security and public health
- Staff (building related)
- Rent
- Management charges
- Land charges

❖ Maintenance costs
- Life cycle asset replacement (specific)
- Annual maintenance (general)
- Annual grounds maintenance (general)

❖ Residual values
- Disposal of existing buildings, land, etc.
- Disposal of temporary decant accommodation
- Retained value at end of evaluation period

❖ Revenue
- Other income derived from the accommodation
- Benefit of capital allowances or other incentive.

The sequence linking LCCA, LCCP and LCCM

| Adjusting the LCCA data | Life cycle cost planning |

Sample occupied building

Cost Data
Physical Data
Performance Data
Qualitative Data

If data on each building available for more than one year establish trend and take one year's figures

| Building No. 1 | Building No. 2 | Building No. 3 |

Adjust for time. Bringing to a present day cost using published cost indices

Measurement data on proposed building
1 Total area
2 Functional area
3 Wall area
4 Window area
5 Volume, etc.

Adjust for occupancy to take account of the type of occupancy hours of use and management efficiency

Energy analysis
from engineer simple calculations

Adjust for location and size if appropriate

Expert advice
Cleaning, rates, water rates, maintenance, insurance

Adjust for design, performance and quality differences such as age, condition, specification design characteristics maintenance

Statistical adjustment for 3 building use mean, median or mode

Assumptions
1 Discount rate
2 Inflation rate
3 Occupancy timers
4 Maintenance needs
5 Life cycles (the building and elements)
6 Period of analysis
7 Taxation aspects

Input data
LCCA of occupied buildings

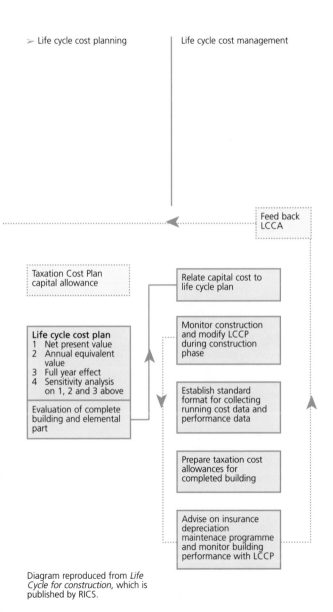

> Life cycle cost planning | Life cycle cost management

Feed back
LCCA

Taxation Cost Plan
capital allowance

Relate capital cost to
life cycle plan

Life cycle cost plan
1 Net present value
2 Annual equivalent
   value
3 Full year effect
4 Sensitivity analysis
   on 1, 2 and 3 above

Evaluation of complete
building and elemental
part

Monitor construction
and modify LCCP
during construction
phase

Establish standard
format for collecting
running cost data and
performance data

Prepare taxation cost
allowances for
completed building

Advise on insurance
depreciation
maintenace programme
and monitor building
performance with LCCP

Diagram reproduced from *Life
Cycle for construction*, which is
published by RICS.

Other considerations

The discount rate and inflation

When compiling life cycle cost plans, it is important to distinguish between the interest rate and the discount rate. Where project cash flows include an allowance for inflation, the discount rate should make an equivalent allowance. Alternatively, where estimates are in current prices, they should be discounted at the real discount rate.

While there is no definitive approach, it is reasonable to state that if all cost estimates are expected to inflate at the same rate then it is not unreasonable to perform all calculations in current prices, applying a real discount rate. Alternatively, where cost estimates are likely to inflate at different rates (e.g. energy costs inflating significantly faster than construction prices) then it may be beneficial to account for the differing rates of inflation.

In the case of financing through borrowing, the discount rate will equal the long term cost of borrowing money in the market place (net of inflation). While the discount rate will vary with the source of funding, it is worth noting that HM Treasury apply a discount rate of 3.5% in public sector option appraisal.

Project life

An estimate of the probable life of the project should be made. When ranking projects with identical lives, the option with the lowest present value should be chosen. However, where the options have different lives, the cost of each alternative should be expressed as an annual equivalent and the option with the lowest annual equivalent chosen.

Reinstatement valuations for insurance purposes

Generally it is considered prudent to insure a property for the value of complete reinstatement following total destruction (including partial destruction that necessitates demolition and rebuild). However, some clients request that only a portion of less vulnerable elements of the building (for example, external areas such as car parking and hardstandings) are included in the valuation.

When compiling a reinstatement valuation the following points should be considered:

❖ Demolition cost to be valued.

❖ Rebuilding costs to be valued (initially at 'day one' rates). Care must be taken here to include for any special features that are to be included to enable replacement of the property on a like for like basis. Examples include facade treatments such as stonework embellishments or internal features such as specialist decorations.

❖ Extent of the valuation to be discussed and agreed with the client: whether tenant's fixtures and fittings are to be valued; whether a basic landlord fit out is to be included; or a shell only valuation with all other items to be included under separate policies. This may be done on agreement with the client or by reference to leases which state the obligations of the landlord and tenant.

❖ Professional fees to be included at an appropriate level, depending on the complexity and location of the property.

❖ Geographical location factors to be accounted for either in rebuilding rates or separately by reference to recognised indices.

❖ Local authority planning and building regulation fees must be included as they are an unavoidable expense.

If the valuation is being projected to cover the period of the policy (as opposed to Day One valuation) then account should be made for the:

❖ period of the policy;

❖ design period;

❖ planning period;

❖ construction period; and

❖ void (letting) period (if required by the owner).

This may result in projecting costs for anything up to and beyond a three year period. In addition, as with any construction scheme, a contingency may be included.

In summary, a 'day one' valuation may increase by upwards of 30% on the basic rebuild costs to take account of the issues listed above. Property owners should always seek a realistic valuation of their property to avoid being over or under-insured. At best the premiums may be based on an exaggerated value and at worst, following destruction, there will be insufficient funds to reconstruct.

Official Journal of the European Union

The Official Journal of the European Union (OJEU) (sometimes also known as OJ – see page 45) is the electronic gazette of the EU. Published since the Nice Treaty of 1 February 2003, in all of the languages of the member states, it covers such matters as new EU legislation, regulations and directives, etc.

There is a 'supplement' to the journal where every week approximately 2,500 notices and tenders for works and services are advertised.

See pages 40 and 41 for information on OJEU procurement and tendering procedures and the tables on page 44 for OJEU public procurement thresholds and timescales.

Town and country planning in the UK

Present and future planning in the UK

The Planning and Compulsory Purchase Act 2004 is the present cornerstone of the planning system in England and Wales. It represented the first major legislative change to the planning system for nearly 14 years and gave effect to the government's policy of reforming planning and creating 'sustainable communities'. Sustainable development is now the core principle underpinning planning.

This Act introduced powers for the reform and speeding up of the development plan system and increasing the predictability of planning decisions.

The Act extends to England and Wales with certain provisions only relevant to Scotland. The Explanatory Note found at www.opsi.gov.uk/acts/en2004/2005en05.htm gives a most useful overview guide.

The publication of the Barker Review of Land Use Planning in December 2006 suggested that further reforms of the planning system would be undertaken. The White Paper *Planning for a Sustainable Future* of 21 May 2007 proposes considerable changes to the planning process, particularly in regard to sustainability in the face of 'global warming and carbon emissions' and developments that concern proposals of National Importance has now completed its consultation process on 17 August 2007. The summary review of the White Paper available on www.communities.gov.uk/publications/planningandbuilding/planningsustainablefuturewhite is worthy of reading. The Planning Bill introduced to Parliament on 27 November 2007 as yet has no enforcement date.

Accompanying the publication of the White Paper were further consultations on:

- ❖ Planning Performance Agreements;
- ❖ Planning Fees;
- ❖ Changes to Permitted Development Rights for Householders;
- ❖ Improvements to the Appeal Process; and
- ❖ Changes to Permitted Development Rights for Householder Microgeneration.

The law covering most aspects of planning in Scotland is the *Town and Country Planning (Scotland)* Act 1997 and www.scotland.gov.uk has excellent guidance on Scottish legislation.

Northern Ireland has devolved Planning under the *Planning (Northern Ireland)* Order 1991 and the *Planning Reform (Northern Ireland)* Order 2006.

Further confirmation of the ongoing reform of the current planning system was evident in the Queen's Speech in November 2007, which highlighted the government's intention to promote four bills which will be of significance to planning:

- ❖ *Planning Reform Bill* – which would streamline and improve the planning regime particularly in regard to major infrastructure projects;
- ❖ *Housing and Regeneration Bill* – which would support the delivery of three million new homes by 2020 by making better use of surplus public sector land and maximising the potential for brownfield land;
- ❖ *Climate Change Bill* – which would create a long-term legal framework to reduce CO_2 emissions; and
- ❖ *Local Transport Bill* – which would support the government's strategy to improve public transport, tackle road congestion and allow local authorities to take local action to meet local transport needs.

Development applications and fees

Development comprises the carrying out of building, engineering, mining or other operations in, on, over or under land or the making of any material change in the use of any buildings or other land. The demolition of buildings also comprises development. Planning permission is required for undertaking development. However, certain categories of minor development and demolition are granted permitted development rights and are therefore do not require planning permission.

Other minor forms of development are expressly excluded from requiring permission by the provisions of the Planning Acts. Such works include the maintenance, improvement or other alteration of any building, or works which affect only the interior of a building, or do not materially affect the external appearance of a building.

Permitted development rights are confirmed in the *Town and Country Planning (General Permitted Development) Order* 1995 and demolition controls in the *Town and Country Planning (Demolition – Description of Buildings) Direction* 1995. Both regulations have recently been subject to review and are therefore likely to be amended.

There are a number of parallel consents that are required in the case of special buildings or areas. Buildings which are listed as being of special historic or architectural interest (Grades I, II* and II) may not be altered (or demolished) in any way that might affect their character without a separate grant of listed building consent. Unlisted buildings within conservation areas may not be demolished without conservation area consent. Scheduled Monument consent is required for works affecting a Scheduled Ancient Monument. Consent is also required to display an advertisement, although there exist a number of deemed consents for certain categories of advertisement.

Fees are payable for planning and advertisement applications. The current fees are prescribed in the *Town and Country Planning (Fees for Applications and Deemed Applications) (Amendment) (England) Regulations* 2005. Some exemptions from fees are granted. For example, applications submitted within 12 months following a withdrawal or refusal of a previous application for the same development on the same site and submitted by the same applicant are not subject to a fee. No fees are liable for applications for listed building or conservation consent. There are no fees for submitting an appeal against the refusal of planning permission, but a fee is due for lodging an appeal against an enforcement notice.

Planning application fees are subject to regular increases and the last increase in 2005 was significant and resulted in a new maximum fee ceiling of £50,000.

Planning application fees have recently been subject to consultation with the result that a further increase is proposed which will take effect in April 2008, together with other adjustments to the scale of fees.

There is a proposal which has also been subject to consultation to introduce a fee for planning appeals.

Appeals and called-in applications

Rights of appeal exist in respect of a refusal of planning permission, a conditional grant of permission or the failure of a local planning authority to determine an application within the statutory time period – 8 weeks for most applications, but 13 weeks for major applications and 16 weeks in the case of development proposals that are subject to Environmental Impact Assessment.

Appeals against a refusal or conditional approval must be made within six months of the decision date. In the case of an appeal against the failure of the authority to determine an application, this must be lodged within six months of the date when the decision was due.

Appeals are determined by independent inspectors employed by the Planning Inspectorate, a government agency specialising in the administration and determination of all appeals.

There are three types of procedure for processing an appeal. Written representations are the simplest and are processed on the exchange of written submissions. Informal hearings allow an opportunity of an oral presentation of evidence, but in an informal session; whilst public inquiries require the evidence to be submitted orally and then subjected to cross examination by the opposing party.

There are stringent timescales and procedures imposed by secondary legislation which govern the appeal process. Guidance on the appeal process is provided in Circular 05/00. Whilst each party to the appeal is expected to bear its own costs, an opportunity to apply for an award of costs is available in the case of inquiries and informal hearings. However, awards are normally only contemplated when one party has behaved unreasonably and Circular 08/93 contains guidance on the situations where an award of costs may be justified.

The majority of appeals in England are decided by Inspectors. A small percentage are however decided by the Secretary of State for Communities and Local Government. Clarification of the type of appeals which are likely to be recovered by the Secretary of State was provided in a Parliamentary Statement in July 2006. In general the recovery criteria relate to major or controversial development proposals.

Development plans and monitoring

Since 1991 the planning system in England has been plan-led, requiring that where the development plan contains relevant policies, planning applications should be determined in accordance with the plan unless material considerations indicate otherwise. This requirement is now embodied in section 38(6) of the *Planning and Compulsory Purchase Act* 2004.

The *Planning and Compulsory Purchase Act* 2004 introduced a new system of development planning based on Local Development Frameworks (LDFs) and Regional Spatial Strategies (RSSs). In due course structure and local plans, and unitary development plans and regional planning guidance will be replaced by LDFs and RSSs. All local planning authorities are engaged on a review of their existing development plans and preparation of LDFs. These review processes, therefore, provide opportunities for submitting representations to promote development opportunities or minimise development constraints and this is a critical component of sound estate management.

General Development Order and Use Classes Order

Town and Country Planning (General Permitted Development) Order 1995 (as amended)

This order (the GPDO) grants permission for certain defined classes of development or use of land. These are mainly of a minor nature. The most commonly used class permits a wide range of small extensions or alterations to dwellings, and there are many other minor permitted developments.

The permitted developments granted under the GPDO can be withdrawn in a defined area under the terms of an article 4 direction made by the local planning authority or Secretary of State.

Town and Country Planning (General Development Procedure) Order 1995 (as amended)

This Order (the GDPO) details procedural matters in respect of planning applications, including a full list of statutory consultees, as well as requirements for a register of applications, specimen copies of forms and guidance on appeal submissions.

Amendments to the GDPO are currently proposed and will take effect on 6 April 2008. These amendments will introduce a standard planning application form and national requirements for the content of planning applications. Local Planning Authorities can, subject to public consultation, adopt their own local lists for planning applications to supplement the requirements of the national list.

Town and Country Planning (General Development Procedure) (Amendment) (England) Order 2005

Further procedural arrangements in respect of planning applications were introduced by the *Planning and Compulsory Purchase Act* 2004 to complement those contained in the 1995 Order. These powers included:

- ❖ the power to decline to determine repeat applications;
- ❖ the duration of permission and consents which require that development or works must be begun within three years from the date when permission is granted;
- ❖ a duty to respond to statutory consultations; and
- ❖ confirmation that Regional Planning Bodies are statutory consultees on major development proposals.

Town and Country Planning (General Development Procedure) (Amendment) (England) Order 2006

This Order introduced further procedural changes to the development control system. These included:

- ❖ powers for local planning authorities to make local development orders;
- ❖ changes to the outline planning permission process with the result that additional information is required to support an application for outline permission;
- ❖ a requirement that applications for certain types of development must be accompanied by design and access statements;
- ❖ powers controlling internal floorspace additions such as mezzanines; and
- ❖ changes to the decision period for determining major planning applications.

Town and Country Planning (Use Classes) Order 1987

Section 55 of the 1990 Planning Act provides that changing the use of some buildings or land does not constitute development and that this applies to changes of use where both the existing and proposed use fall within the same use class as defined within the *Use Classes Order* 1987. In addition some changes of use between different use classes are also permitted development.

There are some uses which do not fall within any use class and these are referred to as *sui generis* uses.

The use classes have been subject to amendment and in the *Use Classes Amendment Order* 2005 the following changes were made:

❖ retail warehouse clubs and nightclubs are excluded from any use class;
❖ internet cafes are included within the A1 shops class; and
❖ the former use class 'food and drink' is divided into three separate classes:
  – restaurants and cafes;
  – drinking establishments; and
  – hot food takeaways.

One effect of these changes is that it is necessary to apply for planning permission to change from a restaurant or cafe to a drinking establishment such as a bar or pub or to a hot food takeaway.

The following list gives the use classes based on the *Town and Country Planning (Use Classes) Order* 1987 (SI 1987/764) and all subsequent amendments:

❖ **A1 Shops:** Shops, retail warehouses, post offices, hairdressers, travel and ticket agencies, pet shops, showrooms, sandwich bars, domestic hire shops, undertakers, dry cleaners and funeral directors.

❖ **A2 Financial and professional services:** Banks, building societies, professional and financial services, estate agencies, employment agencies and betting offices.

❖ **A3 Restaurants and cafes:** Places where the primary purpose is the sale and consumption of food and light refreshments on the premises, e.g. restaurants, cafes, snack bars.

❖ **A4 Drinking establishments:** Public houses, wine bars, etc. but not nightclubs.

❖ **A5 Hot food takeaways:** Places where the primary purpose is the sale of hot food to take away.

❖ **B1 Business:** Offices, research and development and light industry, appropriate in a residential area.

❖ **B2 General industrial:** Covers a variety of industrial uses.

❖ **B3–B7 Special Industrial Groups:** See the Schedule to the *Use Classes Order* 1987.

❖ **B8 Storage or distribution:** Includes open-air storage.

❖ **C1 Hotels:** Hotels, boarding houses and guest houses where there is no care provided.

❖ **C2 Residential institutions:** Residential care homes, nursing homes, hospitals, boarding schools, residential colleges and training centres.

❖ **C2A Secure residential institutions:** Secure residential accommodation, e.g. prisons, detention centres, young offenders institutions, secure training centres, custody centres, short term holding centres, secure hospitals, secure local authority accommodation or military barracks.

❖ **C3 Dwellinghouses:** Family houses or houses occupied by up to six people living as a single household including one where care is provided.

❖ **D1 Non-residential institutions:** Clinics, health centres, crèches, day nurseries, day centres, schools, art galleries, libraries, museums, halls, places of worship, church halls, non-residential education and training centres, law courts.

❖ **D2 Assembly and leisure:** Cinemas, music and concert halls, bingo and dance halls (but not night clubs), skating rinks, swimming baths, gymnasiums and sports arenas (except motor sports or where firearms are in use).

❖ **Sue generis:** Theatres, houses in multiple paying occupation, hostels providing no significant care, scrap yards, filling stations, shops selling and/or displaying motor vehicles, retail warehouse clubs, nightclubs, casinos, amusement centres, launderettes, taxi businesses.

Planning policy guidance notes, policy statements, technical advice notes and circulars

Planning Policy Guidance Notes (PPGs) and Planning Policy Statements (PPSs) set out the government's national policies on different aspects of planning in England. PPSs are gradually replacing PPGs and they are a material consideration in the preparation of development plans and in the determination of individual planning applications. PPSs are aimed at providing a more succinct statement of the government's planning policies.

Devolved government to Scotland, Wales and Northern Ireland does mean there are equivalent National Planning Policies and Guidance Notes for each administration.

In all four constituents of the United Kingdom the various Technical Advice Notes, Circulars, Planning Policy Guidance Notes or Statements are particularly relevant when the development plan is outdated and does not reflect current government planning policies.

Scotland

In Scotland, Planning Policy is contained in the *National Planning Framework for Scotland* (due to be replaced by the Second National Planning Framework sometime in 2008). This is supplemented by 21 Scottish Planning Policies comprising 14 SPP documents and 6 NPPG documents, of which 3 SPPs are presently under review. These are supplemented by PAN or Planning Advice Note Documents. The website www.scotland.gov.uk/Topics/Planning/Policy Legislation/Policy will lead you to the relevant documentation.

Current SPPs and NPPGs	
SPP1	The Planning System
SPP2	Economic Development
SPP3	Planning for Housing
SPP4	Planning for Minerals
NPPG5	Archaeology and Planning
SPP6	Renewable Energy
SPP7	Planning and Flooding
SPP8	Town Centres and Retailing
SPP10	Planning for Waste Management
SPP11	Sport, Physical Recreation and Open Spaces
NPPG12	Skiing Developments
NPPG13	Coastal Planning
NPPG14	Natural Heritage
SPP15	Planning for Rural Development
SPP16	Opencast Coal
SPP17	Planning for Transport

Current SPPs and NPPGs	
NPPG18	Planning and the Historic Environment
NPPG19	Radio Telecommunications
SPP20	Role of Architecture and Design Scotland
SPP21	Green Belts
SPP22	Planning for Fish Farming
SPP23	Historic Environment (**draft presently in circulation**)

Wales

In Wales, land use policy is contained in *Planning Policy Wales* (March 2002). This is supplemented by 20 topic based 'Technical Advice Notes (Wales)' or 'TANs'. Procedural guidance is given separately in Welsh Office/National Assembly for Wales circulars. The website http://new.wales.gov.uk/topics/planning/policy/tans/?lang=en will lead you to the relevant documentation.

Current TANs	
TAN1	Joint Housing Land Availability Studies
TAN2	Planning and Affordable Housing
TAN3	Simplified Planning Zones
TAN4	Retailing and Town Centres
TAN5	Nature Conservation and Planning
TAN6	Agricultural and Rural Development
TAN7	Outdoor Advertisement Control
TAN8	Renewable Energy
TAN9	Enforcement of Planning Control
TAN10	Tree Preservation Orders
TAN11	Noise
TAN12	Design
TAN13	Tourism
TAN14	Coastal Planning
TAN15	Development and Flood Risk
TAN16	Sport and Recreation
TAN18	Transport
TAN19	Telecommunications
TAN20	The Welsh Language – Unitary Development Plans and Planning Control
TAN21	Waste

Northern Ireland

In Northern Ireland, planning has long been devolved with Regional and Local Development Plans supplemented by (presently) a total of 16 Planning Policy Statements (PPSs) with 5 further Clarification, Revision or Draft PPSs. Here www.planningni.gov.uk/AreaPlans_Policy/PPS/PPS.htm will take you to the detailed documents.

Current PPSs	
PPS1	General Principles
PPS2	Planning and Nature Conservation
PPS3	Access, Movement and Parking

Current PPSs	
PPS4	Industrial Development
PPS5	Retailing and Town Centres
PPS6	Archaeology, The Built Heritage and Area of Townscape Character
PPS7	Quality Residential Environments
PPS8	Open Space, Sport and Outdoor Recreation
PPS9	The Enforcement of Planning Control
PPS10	Telecommunications
PPS11	Planning and Waste Management
PPS12	Housing in Settlements
PPS13	Transportation and Land Use
PPS14	[Draft] Sustainable Development in the Countryside
PPS15	Planning and Flood Risk
PPS17	Control of Outdoor Advertisements

England

In England, there are at present 25 Planning Policy Guidance Notes or Statements. Governmental intention prior to 2004/2006 had been to gradually replace Planning Policy Guidance Notes (PPGs) with equivalent Planning Policy Statements (PPSs).

A check on the current status of a PPG or PPS is therefore advisable and this can be undertaken on www.communities.gov.uk/ planningandbuilding/planning/planningpolicyguidance/planningpolicy statements. From May 2006 the Department for Communities and Local Government (DCLG, now CLG) assumed responsibilities for planning and Building Regulations in England from the Office of the Deputy Prime Minister (ODPM). The DCLG ministerial statement of 5 May 2006 stated that the replacement of PPGs by PPSs will only take place as and when necessary.

With the exception of PPG4 *Industrial, commercial development and small firms*, all of the old style PPGs that were targeted for review in June 2004 have either been replaced or a draft replacement has been published for consultation.

PPG/PPS number	Title	Date
PPS1	Delivering Sustainable Development	2005
PPG2	Green Belts	1995 (amended 2001)
PPS3	Housing	2006 (updated 23/3/07)
PPG4	Industrial, commercial development and small firms	1992
PPG5	Simplified Planning Zones	1992
PPS6	Planning for Town Centres	2005
PPS7	Sustainable Development in Rural Areas	2004
PPG8	Telecommunications	2001
PPS9	Biodiversity and Geological Conservation	2005
PPS10	Planning for Sustainable Waste Management	2005
PPS11	Regional Spatial Strategies	2004

PPG/PPS number	Title	Date
PPS12	Local Development Frameworks Note: PPG12 remains relevant for any Development Plans being prepared under the 1999 Development Plan Regulations.	2004
PPG13	Transport	2001
PPG14	Development on unstable land	1990
PPG15	Planning and the historic environment	1994
PPG16	Archaeology and planning	1990
PPG17	Planning for Open Space, Sport and Recreation	2002
PPG18	Enforcing planning control	1991
PPG19	Outdoor advertisement control	1992
PPG20	Coastal planning	1992
PPG21	Tourism – cancelled September 2006	
PPS22	Renewable energy	2004
PPS23	Planning and Pollution Control	2004
PPG24	Planning and noise	1994
PPS25	Development and Flood Risk	2006

Some PPGs/PPSs are supplemented by further guidance in the form of annexes or *Good Practice Guides*. PPS1 is accompanied by a statement on *The Planning System: General Principles*. PPS3 is accompanied by a statement *Delivering Affordable Housing* and advice notes. PPS6 has a Guidance Document. Circular 06/05 and a Good Practice Guide complement the guidance provided in PPS9. PPS10 has a Companion Guide, PPS11 a Good Practice Guide. PPG14 has two Annexes on Landslides and Subsidence. PPG12, which was published in 1999, remains in force for those development plans that are still being prepared under the 'old-style' development plan regulations. Circulars 01/01 and 09/05 amend the guidance contained in PPG15 in respect of the arrangements for handling heritage applications. *A Good Practice Guide on Planning for Tourism* published in May 2006 provides national planning guidance on tourism and replaces PPG21 which was cancelled in September 2006.

An additional PPS1 on *Planning and Climate Change* was published on 17 December 2007 to form a supplement to PPS1.

A consultation paper for PPS4 *Planning for Sustainable Economic Development* was also published on 17 December 2007, with a closing date for responses of 17 March 2008.

Government policy on minerals and planning issues is contained within Minerals Planning Guidance Notes (MPGs) and their replacements, Minerals Policy Statements (MPSs).

Regional Planning Guidance has now been replaced by the Regional Spatial Strategy which, following the enactment of the *Planning and Compulsory Purchase Act* 2004, is now part of the statutory development plan. Each of the regions in England is subject to either a RPG or Draft RSS. Where RPGs have not yet been reviewed they have been renamed and now form part of the statutory development plan for the region.

In Greater London the regional spatial strategy is provided by the London Plan which was published in February 2004. The Plan has been reviewed and is subject to two separate Alterations. The *Early Alterations* were subject to 'Examination in Public' in June 2006 and the *Further Alterations* were published for consultation in September 2006.

Departmental Circulars are also material considerations in the discharge of planning powers, but are more restricted and focus on advice on legislative matters and planning procedures.

The following are most relevant:

No	Title
04/06	The Town and Country Planning (Flooding) (England) Direction 2007
02/06	Changes to Planning Regulations for Casinos
01/06	Guidance to Changes in the Development Control System
11/05	The Town and Country Planning (Green Belt) Direction 2005
08/05	Guidance on Changes in the Development Control System
05/05	Planning Obligations
03/05	Changes of Use of Buildings and Land – The Town and Country Planning (Use Classes) Order 1987
01/05	The Town and Country Planning (Residential Density) (London, South East England, South West England, East of England and Northamptonshire) Direction 2005
05/00	Planning appeals procedures (including inquiries into called-in planning applications)
02/99	Environmental impact assessment
11/95	Use of conditions in planning permission
08/93	Awards of costs incurred in planning and other (including compulsory purchase order) proceedings

A number of circulars have been subject to review and consultation and are likely to be superseded. Consultations have been undertaken on:

❖ a revised circular on Environmental Impact Assessment; and
❖ the introduction of a 'Planning Gain Supplement' and changes in the process of securing planning obligations.

Listed buildings and conservation areas

Listed buildings 'buildings of special architectural or historic interest' have long been recognised as a major asset in the built environment.

The joint RICS, British Property Federation and English Heritage publication *Heritage Works* concluded for example that 'listed office buildings can be a sound financial investment'.

In a world increasingly concerned about reducing carbon emissions and protecting the environment, the 2002 study by the investment property databank for English Heritage and the RICS Foundation concluded that 'the creative new use of historic buildings can bring a return on investment as good as any other type of building and is certainly the best form of "green" development'.

This very much connects with the emphasis in PPG15 on keeping historic buildings in active use and urging planning authorities to be flexible and imaginative in their approach to achieve the right balance between protecting the building's special architectural and historic interest and adapting it for different uses.

The replacement of the present PPG15 by a projected Planning Policy Statement on the Built Heritage is part of the comprehensive review of legislation and policies for heritage protection which has been the subject of a recent White Paper as regards England and Wales – *Heritage Protection in the 21st Century*, which has now completed its consultation period. There would appear to be no immediate likelihood now of the replacement of PPG15 by a PPS and indeed PPG15 may well remain legally applicable for the immediate future and indeed the medium term. At the time of publication, no legislative changes are anticipated before 2009/2010.

This has built on the results of two major consultation papers:

- *Protecting our historic environment: making the system work better* (2003); and
- *The review of heritage protection: the way forward* (2004).

The White Paper included both immediate and long-term measures for comprehensive changes to the heritage protection process in England and Wales. The only matter that has happened was the transfer in 2005 of the process for new listings of buildings to English Heritage.

The key proposals for implementation post the White Paper and relevant primary legislation in England and Wales are:

- The new unified register of historic sites and buildings (RHSBE and RHSBW) – This is intended to offer a holistic approach to the statutory protection of the historic environment through a single designation regime and a new definition of 'historic assets'.
- A reformed heritage consent regime – This is to be implemented by local authorities with assistance from English Heritage and CADW. It is presently understood that this process is likely to distinguish between the following three categories:
  - below ground (and water) archaeology and monumental structures;
  - historic buildings and structures suited to adaptive reuse; and
  - historic landscapes and seascapes.
- Voluntary heritage partnership agreements – These are intended to provide an alternative management regime for:
  - large assets;
  - complex entities that comprise many similar or several different assets;
  - assets of similar type and single ownership and management but in dispersed locations; and
  - assets better managed alongside other regimes.
- New statutory requirements relating to Historic Environment Records (HER) – Local authorities will be required to maintain or ensure that they have access to an HER that meets nationally defined standards.

In Scotland, the Historic Environment Advisory Council for Scotland (HEACS) announced, in its 2007 annual report, the subjects of the four core topics for review requested by the Minister for the current three-year term:

- the infrastructure of the historic environment sector;
- the economic impact of the historic environment;
- a strategy for conservation of ecclesiastical heritage; and
- strategies for engaging the interest of young adults in the historic environment.

This is, however, all in the future and for the present the provisions are as follows.

Listed buildings in the United Kingdom

The principal current legislation is the *Planning (Listed Buildings and Conservation Areas) Act* 1990, in Scotland the *Planning (Listed Buildings and Conservation Areas) (Scotland) Act* 1997. This sets out the statutory framework relating to listed buildings and conservation areas.

Listed Building or Conservation Area Consent is not required for a material change of use. Change of use is covered under the *Town and Country Planning Act* 1990.

Grade I: (Grade A in Scotland, Grade A in Northern Ireland)

Buildings of exceptional interest (about 2% of listed buildings).

Grade II*: (Grade B in Scotland, Grade B+ in Northern Ireland)

Particularly important buildings of more than specialist interest (about 4% of listed buildings).

Grade II: (Grade C(S) in Scotland, Grades B1 and B2 in Northern Ireland)

Buildings of special interest which warrant every effort being made to preserve them. In Northern Ireland Grades B1 and B2 are buildings of local importance or good examples of some period or style.

Listing

The basic criteria for listing are set out in PPG15 (as modified for England alone by Circular 01/07 *Revisions to Principles of Selection for Listed Buildings*) and 'spot listing' will still be considered for individual buildings overlooked or under threat, by reference of details by any member of the public to English Heritage, Historic Scotland, CADW (Welsh Heritage), and the Northern Ireland Environment and Heritage Service. The list reviews will concentrate on finding the best examples of types and periods of buildings under-represented in the current list. Historic Scotland in www.historic-scotland.gov.uk/index/historicbuildings/whatwelist/listingprinciples has a simple and helpful statement.

CADW in www.cadw.wales.gov.uk/upload/resourcepool/whatislisting-e20057855.htm gives similar useful guidance for Wales.

Equally the Environment and Heritage Service of Northern Ireland has useful guidance on www.ehsni.gov.uk/built/listing.htm. Do note that Northern Ireland uses Grades A, B+, B1 and B2.

What is a listed building?

A listed building is any structure or erection, and any part of a building including any object or structure within the curtilage, that forms part of the land and did so before 1 July 1948. There are of course 'Modern Movement' Listed Buildings that postdate 1948.

Material change of use

It is accepted that new uses for old buildings, the 'adaptive reuse of historic buildings', may often be the key to their conservation. In some instances, it may be appropriate that controls should be relaxed where this would enable historic buildings to be given a new lease of life.

The best use for an historic building is obviously the use for which it was designed and, wherever possible, the original use should continue.

Works for which listed building consent is necessary

Demolition of a listed building, or its alteration or extension in any manner that would affect its special architectural or historic interest, requires consent. It should be noted that the setting of an historic building is considered of great importance and an essential feature of its interest and character. Consent is not normally required for works of repair that are on the basis of like-for-like materials and exact matching original details. However, this is a grey area.

Application for listed building consent

Applications for listed building consent should be made to the local planning authority.

Listed building consent decisions

The local planning authority has eight weeks in which to consider an application. This can be extended by agreement with the applicant or revision of proposals, etc.

The legislation requires all listed building consents to have conditions, even if only time/recording conditions.

Listed building consent for works already executed

Listed building consent may be sought even though the works have already been completed. If consent is granted this is not retrospective; the works are authorised only from the date of consent.

Conservation areas

Local authorities have a duty imposed by section 71 of the *Listed Buildings Act* 1990 and equivalent sections of the *Scotland Act* of 1997, that they must regularly formulate and publish proposals for the preservation and enhancement of conservation areas, after consultation with local people at a public meeting. The advice insists that simply designating a conservation area will not ensure its protection and that planning authorities should analyse what makes an area special and develop policies to protect it, in consultation with local residents and businesses.

Other powers

The guidance gives powers to councils to control some minor developments in conservation areas including alterations to roofs, doors and windows, so as to prevent damage to the area's special character and to avoid councils having to pursue individual article 4 directions. From October 1994 many churches, previously exempt, were brought within conservation controls, although Christian churches in active use still have ecclesiastical exemption.

Following publicity for the English, Welsh, Northern Irish and Scottish Heritage list of battlefields, PPG15 and the equivalent documentation in Scotland, Wales and Northern Ireland reminds developers and councils to also protect wider features of the historic environment, such as important gardens and parks, which are now separately listed and graded. World Heritage Sites have separate high measures of protection.

Preservation presumption

PPG 15 and its equivalents reaffirms the presumption in favour of preserving listed buildings of special architectural or historic interest and a presumption in favour of retaining unlisted buildings which make a positive contribution to the character or appearance of a conservation area.

Environmental impact assessments

Environmental Impact Assessment (EIA) is the process for identifying the environmental impact of proposed developments. The legal requirements derive from the *Town and Country Planning (Environmental Impact Assessment) Regulations* 1999 as amended by the *Town and Country*

Planning (Environmental Impact Assessment) (England and Wales) (Amendment) Regulations 2006.

The requirement for an EIA to be undertaken is mandatory for certain development projects. These projects are referred to as 'Schedule 1' developments and are defined in the Regulations. For other developments, which are defined in the Regulations and referred to as 'Schedule 2' developments, the decision as to whether an Environmental Statement is required to support the planning application is contingent on:

❖ whether any part of the development is located within a defined sensitive area;

❖ whether the development exceeds an applicable development threshold or criterion; and

❖ whether the development is likely to have significant environmental effects.

A procedure is set out in the Regulations which allows the need for an EIA to be subject to a screening opinion (regulation 5(1)) obtainable on application to the local planning authority. The decision of the local planning authority in response to the request for a screening opinion must be made within three weeks from receipt of the request, although there is provision for the local planning authority to request an extension. There is further provision within the Regulations for an applicant who disagrees with the local planning authority's screening decision to 'appeal' to the Secretary of State.

The Regulations also provide for a 'scoping opinion' to be obtained from the local planning authority. This provides guidance on the content and extent of matters that the authority considers should be covered by the EIA.

Further guidance on the EIA process can be found in the following:

❖ *Environmental Impact Assessment: A guide to procedures* produced by the Office of the Deputy Prime Minister, 2000;

❖ *Preparation of Environmental Statements for Planning Projects that Require Environmental Assessment: A good practice guide* produced by the Department of the Environment, 1995; and

❖ *Evaluation of Environmental Information for Planning Projects – A good practice guide* produced by the Department of the Environment, 1994.

European Community Directives, UK case law and European Court of Justice judgements have also aided the interpretation of the EIA Regulations. To clarify the requirements the then ODPM issued a *Note on Environmental Impact Assessment Directive for Local Planning Authorities* in April 2004 and this provides a further useful guidance note on the process. The CLG also issued a letter to all local planning authorities in June 2006 providing further guidance in response to recent ECJ judgements.

A revised Circular and Practice Guide (*Amended Circular on Environmental Impact Assessment*) replacing Circular 02/99 was published in 2006 for consultation purposes and provides an updated policy and practice context for EIAs reflecting the changes brought about by UK and European case law.

Occupier obligations

The Regulatory Reform (Fire Safety) Order 2005

The *Regulatory Reform (Fire Safety) Order* 2005 (RRFSO) received Parliamentary Approval on 7 June 2005 and came into force on 1 October 2006. The main effect of the Fire Safety Order is a move towards greater emphasis on fire prevention in all non-domestic premises. However, the RRFSO does apply to the common parts of multi-tenanted residential accommodation such as flats. The Fire Safety Order applies in England and Wales while Northern Ireland and Scotland have devolved responsibility for safety law (see subsequent sections below).

The Order is not in fact 'new' but a reform of all previous fire safety law, which is contained in over 100 separate pieces of legislation. The reform was brought in to simplify, rationalise and consolidate existing legislation in respect of fire safety. The aim was to reduce burdens on businesses caused by previous multiple overlapping fire safety regimes and consequently, the overlap of the responsibilities of enforcing authorities. Accordingly, this reduces the number of enforcing authorities dealing with general fire safety matters.

Under the reform, as of 1 October 2006, fire certificates were abolished and ceased to have legal status. Instead, under the RRFSO, a 'responsible person' for each premises is required to carry out an assessment of fire risk and take reasonable steps to reduce or remove that risk. As with previous Fire Risk Assessments required under the former *Fire Precautions (Workplace) Regulations* 1997 and *(Amendment) Regulations* 1999 (which are now revoked), these will need to be kept under review. Responsibility for complying with the Fire Safety Order rests with the 'responsible person'. There is no separate formal validation process for higher risk premises, although fire authorities will base their inspection programmes on premises that they consider to present the highest risk.

Multi-tenanted buildings

Where two or more responsible persons share or have duties in respect of premises, the RRFSO requires cooperation and coordination between the parties. For example, the landlord will generally be responsible for the common parts and the tenants responsible for their respective demised areas, with coordination between all of the parties concerned, ideally managed by the landlord.

Definition of 'responsible person'

Article 3 of the RRFSO defines 'responsible person' as:

    (a) 'in relation to a workplace, the employer, if the workplace is to any extent under his control;

    (b) in relation to any premises not falling within paragraph (a)

        (i) the person who has control of the premises (as occupier or otherwise) in connection with the carrying on by him of a trade, business or other undertaking (for profit or not); or

        (ii) the owner, where the person in control of the premises does not have control in connection with the carrying on by that person of a trade, business or other undertaking.'

Fire safety duties

Under article 8 of the RRFSO, the 'responsible person' must:

    (a) 'take such general fire precautions as will ensure, so far as is reasonably practicable, the safety of any of his employees; and

(b) in relation to relevant persons who are not his employees, take such general fire precautions [as described below] as may reasonably be required in the circumstances of the case to ensure that the premises are safe.'

General fire precautions

The RRFSO cites, under article 4, the meaning of 'general fire precautions' as:

(a) 'measures to reduce the risk of fire on the premises and the risk of the spread of fire on the premises;

(b) measures in relation to the means of escape from the premises;

(c) measures for securing that, at all material times, the means of escape can be safely and effectively used;

(d) measures in relation to the means for fighting fires on the premises;

(e) measures in relation to the means for detecting fire on the premises and giving warning in case of fire on the premises; and

(f) measures in relation to the arrangements for action to be taken in the event of fire on the premises, including –
(i) measures relating to the instruction and training of employees; and
(ii) measures to mitigate the effects of the fire.'

Crown Copyright material is reproduced with the permission of the Controller of HMSO and the Queen's Printer for Scotland.

Risk assessment

The 'responsible person' is required to undertake a risk assessment, which will need to address, among other things, the following:

❖ assessed risks of young persons employed (i.e. under 18 years of age);

❖ elimination or reduction of risks from dangerous substances;

❖ fire fighting and fire detection provision;

❖ emergency routes and exits; and

❖ evacuation of disabled people.

The government has produced 11 guidance documents which deal with fire safety in different types of premises and which reflect the new legislation. There is also a supplementary guide dealing with means of escape for disabled people.

In addition to the above, the 'responsible person' will (in most cases) need to appoint a competent person to assist him or her in undertaking the risk assessment and fulfilling the obligations under the Order. 'Competent' is described in the Order as 'where he has sufficient training and experience or knowledge and other qualities to enable him properly to implement the measures referred to' in the Order. On small simple buildings this might be the employer him- or herself. However, on larger and more complex buildings, it is likely that the responsible person will need to appoint a qualified professional, trained and experienced in fire safety management.

Enforcement

The enforcing authority under the RRFSO will depend upon the type of premises. The enforcing authorities include the fire and rescue authority for the area in which the premises falls, the Health and Safety Executive, the fire service, the relevant local authority, fire inspector or any other person authorised by the Secretary of State. The enforcing authority is empowered to serve a prohibition notice, an alterations notice or an enforcement notice. Failure to comply with the RRFSO is an offence resulting in a fine up to the statutory maximum limit and/or imprisonment for a maximum of two years.

Amendments to existing legislation

The following legislation was revoked/repealed by the RRFSO. Note: This list is not exhaustive:

- ❖ the *Fire Precautions Act* 1971;
- ❖ the *Fire Certificate (Special Premises) Regulations* 1976;
- ❖ the *Fire Precautions (Workplace) Regulations* 1997; and
- ❖ the *Fire Precautions (Workplace) (Amendment) Regulations* 1999.

Northern Ireland

Sections 1 and 2 of the *Regulatory Reform (Fire Safety) Order* were implemented in May 2006 following public consultation and approval by Parliament. These sections are relevant to the Northern Ireland Fire Brigade only. Section 4 is currently under consultation and will concentrate on the operational side of the Fire Authority. Section 3 will enforce the need for a relevant risk assessment to be carried out to all workplaces by a relevantly trained competent person. The Fire Authority are currently retraining their staff to ensure they are prepared to review fire risk assessments. Consultation is still ongoing and has still to be formally activated by the Secretary of State, therefore, implementation of the outstanding section (section 3), of the Regulatory Reform Order is now targeted for March 2008.

Please refer to the website for the Northern Ireland Assembly www.niassembly.gov.uk for an updated position on the fire legislation.

Scotland

The *Fire (Scotland) Act* 2005 received Royal Assent on 1 April 2005. The 2005 Act came into force on 2 August 2005 with the exception of Part 3 which introduces a new fire safety regime in Scotland and came into force on 1 October 2006.

The main purpose of the Act is to reform fire safety legislation in Scotland, modernising fire and rescue services. It also provides for the implementation of the provisions of a number of EU Directives on health and safety at work.

The new Act revokes/repeals the following legislation:

- ❖ the *Fire Precautions Act* 1971;
- ❖ the *Fire Certificate (Special Premises) Regulations* 1976; and
- ❖ the Workplace Fire Precautions Legislation, in respect of: the *Fire Precautions (Workplace) Regulations* 1997 ('the 1997 Regulations') and the general fire safety provisions of the *Management of Health and Safety at Work Regulations* 1999 ('the 1999 Regulations') (the health and safety provisions of these regulations will be unaffected).

The Act does not include private dwellings but common areas of private dwellings will be dealt with.

The Act consolidates existing legislation relating to duties of employers to their staff and in respect of premises. Provision is made regarding fire safety measures, risk assessment and enforcement.

Provision is also made for a Fire and Rescue Framework for Scotland that will set out priorities and objectives for the relevant authorities. This document will be designed to promote public safety and the efficiency and effectiveness of the rescue authorities.

The introduction of the Act has allowed enabling orders and regulations to be made. In conjunction with Part III of the Act, the *Fire Safety (Scotland) Regulations* 2006 came into force on 1 October 2006. The Regulations, inter alia, cover fire safety, means of fighting fire, means of escape, procedures in dangerous areas, maintenance of premises and equipment, and information to and training of employees.

Please see www.scotland.gov.uk for up to date news on the Act and the accompanying Regulations.

Fire, residential property and houses in multiple occupation (HMOs)

Purely domestic properties are excluded under the RRFSO, however, it still applies to the common areas of houses in multiple occupation and the common parts of flats. Residential landlords also have a general common law duty to keep tenants' homes fit for them to live in and to ensure that they do not endanger tenants' health, including ensuring that there are no fire hazards. Where a house is in multiple occupation and meets the 'HMO' classification, there are additional fire safety responsibilities. (For details: see: www.communities.gov.uk/housing/rentingandletting/privaterenting/housesmultiple/). This will include the provision of adequate fire precautions such as fire alarms and extinguishers and suitable and sufficient means of escape, usually providing at least 30 minutes protection. The local council or Fire and Rescue Service can inspect the property to see whether the landlord or managing agent is complying with the law. If the property is not an HMO, there are no specific fire safety laws to comply with, although there is a general duty to keep the property habitable. There is also an obligation to ensure that the property is properly maintained, so for example, a fire hazard does not occur as a result of a faulty electrical installation. There is also a requirement to ensure that upholstered furnishings provided in the property are fire resistant.

The Disability Discrimination Act and access for disabled people

Disability facts

- ❖ There are estimated to be more than 10 million disabled people in Britain.
- ❖ There are 3.4 million people with a disability or long-term health condition already working in this country. Another 1 million are currently out of work but want a job.
- ❖ Disability increases with age: only 10% of adults aged 16–24 are disabled, while one third of people between aged 50 and retirement age are disabled.
- ❖ By 2020, 50% of us will be aged over 50.
- ❖ Only 50% of disabled people of working age are in employment compared to 81% of non-disabled people.
- ❖ Disability is too often associated with wheelchairs: in fact only 5% of disabled people use wheelchairs.

The DDA (the Disability Discrimination Act 1995 as amended by the Special Educational Needs and Disability Act 2001 and the Disability Discrimination Act 2005)

The *Disability Discrimination Act* 1995 (DDA) came into force on 2 December 1996. It brings in measures to prevent discrimination against disabled people. The *Disability Discrimination Act* 2005 (which further amends the DDA 1995) received Royal Assent on 7 April 2005, increasing and creating new rights for disabled people.

Territorial coverage of the DDA

The DDA 1995 applies to England, Wales, Scotland and (with modifications) to Northern Ireland. The DDA 2005 extends to Great Britain only with the exception of section 9 (Blue badge parking provisions) and section 16 (Improvements to let dwellings) which extend only to England and Wales. The 2005 Act does not extend to Northern Ireland since disability discrimination and transport are classed as 'transferred matters' under the *Northern Ireland Act* 1998. The provisions on rights for disabled people in education extend to England, Wales and Scotland, although there is no duty to produce an accessibility strategy or plan in Scotland. The education provisions (SENDA) do not extend to Northern Ireland.

The Act

The DDA 1995 is split into different sections.

❖ Part 1 – defines the term 'disability'.

❖ Part 2 – deals with discrimination in employment, trade organisations and qualifications bodies.

❖ Part 3 – deals with discrimination in the provision of goods, facilities and services to members of the public and the disposal and management of property. The DDA 2005 further amends Part 3 to now include public authority functions, private clubs with more than 25 members and letting of premises. More recent changes as a result of the DDA 2005 amend the Part 3 duties to clarify the scope of the exemption in relation to transport providers. Therefore, the Part 3 duties now extend to certain types of transport vehicles.

❖ Part 4 – deals with provisions for education.

❖ Part 5 – deals with provisions for public transport.

❖ Part 6 – deals with the setting up of the National Disability Council.

❖ Part 7 – supplemental provisions (details duties and responsibilities covering Codes of Practice, victimisation, liability of employers, help for people suffering discrimination, aiding unlawful acts and exclusion for acts done with statutory authority or done for the purpose of safeguarding national security).

❖ Part 8 – miscellaneous provisions (including government appointments, regulations and interpretation).

Part 1 – Definition of disability within the Act

A physical or mental impairment, which has a substantial and long-term (12 months' minimum) adverse effect on a person's ability to carry out normal day-to-day activities. The DDA 2005 extends the definition to include people with HIV, cancer and multiple sclerosis, from the point of diagnosis.

Part 2 – Employment, trade organisations and qualifications bodies

Employment

This section of the Act came into force on 2 December 1996 and applies when a disabled person is employed, or an employee becomes disabled. The Act places a duty on all employers (the previous threshold exemption of less than 15 employees being removed from 1 October 2004) to make reasonable adjustments to enable disabled employees to carry out their work. (The armed forces are excluded under the employment provisions.)

An employer is expected to take reasonable measures to allow a person to do his or her job. This may involve:

- ❖ making adjustments to premises;
- ❖ moving a disabled person's place of work;
- ❖ altering hours of work;
- ❖ reallocating a disabled person's duties;
- ❖ acquiring or modifying equipment; and
- ❖ providing a reader or interpreter.

In addition to the above, employers should ensure that their equal opportunities policy addresses disability, in addition to preparing a disability statement and policy. Employers are not required to make changes in anticipation of employing a disabled person, however the Code of Practice suggests that employers should take opportunities to make improvements as they arise, e.g. as part of planned maintenance or refurbishment works. In addition, employers must not unjustifiably discriminate against current employees or job applicants on the grounds of disability, and may have to make reasonable adjustments to their employment arrangements or premises if these substantially disadvantage a disabled person.

There are also significant improvements to the legislation, which became effective as of 1 October 2004. The October 2004 changes also include people who are not technically employees, i.e. whereby a contract of employment does not exist. Contract workers, office holders, police officers, partners in firms, barristers and advocates and people undertaking practical work experience for the purposes of vocational training are now included. Others to whom Part 2 of the Act applies are contained within the revised 2004 Code of Practice.

Trade organisations and qualifications bodies

Qualifications bodies is an alteration to the trade association provisions of the DDA. These have come about as a result of a European Directive on discrimination in employment, which includes disability. These changes are contained in the *Disability Discrimination Act 1995 (Amendment) Regulations* 2003, which were implemented in October 2004.

The duty of a trade organisation or qualification body to make reasonable adjustments applies in respect of its disabled members and, also, in respect of any disabled person who is, or who has notified the organisation that he or she may be, an applicant for membership. Further information can be found within the Code of Practice. This is being updated 2007/2008 to cover new anti-disability discrimination legal duties which came into force on 1 September 2007 and also to cover changes that have occurred since the introduction of the 2004 Code.

Part 3 – The provision of goods, facilities and services including discrimination in relation to premises

Note: A revised Code of Practice for Part 3 came into force on 4 December 2006, see www.equalityhumanrights.com/pages/eocdrccre.aspx

The Act covers:

- ❖ any place where the public may enter;
- ❖ accommodation in hotels, boarding houses, etc.;
- ❖ all retailers or tradesman's premises;
- ❖ any building owned by a public authority; and
- ❖ facilities for entertainment or recreation.

Discrimination is deemed to have arisen if a provider of services treats a disabled person less favourably than he or she would treat others and:

- ❖ cannot show the treatment in question was justified; and
- ❖ failed to undertake his or her duty to make adjustments as described below.

Part 3 came into force in three distinct sections.

The following duties came into force in December 1996:

- ❖ a duty not to discriminate;
- ❖ a duty not to refuse service;
- ❖ a duty not to provide a worse standard of service; and
- ❖ a duty not to offer worse terms.

The following duties came into force in October 1999:

- ❖ a duty to change practices, policies and procedures that are discriminatory;
- ❖ a duty to provide extra help such as auxiliary aids; and
- ❖ a duty to overcome physical restrictions by the provision of alternative methods.

The following duties came into force in October 2004:

Where a physical barrier makes the use of any service which is offered to the public impossible or unreasonably difficult, a service provider must take reasonable steps to:

- ❖ remove the feature;
- ❖ alter it so it no longer has an effect;
- ❖ provide a reasonable means of avoiding the feature; or
- ❖ provide a reasonable alternative method of making the service available to disabled people.

The Act does not specify what is reasonable, as it varies according to the characteristics of each area of provision. Account may be taken of:

- ❖ the type of services being provided;
- ❖ the nature of the service provider and its size and resources;
- ❖ the effect of the disability on the individual disabled person;
- ❖ the amount of time that the service provider has had prior to that date to make preparations;
- ❖ whether taking any particular steps would be effective in overcoming the difficulty that disabled people face in accessing the services in question;
- ❖ the extent to which it is practicable for the service provider to take the steps;
- ❖ the financial and other costs of making the adjustment;
- ❖ the extent of any disruption which taking the steps would cause;
- ❖ the amount of any resources already spent on making adjustments; and
- ❖ the availability of financial or other assistance.

The Act does not require a service provider to take any steps which would fundamentally alter the nature of its service, trade, profession or business.

Further interpretation of 'reasonableness' is expected through the courts, although there is currently limited case law. The latest update on this can be found at the Equality and Human Rights Commission website: www.equalityhumanrights.com/pages/eocdrccre.aspx

Public authority functions

The DDA 2005 introduces new duties (which amend part 3 of the DDA 1995) in respect of public authority functions. The Act now prohibits discrimination in relation to every function of a public authority. The new duties came into force on 4 December 2006. The Act does not define a public authority but states that a public authority 'includes any person certain of whose functions are functions of a public nature'. For example, this includes NHS Trusts and Boards, the Prison Service, Courts and Tribunals, Police Authorities, governing bodies of higher education institutions, colleges and universities and local authorities amongst others, details of which are provided in the Code of Practice. It is important to note and differentiate between a service to the public by a public body (which falls under part 3 of the DDA 1995) and a function of a public body. A large majority of the activities of a public authority constitute the provision of goods, facilities and services (and are NOT public authority functions).

The Code of Practice gives a helpful example of a public authority function. Where a highway authority is deciding where to site a pedestrian crossing and what type of crossing to adopt, it is likely to be carrying out a public function rather than acting as a service provider.

Public authorities have duties to make reasonable adjustments, which fall into three distinct areas:

❖ Practices, policies and procedures: the public authority has a duty to take reasonable steps to change any practice, policy or procedure that might make it impossible or unreasonably difficult for a disabled person to receive any benefit that is or may be conferred, or, unreasonably adverse for a disabled person to experience.

❖ Auxiliary aids and services: under s. 21E(6) of the DDA 2005, the public authority has to take reasonable steps to provide an auxiliary aid or service.

❖ Physical features: under s. 21E(4) of the 2005 Act, a public authority has a duty to take reasonable steps to:

– remove the feature;

– alter the feature so it no longer has that effect;

– provide a reasonable means of avoiding the feature; or

– adopt a reasonable alternative method of carrying out the function.

Disability Equality Duty

The DDA 2005 introduces a duty on public authorities to promote disability equality to cover disabled people in every area of their work. The duty is not necessarily about alterations to buildings or adjustments for individuals.

There are both general duties and specific duties under the Disability Equality Duty. The general duty came into force on 4 December 2006. Primary schools in England had until 3 December 2007 to publish their Disability Equality Scheme and all schools in Wales were to publish their schemes no later than 1 April 2007. The Secretaries of State, National Assembly in Wales and Scottish Ministers must produce their first report by December 2008.

Guidance on the Disability Equality Duty can be found at www.dotheduty.org

Private clubs

A further amendment to Part 3 affects private clubs with more than 25 members, which have been included since December 2005. The duty to make reasonable adjustments to policies, practices and procedures with the provision of auxiliary aids and services was introduced from December 2005, under the first stage of the new DDA 2005. The second stage came into force on 4 December 2006, where private clubs with more than 25 members are required to undertake reasonable adjustments to physical features. As a practical example, the private club provisions will apply to a private golf club, however, if they also have a function room available for private hire such as wedding receptions, this will fall under the services to public provisions. A local authority run golf club will have duties under the services to public provisions regardless of how they run their facilities.

Discrimination in relation to selling, letting and management of premises

The DDA 1995 duties have been extended under the DDA 2005, from December 2006 (in relation to letting of premises), to include a duty to make reasonable adjustments to policies, practices and procedures and to provide auxiliary aids and services, where reasonable to do so. Landlords will therefore have a duty to take reasonable steps to facilitate access for disabled tenants and leaseholders. Reasonable adjustments might include:

- ❖ changing a 'no dogs' policy to allow assistance dogs;
- ❖ changing a term in a lease prohibiting the undertaking of any alterations where the term makes it impossible or unreasonably difficult for a disabled person to enjoy the premises or make use of an associated benefit or facility; or
- ❖ providing a clip-on receiver, that vibrates when the doorbell rings, for a tenant with a hearing impairment.

However, landlords will not be under any duty to carry out adjustments to physical features of the premises. Furthermore, the cost of any reasonable adjustments that a landlord may have to make (in respect of policies, practices, procedures, auxiliary aids and services) cannot be recovered by way of increased rent or service charges. However, it is permissible to share the cost between all of the tenants in a building through the service charge provision, providing the tenancy agreements permit this. **The duty to make adjustments in respect of let premises is owed directly to the individual disabled person once certain conditions have been met and only arises when requested by the disabled person.** It is **not** an anticipatory duty. The request for the adjustment does not have to be in writing and furthermore, does not need to refer to the DDA.

Landlords have an obligation under the DDA to change letting terms, where reasonable to do so, to enable a tenant to undertake alterations which ordinarily might not be permitted under the lease.

Landlord responsibilities for common parts under the DDA

The duties of landlords under Part 3 of the DDA 1995 is unclear. The Code of Practice (Part 3) states that 'there is no legal duty to make reasonable adjustments to premises which are sold, let or managed'. In addition, 'those who are selling, letting or managing premises do not have to make adjustments to make those premises more suitable for disabled people'. The issue surrounding landlords' responsibilities is complex and therefore landlords of premises with more than one occupier should not assume that they are not service providers for the purposes of the Act. The Code of Practice states that 'they should anticipate that they may have responsibilities to make the common parts accessible to disabled people. They are advised to keep up to date with how the law in this respect is being interpreted'. The Code of Practice goes on to say 'if tenants are providing services to the public in their own right from the premises, they will have a duty under the Act to take reasonable steps to make the services accessible to disabled people'. However, landlords should be careful in the extent of works that they carry out where they would seek to recover the cost of such works from the tenants through service charge provisions.

Disability Discrimination (Providers of Services) (Adjustment of Premises) Regulations 2001

These apply to service providers and landlords of premises occupied by service holders. The Regulations prescribe particular circumstances in which it is reasonable or unreasonable for service providers to make physical alterations to the premises they rent or own or for lessors to withold their approval to same.

With the introduction of the Disability Equality Duty (DED) from December 2006, public authorities such as councils will need to consider how the DED could affect them as landlords. This is likely, amongst other things, to include the need to consider access improvements to the common and demised parts of rented premises. The provisions of the original DDA 1995 have been extensively amended and extreme caution should be taken when referring to material that may now be out of date. There is no substitute for professional legal advice in an environment where incorrect interpretation of the provisions is widespread.

Part 4 – Education (as amended by the Special Educational Needs and Disability Act)

Provision of education was excluded from Part 3 of the Disability Discrimination Act (Provision of Goods, Facilities and Services) as the *Education Act* 1996 made comprehensive educational provision for children with special educational needs, to which LEAs and governing bodies have a duty to comply. However, the *Special Educational Needs and Disability Act* 2001 (SENDA) was given Royal Assent on 11 May 2001 and came into force from 1 September 2002. The Act removes the previous exemption of education from the *Disability Discrimination Act* 1995, ensuring that discrimination against disabled students will be unlawful. The Act is an amendment to the existing DDA 1995 and only protects people defined as 'disabled' according to that legislation. This definition is based on an individual's ability to carry out normal 'day-to-day' activities, and so may exclude some students who are usually considered disabled by the support systems within their institutions. Education providers need to be aware of the *Learning and Skills Act* 2000, as they may need to make different provision for people covered by this legislation.

Construction professionals should note particularly the differing requirements between schools and post-16 education. Duties under post-16 education apply to higher education, further education, adult and community education, schools providing further education for adults (but excluding sixth form) and youth and community services.

SENDA (post-16 duties)

The duties of SENDA are being implemented in three stages.

The main new sections of the Act came into force on 1 September 2002. These sections make it unlawful to discriminate against disabled people or students by treating them less favourably than others. In addition, they require responsible bodies to provide certain types of reasonable adjustments to provision where disabled students or other disabled people might otherwise be substantially disadvantaged.

A duty on responsible bodies to make adjustments involving the provision of auxiliary aids and services came into force on 1 September 2003.

The duty on the responsible body to make adjustments to physical features on premises where these put disabled people or students at a substantial disadvantage came into force on 1 September 2005.

Duties under SENDA apply to higher education, further education, adult and community education, schools providing further education for adults (but excluding sixth form) and youth and community services. Note: the post 16 duties do not apply to private or independent companies running courses. This would be covered by the DDA Part 3 duties.

SENDA (schools)

The disability discrimination duties provide protection for disabled pupils by preventing discrimination against them at school on the grounds of disability. There are two key duties involved in ensuring that schools do not discriminate against disabled pupils. These are:

- ❖ not to treat disabled pupils less favourably; and
- ❖ to take reasonable steps to avoid putting disabled pupils at a substantial disadvantage.

The reasonable adjustments duty does not require the responsible body to provide auxiliary aids and services, nor does it require the responsible body to make alterations to the physical features of the school. The reasonable adjustment duty does not apply to auxiliary aids and services because it is anticipated that in schools in the maintained sector, such provision will be made through the SEN framework. Physical alterations to schools are not required under the reasonable adjustments duty as it is anticipated that these will be achieved through a longer term and more strategic approach to improving access to school buildings through the planning duties.

The planning duties require that schools prepare and develop accessibility plans, which should address three distinct elements of planned improvements in access for disabled pupils:

- ❖ improvements in access to the curriculum;
- ❖ physical improvements to increase access to education and associated services; and
- ❖ improvements in provision of information of a range of formats for disabled pupils.

The planning duties also update the requirement on governing bodies to provide information in their annual reports about arrangements for disabled pupils at the school.

The DRC has published two Codes of Practice that set out, separately, in detail, the duties and responsibilities for both schools and post-16 education. The codes warrant detailed examination for those who are involved in educational establishments as they provide clarification and examples of potential scenarios covering the various duties and responsibilities under the Act.

The codes are available on the EHRC website
www.equalityhumanrights.com/pages/eocdrccre.aspx

Part 5 – Public transport

Part 5 of the Act allows the government to set access standards for buses, coaches, trains, trams and taxis. Regulations have been introduced by the government to apply minimum access standards. Part 5 of the DDA applies specifically to the actual means of transport and does not include, for example, railway stations, ferry terminals, bus stations, airports and the like. These are covered under Part 3 of the Act. Under the Code of Practice, the following example is given: 'A wheelchair user has no protection under Part 3 of the Act if a ferry on which he wishes to travel is not accessible. However, if he is refused service in the buffet bar of the ferry terminal because of his disability, this is likely to be unlawful.'

The *Disability Discrimination Act* 2005 will result in further changes and improvements including extending some areas of Part 3 to include public transport. The 2005 Act provides a flexible framework which has allowed the introduction of regulations to include forms of transport into Part 3 of the DDA. The 2005 Regulations apply to breakdown recovery vehicles, hire or rental vehicles, private hire vehicles, public services vehicles (such as buses and coaches), rail vehicles (including underground rail and trams), taxis and vehicles used on a system using a mode of guided transport (e.g. monorails and guided buses). They do not yet currently include aircraft and shipping vessels, although the Act empowers the government to lift the transport exemption in respect of any form of transport service.

The transport duties introduced under Part 3 of the DDA, as amended by the *Disability Discrimination Act* 2005 and its supporting regulations, came into force on 4 December 2006. Section 6 of the DDA 2005 requires rail vehicles to be accessible by 2020.

Providers of transport services in respect of the provision or use of a vehicle covered by the 2005 Regulations are now deemed providers of services to the public for the purposes of Part 3 of the DDA.

Codes of practice and advice notes

The government has drawn up various codes of practice to help implement the Act and interpret its requirements. The codes can be downloaded from the Equality and Human Rights Commission (EHRC) website at www.equalityhumanrights.com/pages/eocdrccre.aspx

The DDA and the Building Regulations

Where a physical feature of a building is covered by Approved Document M of the Building Regulations, if that feature conforms or is deemed to conform to the requirements of the edition current at the time of approval or installation, a ten-year exemption applies to that specific feature from the date of installation or construction. This exemption applies to service providers only.

BS 8300:2001

British Standard 8300:2001 *Design of buildings and their approaches to meet the needs of disabled people – Code of Practice* was amended in June 2005. This is an important document in the field of access for disabled people and provides extensive and detailed guidance on good practice in the design of and access to buildings and their approaches. It forms the basis for much of the amendment to the Part M Approved Document under the Building Regulations. This document is much more comprehensive than the Approved Document and, therefore, it may not be sufficient to rely uniquely on Part M.

Part M Approved Document

This recently revised guidance is based on and is complementary to BS 8300:2001, although the BS contains much additional material that is not included in the new Part M Approved Document. In some cases, the guidance in the Part M Approved Document differs from the recommendations in BS 8300. Compliance with the recommendations in the BS, therefore, while ensuring good practice, is not necessarily equivalent to compliance with the guidance in the Part M Approved Document and appropriate care should be taken when dealing with both documents.

The National Register of Access Consultants

The National Register of Access Consultants (NRAC) was established in 1999 to accredit access auditors and access consultants. Its website can be accessed at www.nrac.org.uk. There are two levels of membership: auditor or consultant. The fundamental difference between an auditor and a consultant is that consultants are required to have construction-related qualifications. Therefore, there are some limitations to the extent and detail of the advice that auditors can provide. Construction professionals such as surveyors and architects are therefore well placed to advise in this field.

The Royal Institution of Chartered Surveyors (RICS) 'Certificate in Inclusive Environments'

The RICS scheme was introduced in spring 2006 to 'promote excellence in the field of inclusive environments'. The scheme is similar to that of the NRAC with the setting up of a register of individuals with appropriate knowledge, experience and skills in inclusive environments. However, it is focused at RICS members, in particular, chartered building surveyors. See www.rics.org for more information.

Case law

Since the DDA was introduced, there have been a number of cases brought forward, although case law, particularly covering Part 3, is still largely undeveloped. Please refer to the full list of DRC cases to be found on the EHRC website www.equalityhumanrights.com/pages/eocdrccre.aspx

Legislation update

It must be noted that the DDA is complex, particularly so with the DDA 2005 amendment and the introduction of new regulations and codes of practice. Care must be taken when referring to the above in the light of continuing changes and developments in the DDA and the access field. In any event, legal advice may need to be sought in respect of interpretation of the law.

Access Statements

Essentially, an Access Statement is a document which shows how an applicant is addressing accessibility issues within the design of a building or space. The document would usually start off as being prepared to submit with a Planning or Building Regulation Application. Eventually, the document would be handed over to the end user to assist him or her in addressing the occupational side of access for disabled users. The statement should provide details as to the level of accessibility to be provided and in particular, document any deviation from current regulations and best practice. The reasons for deviating from these standards must also be explained. Where these are approved by the local authority, this will assist an end user by providing supporting documentary evidence as to why this has not been possible. This is particularly important where the end user has duties under the DDA.

There is a requirement for the undertaking of Access Statements for both planning and building control purposes. However, in reality, there is misunderstanding by some local authorities as to what should be provided, in addition to issues of inadequate resource and lack of experience on inclusive design to address access as part of Building Control and Planning applications.

Access Statements should be prepared at the planning stage and will need to be submitted for both planning purposes and then subsequently developed for submission with the Building Regulations application. The actual requirement to submit an Access Statement to Building Control will largely depend upon the local enforcing authority. As a minimum, any deviations from the Approved Document M will almost certainly require the submission of an Access Statement.

There is limited guidance on Access Statements, although some guidance has been produced by the Disability Rights Commission entitled *Access Statements – Achieving an inclusive environment by ensuring continuity throughout the planning, design and management of buildings and spaces*. There is also the guidance issued by the department for Communities and Local Government (CLG) through the Commission for Architecture and the Built Environment entitled *Design and access statements – How to write, read and use them*.

As of 10 August 2006, an Access Statement is required to be submitted with all planning applications with the exception of householders and changes of use. Access statements are recommended to be submitted with all Building Regulation applications and should certainly be provided where the applicant deviates from Approved Document M.

The DDA, listed buildings and conservation areas

Contrary to popular belief, listed buildings are not excluded from the DDA. There is nothing in the Act stating that if a building is listed or located within a conservation area there is any exemption from the DDA. Buildings that fall into this category will invariably be more difficult to work with in improving physical access. However, access improvements have been made to numerous historic buildings where alterations have remained sympathetic to the original character and features. Any proposed alterations will need to meet the approval of the Conservation Officer and English Heritage.

Lifetime Homes

The Lifetime Homes concept was developed by a group of housing experts who came together as the Joseph Rowntree Foundation (JRF) Lifetime Homes Group in 1991. The Lifetime Homes standards have 16 design features which must be incorporated within a new house or flat for it to be approved as a 'lifetime home'.

The idea around the concept of Lifetime Homes is to design with future flexibility in mind and to ensure that a household meets the changing needs of its occupants. This is not just about addressing disability but also takes into consideration the ease in which a property can be subdivided and remodelled to meet changing householder needs.

See the following example from the JRF website:

> 'A common scenario in Germany is: a young couple build a house; the ground and first floor is used "conventionally" as the family grows; in order to supplement their income to finance their mortgage, the basement, or part thereof, is let out as a self-contained flat. As the family grows up, teenagers may move up into the (now finished) attic rooms, which can also be effectively self-contained. Grandparents now becoming more dependent, and requiring less space, may often move into the basement flat.'

From the Joseph Rowntree Foundation's website www.jrf.org.uk/ housingandcare/lifetimehomes/questions/answer.asp?ID=21. Reproduced by permission of the Joseph Rowntree Foundation.

See www.jfr.org.uk for further information.

The Workplace Regulations – Glazing

The *Workplace (Health, Safety and Welfare) Regulations* 1992, regulation 14, require that glazed doors (and gates) be fitted with safety materials where any part of the glazing is below shoulder height. This requirement applies to glazing in the panels at the sides of the doors (and gates) because these areas are often struck or pushed when mistaken for part of the door.

The requirements also apply to windows, walls and partitions where there is glazing below waist height.

In situations where the width of the glass panel exceeds 250mm then safety materials must be used. Safety materials include:

❖ polycarbonates, glass blocks or other materials that are inherently robust; or

❖ glass that will break safely (i.e. shatters without a chance of sharp edges) or ordinary annealed glass that is of sufficient thickness relative to its area, as outlined in the following table.

Nominal thickness	Maximum size
8mm	1100 x 1100mm
10mm	2250 x 2250mm
12mm	3000 x 4500mm
15mm	Any size

Therefore, just because annealed glass exists, it does not follow that additional protection is required.

Glazing should always comply with British Standard BS 6262: Part 4: 2005 *Glazing for Building: Code of practice for safety related to human impact.*

In circumstances where glazing does not comply, it will be necessary to replace it with safety materials or to provide some physical protection that will ensure that it meets the impact performance levels required by BS 6262, Part 4: 2005.

A cheaper alternative would be to apply safety film to achieve the BS 6262 standard. Manufacturers of film should be consulted to ensure an appropriate grade of material for glass size.

All glass should be suitably marked as being of a safety standard. Where glass is protected by film, labelling should identify this.

Identification

Laminated and toughened glass can be detected using proprietary glass testing kits.

Note that ordinary Georgian wired glass does not comply with safety standards, but Georgian wired safety glass does.

The Workplace Regulations – Provision of sanitary facilities

The *Workplace (Health, Safety and Welfare) Regulations* require that sanitary provision shall be suitable and sufficient for the numbers and types of workers employed.

BS 6465: Part 1: 1994 sets out the minimum requirements.

It contains numerous tables illustrating the number and types of sanitary appliances required for a variety of different circumstances, depending on: the number of workers, and where relevant, customers; the ratio of males to females; and the different primary uses of the building in question.

The types of building include offices, shops, factories, restaurants, cafes, canteens and fast-food outlets, swimming pools, stadia, public houses, licensed bars, other places of public entertainment and non-domestic premises.

Comparison of requirements for 100 people evenly divided between the sexes (not including wheelchair users)								
Building type	Male			Female		Total		
	wc	urinal	whb	wc	whb	wc	urinal	whb
Workplaces	3	2	3	3	3	6	2	6
Workplaces (dirtier conditions)	3	2	3	3	5	6	2	8
Shops (customers) 1000–2000m²	1	1	1	2	2	3	1	3
Shops (customers) 2000–4000m²	1	2	2	4	4	5	2	6
Restaurants	1	1	2	2	2	3	1	4
Public houses, etc.	1	2	2	3	2	4	2	4

wc = water closet   whb = wash hand basin

The Workplace Regulations – Falls from height

Falls from height are the most common cause of fatal injury and the second most common cause of major injury to employees in the workplace. Most falls are the result of poor management rather than equipment failure.

Common examples include:

- ❖ failure to recognise a problem;
- ❖ failure to provide safe systems of work;
- ❖ failure to ensure that safe systems of work are followed;
- ❖ failure to provide adequate information, instruction, training or supervision;
- ❖ failure to provide safe plant or equipment; and
- ❖ failure to use appropriate equipment.

HSE has produced a number of free leaflets on falls from height that can be downloaded from their website at www.hse.gov.uk/falls. These include general advice such as *Safe use of ladders and stepladders* as well as the use of specific equipment such as *Safety in window cleaning using rope access techniques*.

The principles of good practice to prevent falls are contained within the *Work at Height Regulations* 2005.

The Work at Height Regulations 2005

These regulations came into operation on 6 April 2005.

They apply to all work where there is a risk of a fall liable to cause personal injury, even if the fall is at or below ground level.

The regulations place duties on employers, the self-employed and anyone who controls the work of others.

Employers must do all that is reasonably practicable to prevent falling by following a hierarchy for managing and selecting appropriate equipment:

- ❖ avoid work at height if possible;
- ❖ if not, use work equipment to prevent falls;
- ❖ where risk of fall cannot be eliminated, use equipment or other measures to minimise the distance and consequences of any fall; and
- ❖ select collective measures to prevent falls (e.g. guardrails and working platforms) before measures which may only mitigate the distance and consequences of a fall (e.g. nets or airbags) or which may only provide personal protection from a fall (e.g. fall arrest lanyards).

Employees must report any safety hazards and properly use the equipment supplied to them.

Duty holders must ensure that:

- ❖ all work is properly planned and organised;
- ❖ work activities take account of weather conditions;
- ❖ persons involved are trained and competent;
- ❖ the place of work is safe;
- ❖ equipment is appropriately inspected; and
- ❖ risks arising from fragile surfaces and from falling objects are properly controlled.

The Workplace Regulations – Lighting

Regulations

The key provisions relating to lighting can be found in the following Regulations:

- ❖ **The Workplace (Health, Safety and Welfare) Regulations 1992**
  - – Lighting in workplaces should be suitable and sufficient to enable people to work and move about safely. If necessary, local lighting should be provided, and at places of particular risk, such as crossing points of traffic routes.
  - – Lighting shall, so far as is reasonably practicable, be by natural light.
  - – Lighting and light fittings should not create a hazard.
  - – Automatic emergency lighting, powered by an independent source, should be provided where sudden loss of light would create a risk.
- ❖ **Health and Safety (Display Screen Equipment) Regulations 1992**
  - – Satisfactory lighting and appropriate contrast between screen and background to suit type of work and visual requirements of the operator.
- ❖ **Provision and Use of Work Equipment Regulations 1992**
  - – Again, these Regulations require lighting to be both suitable and sufficient.
- ❖ **Building Regulations Part L**
  - – Applies to all new non-domestic buildings over 100 square metres and certain buildings undergoing a change of use. Excludes exterior lighting.

– Includes requirements for energy-efficient lighting, lamps and luminaries and controls. Aims to encourage maximum use of daylight and avoid unnecessary lighting when spaces are unoccupied.

Guidance

The Chartered Institution of Building Services Engineers (CIBSE) and the Society of Light and Lighting (SLL) (see www.cibse.org for both) have published a number of useful and authoritative guides:

❖ Guidance Note (GN2:1993) *Healthy Workplaces – on compliance with the Workplace Regulations*;
❖ *Code for Interior Lighting* generally, and other task-specific guides e.g. LG1: *Industrial Environment*;
❖ LG3: *Areas for visual display terminals*; and
❖ TM12: *Emergency Lighting*.

ISO 9241 *Ergonomic requirements for office work with visual display terminals (VDTs)*.

BS 5266 – covers minimum levels and for emergency lighting.

The absolute minimum lighting level for particular tasks is set out in HS(G)38 *Lighting at Work* published by HSE.

Other considerations

Other considerations to take into account in relation to lighting would include:

❖ safe access for cleaning and maintenance;
❖ temperature of fitting(s);
❖ reflection and glare; and
❖ ease of control.

Building and construction

The Building Act 1984 and the Building (Amendment) Regulations 2004

The technical requirements of the Building Regulations are generally expressed as functional requirements; by themselves they may be difficult to interpret or understand. For this reason, the department for Communities and Local Government (CLG) publishes guidance on meeting the requirements in what are known as 'Approved Documents'. The Approved Documents cover all of the parts A–P of the Regulations, although building work will also have to comply with the requirements of any other relevant paragraphs in Schedule 1 to the Regulations. The Approved Documents also refer to additional texts – Associated Guidance.

The Approved Documents are intended to provide guidance for some of the more common building situations. In themselves they are not mandatory and there is no obligation to adopt any particular solution contained in an Approved Document if it is desired to meet the relevant requirement in some other way. They are given legal status by the Building Act 1984.

The most recent versions of the Approved Documents for the 14 technical 'Parts' of the Building Regulations' requirements can be downloaded free of charge from www.planningportal.gov.uk/england/professionals/en/1115314110382.html

Current Approved Documents

Approved Document	Date of publication and comments where applicable	Associated Guidance (all available from the planning portal – refer to the Approved Document for links)
A – Structure	27 April 2006, incorporating 2004 amendments	**Disproportionate collapse** • *DTLR Framework Report: Proposed Revised Guidance on meeting Compliance with the Requirements of Building Regulation A3: Revision of Allot and Lomax Proposal*, Project report number: 205966 • DTLR, *Guidance On Robustness And Provision Against Accidental Actions* • NHBC, *Guidance on Disproportionate Collapse*
		Multi-storey car parks • *Department for the Environment Transport and the Regions Partners in Innovation Scheme Contract Ref: 39/3/570 CC1806 EDGE PROTECTION IN MULTI-STOREY CAR PARKS – Assessment Method For Installed Restraint Systems*, Final Report, October 2001 • *Enhancing the Whole Life Structural Performance of Multi-Storey Car Parks*, September 2002, OPDM and Mott Macdonald

Approved Document	Date of publication and comments where applicable	Associated Guidance (all available from the planning portal – refer to the Approved Document for links)
A – Structure *continued*		**Thaumasite** • *Thaumasite Expert Group One-Year Review* • *Thaumasite Expert Group Report: Review after three years' experience.* **Garden walls** • *Your garden walls: better to be safe*
B – (Fire safety) – Volume 1: Dwelling houses	18 December 2006	• *Building Regulations and Fire Safety: Procedural Guidance*, July 2007 • *Fire Safety in Adult Placements: A Code of Practice*, September 2005
B – (Fire safety) – Volume 2: Buildings other than dwelling houses	18 December 2006	None
C – Site preparation and resistance to contaminates and moisture	28 April 2006	None
D – Toxic Substances	27 April 2006	None
E – Resistance to the passage of sound	27 April 2006	None
F – Ventilation	3 May 2006	None
G – Hygiene	2 May 2006, incorporating 1992 and 2000 amendments	None
H – Drainage and waste disposal	2 May 2006, replaced 2002 edition	None
J – Combustion appliances and fuel storage systems	2 May 2006, replaces 1992 edition	• *Solid fuel, wood and oil burning appliances* – safety leaflet • *Risk assessment of concrete flue liners* • *Danger – carbon monoxide poisoning*

Approved Document	Date of publication and comments where applicable	Associated Guidance (all available from the planning portal – refer to the Approved Document for links)
K – Protection from falling, collision and impact	3 May 2006, replaces the previous edition incorporating 2000 amendments	None
L1A – Conservation of fuel and power (New dwellings)	Since the 2006 Approved Documents for Part L were published on 15 March 2006, CLG (formerly ODPM) has become aware of inaccuracies in those for each of L1A, L1B, L2A and L2B. These inaccuracies have now been amended and the definitive version was placed on the website on 31 March 2006	See www.planningportal.gov.uk/ england/professionals/en/ 4000000000984.html for: • *National Calculation Methodologies* (includes SAP 2005, SBEM and the criteria for assessing software interfaces for SBEM) • *Accredited Construction Details* (for steel, timber and masonry construction) • Other reference documents on multi-foiled insulation, low or zero carbon energy sources, domestic and non-domestic heating systems, gas and oil central-heating boilers and condensing boiler installations • *Monitoring the Sustainability of Buildings* • *Sustainable and Secure Buildings Act 2004, A Biennial report* and supporting documents (Baseline key performance indicators and Impact of policy measures) • *Climate Change and Sustainable Energy Act* 2006 – section 14: A report regarding compliance with Part L
L1B – Conservation of fuel and power (Existing dwellings)	15 March 2006	
L2A – Conservation of fuel and power (New buildings other than dwellings)	15 March 2006	
L2B – Conservation of fuel and power (Existing buildings other than dwellings)	15 March 2006	

Approved Document	Date of publication and comments where applicable	Associated Guidance (all available from the planning portal – refer to the Approved Document for links)
M – Access to and use of buildings	3 May 2006, replaces previous edition	None
N – Glazing – safety in relation to impact, opening and cleaning	3 May 2006, replaces the previous edition incorporating 2000 amendments	None
P – Electrical safety – dwellings	15 March 2006	• *New Rules For Electrical Safety In The Home*, DCLG 2004
Approved Document to support Regulation 7 – Material and work-manship	3 May 2006	None

Part L 2006 compliance

'The only way in which the international community will limit the rise in carbon emissions is if governments, industry and individuals take into account the costs associated with the emissions for which they are responsible. A key role for Government is to put in place a framework which, by placing a value on carbon, provides a financial incentive for business and households to incorporate the climate change impact in their activities.'

The quote above is Crown copyright and is reproduced from the energy review report *The Energy Challenge*, published by the DTI in 2006.

Putting our contribution to the world's carbon emissions into perspective, with just 1% of the world's population the UK produces 2.3% of the world's CO_2. (Source: Friends of the Earth, 2006.)

Overview of Part L

The revised Part L was implemented in April 2006 to improve the energy efficiency standards of new and existing buildings beyond the standards of 2002 Part L Regulations. This was necessary to ensure that the UK is contributing to the reduction of greenhouse gas emissions that are known to cause global warming. The updated Regulations are the means by which articles 3 to 6 of the EU *Energy Performance in Buildings Directive* (EPBD) are being implemented in the UK.

EPBD articles 7 to 10 will be implemented in stages by January 2011:

 ❖ article 7 – for the provision of energy performance certificates for new and existing buildings (implementation between June 2007 and October 2008);

 ❖ article 9 – for the provision of regular inspection of boilers and air-conditioning systems (implementation between January 2009 and January 2011); and

❖ article 10 – for the provision of independent experts to certify, recommend improvements and inspect boilers and air-conditioning systems.

Part L 2006 Building Regulations are implemented through four separate Approved Documents, these are:

❖ AD L1A Work on new dwellings;
❖ AD L1B Work on existing dwellings;
❖ AD L2A Work on new buildings other than dwellings; and
❖ AD L2B Work on existing buildings other than dwellings.

The Regulations focus upon whole building energy performance to control carbon dioxide emissions in use. Flexibility is afforded to designers in selecting a means of compliance to achieve the minimum national energy performance targets. These targets must be reviewed within intervals of no longer than five years. A building that complies with 2006 Part L should emit 25% less CO_2 than a building that complied with 2002 Part L. The next review of Part L is likely to be undertaken in 2010 and is predicted to reduce the emissions benchmark by a further 25% of the 2006 requirements. By 2016 zero carbon emissions will be the target.

No prescriptive technical guidance is provided within the Approved Documents therefore designers are referred to technical data from a range of sources, such as CIBSE, BRE and HVCA. These sources are described as 'Second Tier guidance documents' that are published to assist with achieving target carbon dioxide emissions and energy efficiency.

The Regulations legislate for new and existing buildings and dwellings. New buildings and dwellings are required to comply with whole building carbon dioxide emissions targets, while existing buildings are required to comply with elemental performance standards targets.

A provision is made to include a contribution from low or zero carbon (LZC) technologies to achieve emissions targets, such as solar hot water heating, wind turbines, biomass heating and combined heat and power systems. All of these LZC technologies are subject to their own specific efficiency, feasibility, planning and cost issues and in some buildings the cost could be a significant proportion of the total construction cost.

New buildings should be designed and constructed:

❖ to conserve fuel and power to minimise CO_2 emissions in connection with occupancy and operation;
❖ to avoid overheating in summer time particularly with regard to unconditioned buildings;
❖ to reduce heat losses and heat gains through the external building fabric and also from pipes, ducts and vessels used for building services;
❖ to avoid unwanted and excessive solar gain and to reduce the requirements for mechanical cooling;
❖ to incorporate renewable and/or decentralised energy systems where feasible;
❖ to limit air leakage through the external fabric and ductwork;
❖ to demonstrate compliance upon construction completion by the undertaking of commissioning activities and providing certification; and
❖ to have operation and maintenance manuals and log books in place to ensure that efficiency of the installed systems is maintained in operation.

National calculation methodology (NCM)

A calculation methodology is a requirement of EPBD (see the section beginning on page 352) article 3 for validating a building's compliance. The implementation of this in the UK is through the Simplified Building Energy Model (SBEM). SBEM is the Part L specified national calculation software tool created by the BRE for calculating carbon dioxide emissions for dwellings over 450m² and for all buildings other than dwellings. The process for calculation involves inputting all aspects of the building design into the SBEM software to establish the Building Emissions Rate (BER), which must improve upon the Target Emission Rate (TER) set for the type of building being considered. The Part L specified calculation method for dwellings under 450m² is the Standard Assessment Procedure 2005 (SAP).

The Target (carbon dioxide) Emission Rate (TER) is the measurement of a building's efficiency. This is the mass of CO_2 emitted per year, per square metre of the total useful floor area of the building shown as kg/m²/year. The type of fuel to be used for a building will have a direct impact upon the carbon dioxide emissions calculation. Natural gas, for example, has an equivalent CO_2 emission of 0.194kg CO_2/kWh, whereas grid supplied electricity has an equivalent CO_2 emission of 0.422kg CO_2/kWh. The fuel factor applied to grid electricity is higher than natural gas when calculating building carbon dioxide emissions due to the inefficient nature of its production and delivery. The use of fuel factors will have a direct impact upon the Emissions Rate for a building.

SBEM has been the subject of much criticism due to its viability to be applied to non-simplified designed buildings. It has also been revised following feedback from users of the software. Unfortunately there have been issues where a building deemed to comply with Part L under the earlier versions of the SBEM software have subsequently failed using the revised versions.

There are a number of commercial software tools now available which have been approved for use by the department for Communities and Local Government (CLG) which can assist with checking for Part L compliance. These tools are designed to be more flexible, dynamic and user friendly than the SBEM tool.

A number of consultants have licences for more than one of these commercial software tools and use these simultaneously for the same building designs to ascertain how well the design performs against the TER. This is because it has become apparent that different software tools produce slightly different results and could make a difference to the extent of design and associated cost implications.

Emissions calculations will need to be undertaken around outline and scheme design stages to ensure that the building design being considered is likely to achieve compliance against the TER and by what margin, before progressing onto more detailed design and to avoid abortive design works. When the design becomes fixed, the calculations should then be updated to serve as a final check for design compliance with the TER. This is likely to impose limitations for the design team to make substantial changes to the design later on in, if they are to avoid abortive work and costs. Early energy and carbon assessments of a proposed design have become essential to undertake on most projects in order to influence how a building should be designed to comply with Part L.

Part L compliance must be proved at building control submission stage and then again upon completion of the building. There is a risk that, if the construction deviates from the prescribed specification and workmanship upon which Part L compliance relies upon, the completed building could fail to comply and may potentially be costly to remedy.

Design features to achieve whole building energy and carbon performance

The specifications listed below can contribute to achieving Part L compliance:

- ❖ Solar shading to reduce solar gain, through external shading and/or double wall facades, for example.
- ❖ Low 'e' double or triple glazing.

- ❖ Orientate the building in accordance with the direction of the sun and its angle, particularly during the winter season to maximise solar gain (without causing overheating).
- ❖ High boiler, chiller fans and pump efficiencies.
- ❖ High levels of external envelope airtightness.
- ❖ High artificial lighting efficiency and lighting control systems which utilise occupation and daylight sensors.
- ❖ Maximise heat recovery using heat exchangers, run around coils and thermal wheels, for example.
- ❖ Narrow plan floor plates, to maximise natural daylight, together with shading control.
- ❖ Utilise exposed thermal mass of structure and fabric together with night-time ventilation/purging for passive cooling.
- ❖ Combined heat and power systems.
- ❖ Utilise heat pumps for heating and cooling; either through traditional mechanical plant or ground coupling.
- ❖ Building-integrated renewable energy systems.
- ❖ Enhanced thermal insulation levels to walls, floors, roofs and glazing.
- ❖ Optimise the proportion of facade and roof glazing and the type used to limit perimeter and roof heat gains in summer, and losses in winter.
- ❖ Triple glazing.
- ❖ Maximise alternative means of ventilation and cooling involving 'mix mode' ventilation and 'free cooling' where feasible.
- ❖ Effectively use Building Energy Management Systems to optimise services efficiency and energy monitoring.
- ❖ Specify direct current/low energy fan coil systems.
- ❖ Specify chilled beam or chilled ceiling systems.

None of the above items listed are particularly revolutionary and indeed have been incorporated into pre-2006 Part L designed buildings. The Part L Regulations provide the flexibility to consider any and all of the specifications above, however the design solution selected will be a consequence of the most cost effective and practical solution that achieves the TER whilst still meeting the design brief provided by the client.

Regulations compliance for existing buildings

Where a building undergoes alteration, renovation and refurbishment, the following types of work fall within the remit of Part L.

Extensions – an extension over 100m² and greater than 25% of an existing building qualifies as a new building and must comply with AD L1A. Extensions to buildings can also trigger certain requirements to achieve minimum thermal and energy efficiency standards, these are called 'consequential improvements' and are discussed further below.

Material alteration and change of energy status – i.e. where work would lead to non-compliance of a building or service that previously complied and therefore minimum energy efficiency standards must be achieved.

Material change of use – such as the conversion of a private commercial building to a public building.

Extension, alteration or revision of a controlled (thermal) element – captures windows, doors, walls and conservatories, for example, and prescribes minimum energy efficiency standards.

Extension, alteration or revision of a controlled service or fitting – captures lighting, mechanical ventilation and cooling systems, heating and hot water systems, etc. and prescribes minimum energy efficiency standards.

Put simply if work is undertaken on controlled elements or services, requirements for upgrading or replacement may be necessary.

Consequential improvements – for existing non-domestic buildings with a floor area over 1,000m², where a new extension is to be constructed or there will be an increase in the capacity of fixed building services, 'consequential improvements' may have to be implemented to upgrade an existing building's thermal performance. Consequential improvements will be required even where the existing building is not directly affected by the proposed building works. Put simply, this means that where there is an improvement to one element of a building, general improvements are expected to other parts, although subject to the stated economical and technical criteria within the Approved Documents. The extent of consequential improvements as advised in the Approved Documents is limited to works that are technically, functionally and economically feasible and not more than 10% of value of principal works, with a simple payback of not more than 15 years.

For an extension, consequential improvements of not less than 10% of the value of the principal works should be spent (when practical and economically feasible) on measures such as:

❖ upgrading heating, cooling or air-handling systems that are more than 15 years old;

❖ upgrading general lighting systems that cover an area in excess of 100m² which have a lamp efficiency of less than 40 lamp-lumens per circuit-watt;

❖ installing energy metering;

❖ upgrading thermal elements with high U-values;

❖ replacing existing windows to achieve lower U-values; and

❖ incorporating on-site low and zero-carbon energy generating systems to provide at least 10% of a building's energy needs.

With offices a key issue to be aware of is that, although a new office building fitted out to a Category A standard must comply with Part L2A, a subsequent tenant fit-out to Category B must comply with Part L2B. If the Regulations are interpreted in the strictest sense, then consequential improvements could be required. In this circumstance it is necessary to take a sensible and pragmatic approach to the fit-out element and agree the right approach with Building Control.

There are different requirements for historic buildings, particularly those of a listed nature. Listed or 'protected' buildings are exempt from Part L compliance. For buildings which are not exempt the local authority may require certain works are undertaken providing that the original historic character of the building is not affected or compromised.

In assessing the scope of work required, the carbon emissions approach can be used, in addition to elemental performance compliance, to demonstrate that the modified building meets its target.

The approach to achieving compliance for existing buildings is not straightforward. The assessment of the appropriate scope of improvement works for existing buildings will be, by necessity, a trade-off between the ease of implementation, the effectiveness in achieving the TER and of course the capital cost measured against cost-in-use. The energy survey carried out as part of the project to identify and assess the challenges and opportunities will be a key aspect of this process.

How is the Part L compliance influencing the way new dwellings and buildings are designed?

Part L 2006 appears to be enabling fully glazed, sealed and air conditioned office buildings to be designed, despite early fears leading up to it's introduction that they would potentially be phased out. This has become apparent when using the approved software tools and SBEM. An air conditioned building must perform better than an equivalent 2002 compliant building, but a 'quirk' of the calculation methodology means that it is easier to comply with a fully air conditioned than a naturally ventilated building; mainly as there is much less scope to improve on a naturally ventilated building.

When designing buildings with full air conditioning, a key consideration in energy use is the perimeter heat gains in summer and heat losses in winter. These are a function of the proportion of facade glazing and also the type of glazing used in conjunction with the level of shading provided at the facades. If Part L compliance is difficult to achieve with conventional air-conditioning systems, then alternative solutions may have to be explored for ventilation and cooling such as 'mix mode' ventilation and active and passive cooling where the design permits. This may include further facade treatment, such as improving U-values and providing shading.

The thermal mass or inertia of a structure and its thermal elements are becoming more important in achieving compliant design solutions in the future to reduce the reliance upon totally mechanical solutions. This is because natural passive or mix-mode ventilation solutions can be utilised in balance with the thermal mass of a building to regulate changes in temperature without the intervention of total mechanical temperature control. The thermal properties of the structure and thermal elements will determine how swiftly the internal temperatures will respond to heat gains and losses and also how sensitive the internal environment is to temperature fluctuations. Generally speaking, heavyweight structures (such as concrete and brick) have a high thermal mass and lightweight structures (such as cladding, curtain walling and steel) have a low thermal mass.

An easy and low cost way to contribute to achieving Part L is to include energy efficient lamps and luminaires to reduce energy consumption and cooling loads. This is because installing efficient lighting does not require the building envelope to be upgraded and provides a cost effective contribution to carbon dioxide reductions.

Improving the thermal performance of the external fabric and glazing is only generally cost effective up to a point and does not always significantly contribute to the reduction of carbon dioxide emissions for many buildings, particularly when compared to improvements that can be made to the efficiencies of building services installations and providing an airtight facade. Making improvements to the efficiency of building services and the provision of an airtight facade may have a greater capital cost implication, however, buildings would benefit from greater energy efficiency and this could lead to downsizing of central plant, thus reducing operational costs over the life of a building.

In dwellings, space heating and hot water generation produces a significant proportion of the total carbon dioxide emissions. Therefore improving airtightness levels, increasing the thickness of thermal insulation, and incorporating enhanced hot water tank insulation, high efficiency heat sources and solar hot water heating, can significantly contribute to achieving carbon emissions targets. The ideal design condition should be to ensure that the external fabric and glazing is sufficiently insulated and airtight so that minimal space heating is required.

Airtightness issues

To ascertain that the designed airtightness has been achieved for the external fabric of a building to control unintentional air-leakage, air leakage testing is a mandatory method checking for compliance with Part L. Dwellings and buildings that fail the air pressure tests are to be subjected to prescribed methods of re-testing. Establishing liability for air test failures may be difficult, particularly in relation to poor design detailing or poor workmanship on site. Somebody has to pay to rectify the air leakage paths that caused the air test failures and responsibility has to be established. Air leakage testing takes place when a building is almost or entirely complete, therefore the discovery of significant failures could have a significant impact on the completion programme due to additional time spent carrying out remedial works and re-testing. The maximum rate of air leakage allowable is $10m^3/hr/m^2$ and the lower the value achieved below this threshold the better it is for achieving the TER. Airtight external walls, glazing, roof and doors is key to controlling energy use and minimising heat losses.

Revised Part F

Part F *Ventilation* was also revised in April 2006 in line with Part L because the airtightness requirements for buildings have increased and therefore designers must ensure that adequate ventilation is still provided within the occupied spaces. Part F and Part L are closely linked and strategies for compliance by way of a combination of extract ventilation, whole building ventilation and purge ventilation can be adopted to provide the required rates of fresh air and extract.

Part L compliant buildings cost implications?

It is costing more to build new or refurbish existing dwellings and buildings to comply with Part L 2006 than to build 2002 equivalent Part L compliant buildings. Typically, a range of up to 5% is added to construction costs, although the cost uplift is entirely dependent upon the design strategy adopted to achieve the carbon performance requirements based upon SAP or SBEM calculations. Where life cycle performance is particularly crucial, the additional costs have been greater than 5%, particularly for PFI schemes. The influence of consequential improvements has incrementally increased costs associated with works to existing buildings.

The introduction of the *Code for Sustainable Homes* (CSH) and the cost implications of its carbon dioxide emissions reduction targets over the next ten years has somewhat overshadowed the limelight Part L1 was exposed to, since the energy targets of the CSH go significantly beyond the standards of Part L 2006. Code Level 3 of the CSH has become the current best practice standard to achieve in new housing and demands a 25% improvement over Part L1.

Important note

Note that this section is a brief summation of the Part L 2006 Building Regulations and its applications. Therefore, the Approved Documents and their specified 'Second Tier Guidance Documents' should be referred to in the first instance for specific project application.

Further information

Department for Communities and Local Government: Approved Documents Parts L1A, L1B, L2A and L2B: www.planningportal.gov.uk

Part L explained, BRE guide published in 2006 by BRE publications

Airtightness

Parts L1 and L2 of the Building Regulations contain, among other things, a requirement for minimising air leakage from buildings.

Achieving an airtight building means following three essential steps:

- ❖ design for airtightness;
- ❖ build for airtightness; and
- ❖ test for airtightness.

It is not practicable to construct a building and then try to make it airtight. Remedial sealing can be difficult and costly. By designing in airtightness at the drawing stage you can deal with air barrier continuity and sealing details at critical elements – and ensure long-term performance by specifying the correct seal or sealant.

The main air leakage problems in buildings occur typically:

- ❖ around doors, windows, panels and cladding details;
- ❖ in gaps where the structure penetrates the construction envelope;
- ❖ in service entries: pipes, ducts flues, ventilators;
- ❖ in porous construction: bricks, blocks, mortar joints; and
- ❖ in joist connections within intermediate floors.

Designers should identify all the problem areas, for example, sealing around pipe entries, and spell out responsibility for finishing off in the contract documents.

Constructing the building to the airtightness specification is then down to the main contractor and subcontractors. For this to be successful all of the workforce should be aware of airtightness issues in the same way as safety issues and codes of conduct are dealt with.

Inspection during construction is essential. Talking to and working with contractors is the best way of ensuring that the team understands the importance of the airtightness layer and how to incorporate it.

The only real way to be confident that the building meets an airtightness specification is to carry out a fan pressurisation test prior to handover as required in the proposed revisions to Part L. Large buildings, for example, hypermarkets or industrial buildings, need specialist larger capacity equipment.

If the three essential steps listed earlier are followed, the building should pass the test. In the event they are not and the building fails, the proposals in Part L state: 'If on first testing the building fails to comply, the major sources of air leakage should be identified using the techniques described in TM23 [CIBSE Technical Memorandum].' This usually requires specialist help.

Despite improved understanding of construction techniques, few buildings are sufficiently airtight – this is true of new buildings as well as old. In a recent survey, only one out of 39 buildings tested met a good practice benchmark for airtightness. While the degree of leakage varies considerably from building to building, it is not unusual for the problem to be equivalent to having a 9m² hole in the building envelope.

Both the government and CIBSE regard airtightness as a serious issue and encourage protective measures.

Airtightness testing

Within the UK, air pressurisation/depressurisation testing must be undertaken in accordance with relevant national standards (CIBSE TM23 *Testing Buildings for Air Leakage* and BS EN 13829: 2001 *Thermal performance of buildings – Determination of air permeability of buildings – Fan pressurization method*). Testing organisations should have United Kingdom Accreditation Service (UKAS) accreditation in accordance with BS EN 17025 *General requirements for the competence of testing and calibration laboratories* and be members of the Air Tightness Testing and Measurement Association (ATTMA).

ATTMA standard TS1 (applicable to planning applications submitted post 6 April 2006) and TM23 describe the testing methodology for the fan pressurisation testing of buildings to show compliance with Part L of the Building Regulations. In addition to the testing methodology, these documents lay down recommended air leakage specifications for different building types.

Single or multiple fan units can be used to identify whole-building leakage rates by producing artificial positive or negative pressures within a building. Air is supplied to the building through the fan(s) for a range of measured airflow rates, and the resulting pressure differential between the inside and outside of the building is measured for each different rate.

The external barometric pressure and temperature are measured and compared with the internal temperature so that corrections can be applied to the measured airflow rates if necessary.

Wind speeds above 6m/sec. can also influence the measured envelope leakage rates and so tests are usually conducted when weather conditions are favourable.

Smoke tests

Air leakage paths can be determined using smoke and the normal forces acting on the building envelope, or smoke used in conjunction with artificially-induced internal pressurisation or depressurisation. Hand-held generators can be used to pinpoint leakage that may need remedial sealing either before a pressure test, or after a test that has revealed inadequacies.

By comparison, large-scale smoke generators are generally used to smoke log buildings. The buildings are then typically pressurised to blow the smoke out through any discontinuities in the envelope. Smoke leaking from the building can then be identified and recorded photographically.

Smoke logging tests are less accurate a means of detection than hand-held generators, as smoke can travel for significant distances before it escapes. For example, while smoke may appear to be leaking from the ridge of the building, it may in fact be travelling up through a cavity wall from a discontinuity rather than leaking out from the roof void.

Infrared thermography

Infrared thermography produces a visual representation of the surface temperatures of a subject. Large areas can be surveyed in a relatively short time and a visual record of the results produced as the survey proceeds. Instead of using smoke, the infrared camera detects the amount of heat radiated from the surface and by depressurising the building, colder external air can be drawn in through discontinuities in the fabric, cooling the adjacent areas and enabling identification. In the alternative, creating a positive internal pressure will enable the external identification of leakage points as warm air escapes.

Building Regulations and historic building conservation

Striking the balance between energy conservation requirements of the Building Regulations and historic building conservation

The Approved Documents L1B and L2B impose energy conservation requirements on properties when undergoing certain types of refurbishment or alteration works, details of which can be found at www.planningportal.gov.uk. Historic buildings protected under planning law will not necessarily have to comply with the full extent of these documents, however, that is not to say that their protection under planning law will necessarily exempt them from all or part of the requirements.

The fields of energy conservation and building conservation are two very large overlapping subject areas and a pragmatic approach needs to be adopted in order to reach a satisfactory compromise. Due consideration of this is given within the Approved Documents, however further useful guidance can be obtained by reference to the English Heritage publication *Building Regulations and Historic Buildings, balancing the needs for energy conservation with those of building conservation*. In Scotland, Northern Ireland and Wales separate guidance is available from Historic Scotland www.historic-Scotland.gov.uk, www.ehsni.gov.uk for Northern Ireland and www.cadw.wales.gov.uk for Wales.

The Approved Documents provide guidance on buildings that currently do not have to comply with the full requirements, i.e.

- ❖ listed buildings, as listed in accordance with section 1 of the *Planning (Listed Buildings and Conservation Areas) Act* 1990;
- ❖ buildings in a conservation area; and
- ❖ Scheduled Ancient Monuments.

Special considerations apply to buildings which fall into the above three categories where meeting the energy conservation requirements would alter the character or appearance unacceptably.

Sections 9 and 10 of Approved Documents L1B and L2B general guidance go on to point out that improved energy efficiency should not be at the risk of the character or long-term viability of the building. They cite specific instances where taking advice would be beneficial (e.g. restoration, rebuilding and work undertaken to enable fabric to 'breathe') and suggest enlisting the services of local authority conservation officers.

United Kingdom heritage authorities promote the retention and reuse of existing building stock citing BS 7913: 1998 which states 'In global environmental terms, the balance of advantage strongly favours the retention of existing building stock, particularly when performance in terms of energy consumption in use can be improved'.

Although ultimately the extent and type of any energy conservation works to an historic building will be agreed through discussion with conservation and building control officers, the professional contemplating works to such a building should be mindful of the issues discussed.

Further information

Approved Document L1B, *Conservation of Fuel and Power in Existing Dwellings*, (effective 6 April 2007).

Approved Document L2B, *Conservation of Fuel and Power in Existing Buildings Other Than Dwellings*, (effective 6 April 2007).

Building Regulations and Historic Buildings. Balancing the needs for energy conservation with those of building conservation: an Interim Guidance Note on the application of Part L, English Heritage, 2004 (www.english-heritage.org.uk/upload/pdf/ign_partl_buildingregs.pdf).

Health and safety at work for surveyors

Essential legal duties

The *Health and Safety at Work etc. Act* 1974 requires all surveyors to ensure, so far as is reasonably practicable, the health and safety of themselves and any other people who may be affected by their work.

In essence, the places where surveyors' work must be safe and working practices must be clearly defined, organised, and followed to avoid danger. This requires safety training and the distribution of relevant information, followed up by diligent and regular supervision.

These duties extend to anyone who uses surveyors' professional services.

Those who lease part of their premises to other businesses also may be responsible for them with regard to safety matters.

In addition, all working people whether employees, managers, partners or directors (self-employed or not) must behave in a way that does not endanger themselves or others.

Health and safety policy statement

Every firm of surveyors which employs five or more people is obliged by the Act to draw up a health and safety policy statement, which should be kept up to date, with any significant revisions being notified to employees.

The Health and Safety Executive (HSE) in *Writing your health and safety policy statement: how to prepare a safety statement for smaller businesses* describes what the document should say and gives a useful pro-forma.

It is suggested that employees, especially when taking a new job, should satisfy themselves that they have seen and understood the company's policy statement and have been made familiar with safe working practices. If they consider that the Health and Safety at Work Act is not being followed, they ought to say so, and if necessary ask advice from their local HSE office (listed in the telephone directory).

Practical procedures

Surveyors should identify the hazards they may encounter in practice, carry out a risk assessment and plan accordingly. The way they proceed will depend upon the working environment: when surveying old and derelict buildings, for example, there may be holes in floors, parts of the structure may be unstable or there may be health hazards. Particular care should be taken to protect against personal attack.

The Control of Substances Hazardous to Health Regulations 2002

The purpose of the *Control of Substances Hazardous to Health Regulations* 2002 (as amended in 2004) is to safeguard the health of people using or coming into contact with substances that are hazardous to health.

Substances are classified as being very toxic/toxic, harmful, corrosive or irritant. Under these regulations employers are required to evaluate the risk of all products used that may be harmful to the health of their employees and take appropriate measures to prevent or control exposure.

The 'Six Pack' Regulations

This set of original six sets of regulations were introduced in 1993. They were wide ranging and, with some minor exceptions, apply to all places of work, replacing and consolidating various individual acts or regulations applicable to individual industries or sectors of industry, such as the *Factories Act*, the *Offices, Shops and Railway Premises Act*, and the *Construction Regulations*.

Workplace (Health, Safety and Welfare) Regulations 1992

These apply to all workplaces. The regulations set out the minimum requirements in respect of the provision and maintenance of the environmental conditions, space allocation, sanitary and welfare provision of employees. In addition, they impose particular safety requirements on forms of construction or circumstances which are considered to be high risk. They do not apply to construction sites.

Provision and Use of Work Equipment Regulations 1998

These apply to all workplaces. Basically, all existing and new work equipment which includes everything hired or purchased second hand, must comply with the regulations.

Every employer must ensure that all work equipment is so constructed or adapted as to be suitable for the purpose for which it is used or provided. They identify specific hazards that the employer must prevent or adequately control.

Manual Handling Operations Regulations 1992

These require the employer to try to avoid the need for employees to undertake any manual handling operations at work that involve a risk of their being injured. Where this is not reasonably practicable the risk must be assessed and suitable provision made, including equipment, instruction and training for safe manual handling.

Management of Health and Safety at Work Regulations 1999

These regulations are of a wide-ranging general nature and overlap with many others. They require the employer to carry out an assessment of the risks of the hazards to which his or her employees are exposed at work or to others arising from or in connection with this work. The employer must instigate appropriate protective or preventive measures, reviewing and amending these as necessary.

The employer must appoint a 'competent person' to provide assistance in respect of these duties. Emergency procedures must be put in force to deal with any serious and imminent danger. Employees must be informed of these measures and suitably trained where required. They are obliged to comply with these instructions and warn of any situation considered to be a serious and immediate danger to health and safety.

Personal Protective Equipment at Work Regulations 1992

Under these regulations the employer has a duty to provide and maintain suitable personal protective equipment including adequate instruction and training on its correct use when risks to health and safety cannot be avoided by other means. Employees have a duty to make full and proper use of such equipment provided and to report any loss or obvious defects.

Display Screen Equipment Regulations 1992

The need for the regulations is primarily the evidence of repetitive strain injury that is reported by keyboard users, the amount of time lost due to other causes of sickness among users and, of course, the European Directive.

These regulations target full time users of visual display units, mainly in the banking, insurance and data processing sectors but, given that most of the medium and larger companies will have in their offices a number of full time or habitual users, then these regulations will apply. They will also apply in the office facility of a construction site, if any persons are habitual users of visual display units.

The Construction (Health, Safety and Welfare) Regulations 1996

The CHSW Regulations were incorporated within and replaced by the Construction (Design and Management) Regulations 2007 (CDM 2007).

The Construction (Design and Management) Regulations 2007

The Construction (Design and Management) Regulations 2007 (CDM 2007) (SI 2007/320) came into force on 6 April 2007, replacing the previous CDM Regulations 1994 and the Construction (Health, Safety and Welfare) Regulations 1996 (CHSW).

Like the previous CDM Regulations, CDM 2007 provides a statutory framework for managing health and safety during the construction, repair, maintenance and demolition of civil engineering and construction work, with legal duties for everyone involved in the project from design through construction and beyond, including the maintenance, use and demolition of the building or structure.

The Health and Safety Commission has published an accompanying Approved Code of Practice *Managing health and safety in construction* (L144).

The key aim of the Regulations is to integrate health and safety into the management of the project and encourage everyone involved with the project to work together to:

- ❖ improve the planning and management of projects from the very start;
- ❖ identify hazards early on, so they can be eliminated or reduced at the design stage and the remaining risks can be properly managed;
- ❖ target effort where it can do the most good in terms of health and safety; and
- ❖ discourage unnecessary bureaucracy.

Transitional arrangements – there are interim provisions for projects and/or appointments in being before 6 April which give specific time limits to enable the principles of the new Regulations to be incorporated.

The Regulations apply to all 'construction work', with additional requirements if the project is notifiable. In the following text the latter are highlighted with an asterisk.

The key matters are as follows:

* Project notification – a project must be notified to the HSE if it is expected to last more than 30 working days or involve more than 500 person working days. The client is required to confirm his or her agreement of the details.

* CDM co-ordinator (CDMC) – replaces the previous role of the 'planning supervisor' and is the advisor and 'friend' of the client. The CDMC:

- ❖ advises the client on measures necessary for compliance;
- ❖ ensures adequate arrangements are in place for co-operation and co-ordination generally;
- ❖ takes all reasonable steps to ensure designers comply with their duties;
- ❖ liaises with the principal contractor re the contents of the health and safety file, information needed to prepare the construction phase plan and for subsequent design development;
- ❖ prepares, or if existing, otherwise reviews and updates, the health and safety file and passes it to client at the end of the construction phase.

Competence – Anyone who is appointing another party, or is being appointed, must ensure that they are competent for the specific project.

Co-operation and co-ordination – Everyone involved in the project is required to co-operate and co-ordinate their activities with each other and also to co-operate with those involved in concurrent projects on neighbouring sites to ensure the safety of those carrying out the construction work, and others who may be affected by it.

Client – The client:

- ❖ cannot abrogate responsibility to an agent;
- ❖ must ensure that suitable project management arrangements are in place;
- ❖ must ensure that contractors have made arrangements for suitable welfare facilities to be in place from the start and throughout the construction phase;
- ❖ if the project is a fixed workplace, must ensure that the design and materials used comply with the *Workplace (Health, Safety and Welfare) Regulations* 1992;

❖ must ensure that relevant information, likely to be needed by designers, contractors or others to plan and manage their work is passed to them;

❖ must ensure that there are reasonable management arrangements in place throughout the project to ensure that the construction work can be carried out, so far as is reasonably practicable, safely and without risk to health;

❖ * must appoint the CDMC as early in the project as possible and before the scheme design progresses beyond the concept stage;

❖ * must appoint a principal contractor to manage health and safety during the construction phase;

❖ * must provide the CDMC with all available relevant information including minimum time to be allowed for principal contractor for planning and preparation prior to start on site;

❖ * must ensure that the construction phase does not commence until satisfied that the principal contractor has prepared a suitable construction phase plan; and

❖ * must ensure that the CDMC is provided with all relevant information needed for inclusion in the health and safety file, with the information clearly separated for each separate project, site or structure and keep the file available for inspection thereafter.

Pre-construction information (the equivalent of the previous tender stage of the health and safety plan) – This is a collection of information contributed to by all relevant parties to be provided to all designers and to every contractor (who has been, or may be, appointed by the client). It includes information:

❖ about or affecting the site or construction work;

❖ concerning the proposed use of the structure as a workplace;

❖ about the 'mobilisation time' for contractors; and

❖ that contained in any existing health and safety file.

Health and safety on construction sites – Every contractor and every person who controls the way in which construction work is carried out by a person at work must comply with the requirements of regulations 26 to 44 inclusive. These are the general health and safety requirements that were previously described in the CHSW Regulations 1996 and include general matters such as good housekeeping, emergency procedures, fire fighting and detection, and safe working environments, as well as specific high risk activities and forms of construction. In addition, construction workers are obliged to report to their supervisors any defects which they are aware may endanger themselves or others.

Health and safety file – The health and safety file is a record of significant information relevant to health and safety to be retained by the client, made available and used throughout the life of the building or structure to assist its safe maintenance, alteration or demolition.

The file is prepared by the CDMC using information supplied by other duty holders.

Where a file relates to more than one project or structure, the client must ensure that the information relating to each part can be easily identified.

Dispute resolution

Disputants and their advisors have a variety of dispute resolution mechanisms that they can select to resolve their disputes.

The principal dispute resolution procedures are:

Adjudication

This process is enshrined in the *Housing Grants, Construction and Regeneration Act* 1996. A wide variety of the disputes arising under construction contracts can be referred to adjudication. The Act does not deal with disputes with residential occupiers unless the parties agree that adjudication will apply. Adjudication is popular not least because an adjudication award has to be made within 28 days of the case being referred to an adjudicator unless the parties agree otherwise.

Arbitration

Arbitration is based on the contractual provisions agreed by the parties. Procedures under the 1996 Arbitration Act have given the arbitrator wide powers to resolve disputes without unnecessary cost or delay, and in a fair manner without undue interference from the courts. The right of appeal is limited.

Early Neutral Evaluation (ENN)

Technology and Construction Court judges are prepared to arrange a short hearing of a case, on specific issues, on a without prejudice basis and give preliminary views on the merits, as an aid to settlement discussions between the parties. If a judge determines a particular issue by ENN the parties are free to agree whether or not they will be bound by it. If the ENN does not result in settlement, the case can proceed to trial but will be heard by another judge with no knowledge of the outcome of the ENN.

Independent expert

This forms a valuable means for the speedy resolution of technical disputes. The procedure is generally straightforward and flexible. Issues in dispute are referred to an expert to decide using his or her own professional expertise or judgement. It has been successfully used for many years in rent review matters, but has much wider application to technical disputes. If the parties agree to be bound by the expert's decision it cannot be appealed unless there is misconduct on the part of the expert.

Litigation

The *Civil Procedure Rules* 1998 have led to more efficient running of cases both in terms of costs and time. The Technology and Construction Court in the High Court deals with construction disputes and has considerable experience of doing so. Before court proceedings are commenced, the parties should comply with the Pre-Action Protocol for Construction and Engineering disputes. This requires the parties to set out their respective cases in correspondence and to meet on a without prejudice basis to seek to settle the dispute or narrow the issues involved, prior to the issue of court proceedings.

Mediation

Mediation is a voluntary and non-binding procedure. It is a private process in which an independent neutral person helps the parties reach a negotiated settlement. The Mediator usually does not make a determination on the dispute but may do so if the parties agree and he or she considers that it will assist in reaching a settlement.

Latent Damage Act 1986

The *Latent Damage Act* 1986 enhances case law relating to certain cases of negligence, by imposing statutory limits in relation to the time in which cases may be brought to court if a defect is found.

The Act applies specifically to those cases of negligence that relate to latent damage and not to personal injury. In addition, recent case law suggests that in the meaning of the Act, negligence covers only a breach of a tortious duty of care and not a contractual duty of care.

Previous statute exists indicating time limits in which legal action must commence; section 14 of the *Limitation Act* 1980. The 1986 Act enhances section 14 by limiting any claims to six years after the damage occurred. This, however, can be extended under section 14A by a further three years from the date when the defect is discovered. In all cases however, a 15-year time limit is placed under section 14B of the Act. When considering claims for latent defects, the most important points to establish are the dates from when the negligence occurred and the cause of the negligence. For example, the negligence may have been caused by defective construction, design, or a combination of both. The date on which the defect technically arises may be confused by the ongoing contractural state of the project, i.e. whether a final certificate has been issued or a defect liability period is still active. In certain cases proceedings may be delayed on the basis that the damage has not yet occurred, but is in fact imminent.

Discovery of building defects – statutory time limits

The *Limitation Act* 1980 ('the 1980 Act') as modified by the *Latent Damage Act* 1986 (see above) lays down the periods within which proceedings to enforce a right must be brought. Upon the discovery of a defect in a building or structure, possible claims against the designers and constructors of that building or structure could arise in contract, in tort or under statute.

Contract

To bring an action for breach of a simple contract, court proceedings must be commenced within six years of the date on which the breach of contract occurred. If the contract has been completed under seal, rather than hand, then the time limit prescribed by the 1980 Act is 12 years. Under the *Companies Act* 1985 (as amended) the 12-year limitation period also applies to companies when a contract is signed as a deed by two directors or a director and a company secretary.

Tort

The general time limit for actions in tort is six years from the date when the damage was suffered, with the exception that a time limit of three years applies to personal injury actions involving negligence. This period runs from the date of the accident concerned, although special rules apply for illnesses, which may not manifest themselves for many years after exposure to their cause, for example, asbestos.

Also, for negligence claims involving latent damage, the time limit laid down by the *Latent Damage Act* 1986 for commencing proceedings is six years from the date the damage was suffered. However this period can be extended for a further three years from the 'starting date'. The starting date is defined by the *Latent Damage Act* 1986 as the date on which the plaintiff first had both the required knowledge and the right to bring an action. The *Latent Damage Act* also includes a 'long-stop' provision preventing the instigation of any proceedings after the expiry of 15 years from the date of the negligence concerned.

Statute

Where a right derives from a breach of statutory duty, reference should, in the first instance, be made to the particular statute concerned, which may specify a time limit for the commencement of proceedings. The *Defective Premises Act* 1972 provides a particularly germane example. If the statute concerned is silent as to the time limit, then a period of six years will generally apply. If an action is brought in respect of a defective product, under the *Consumer Protection Act* 1987 there is a cut-off point of ten years from the 'relevant time' (usually the date of a supply).

It should be noted that the time limits for both tortious and contractual claims might be postponed where there is concealment, mistake or fraud.

Expert witness

Expert evidence in court proceedings is dealt with by Part 35 of the *Civil Procedure Rules* (CPR) and accompanying practice direction which came into force on 26 April 1999. This has been supplemented by the Civil Justice Council's Protocol for the Instruction of Experts to give Evidence in Civil Claims ('the Protocol') which took effect from 5 September 2005. The Protocol is intended to assist in the interpretation of the provisions of CPR Part 35.

The CPR states that it is the duty of an expert to help the courts on matters within his or her expertise. This duty overrides any obligation to the person from whom he or she has received instructions or by whom he or she is paid. The expert should therefore:

❖ be independent/impartial; the Protocol sets out a useful test of 'independence' namely, whether the expert will 'express the same opinion if given the same instructions by the opposing party';

❖ state any reservations about the case he or she is instructed upon;

❖ identify areas outside his or her expertise;

❖ consider all material facts in his or her report and state all facts and assumptions, upon which his or her opinion is based;

❖ state where necessary that it is only a provisional report, because only limited information/data was available when it was compiled;

❖ advise instructing solicitors if further information, i.e. the other expert's report, changes his or her opinion;

❖ make available all documents referred to in the report (i.e. survey reports, plans, calculations, photographs, etc.); and

❖ keep the report as brief as possible, but without losing the reasoning and conclusions, upon which his or her opinion is based.

The written report

There needs to be a statement setting out the brief and instructions given.

The report is to be written in the first person and it must be an individual who prepares the report and not the company or firm.

The report should be addressed to the court.

Although the report should be as brief as possible, accuracy should not be sacrificed to brevity.

The expert witness must be able to substantiate each and every sentence of the report and highlight any areas where his opinions are based on inadequate factual information. It is not the expert's role to make or advance legal arguments.

The report should contain the expert witness's curriculum vitae (CV).

It is compulsory to include a declaration in the report that the expert understands that his duty is to the court and that he has complied with that duty. A statement of truth must also verify the report. The wording to be included within the expert's report immediately before the signature is as follows:

> 'I believe the facts as stated in this report are true and that the opinions I have expressed are correct.'

The Protocol emphasises that this wording is mandatory and must not be modified.

Under the CPR, each party has 28 days after receipt of the opposing expert's report to put written questions. Unless the court gives permission for more general questions, these can only be for the purpose of clarifying the report.

Without prejudice meetings

Without prejudice meetings between experts are necessary and important. The court, under the CPR, may, and normally does, require the experts to produce a joint statement from 'without prejudice' meetings setting out what has and has not been agreed. Reflecting the provisions of CPR 35, the Protocol states that agreements between experts during discussions 'shall not bind the parties unless the parties expressly agree to be bound by the agreement'. However the Protocol adds a strong caveat that in view of the overriding objective of the CPR which encourages that cases are dealt with expeditiously and fairly, 'parties should give careful consideration before refusing to be bound by such an agreement, and be able to explain their refusal should it become relevant to the issue of costs'.

Giving evidence in court

If the case gets to a hearing, then the expert witness will be required to give evidence. The stages of examination of the evidence will be:

- ❖ examination in chief;
- ❖ cross-examination;
- ❖ re-examination; and
- ❖ questions from the judge.

A few helpful hints in giving evidence are listed below:

- ❖ Take time, don't rush.
- ❖ Succinctly answer only the questions that are asked. Use plain language.
- ❖ Do not digress from the question asked.
- ❖ Do not act as advocate.
- ❖ If the question is not understood nor heard – say so.
- ❖ Know the report 'inside out'.

Cross-examination will challenge credibility; so consider the following:

- ❖ Do not feel obliged to fill a silence.
- ❖ Do not be afraid to answer repeated or different questions with the same answer again and again.
- ❖ If asked a closed question, if appropriate state that there may not be a yes or no answer.

- ❖ Do not be rattled by a number of quick fire questions.
- ❖ Do not argue with counsel.
- ❖ If he or she becomes aggressive, stay cool.
- ❖ Beware of the important question slipped in among a number of trivial questions.

The above notes only deal briefly with the CPR and Protocol. These notes should not be considered as comprehensive text. The role of the expert is evolving through the interpretation of the CPR in case law and any expert should ensure that he or she fully understands that role in the light of the current law.

The Provisions of Part II of the Housing Grants, Construction and Regeneration Act 1996

The following aims to set out a brief outline of the issues which need to be considered when determining whether contractual terms are compliant with Part II of the *Housing Grants, Construction and Regulation Act* 1996 or whether certain provisions will be incorporated into the contract by the Scheme for Construction Contracts (Scheme).

Parties to a construction contract are free to negotiate and agree the terms and conditions under which the works and services are to be carried out. However, there are times where a contract fails to comply with the minimum requirements relating to adjudication and payment laid down by the Act. Consequently, certain provisions will automatically be incorporated into the contract by the Scheme for Construction Contracts.

When does the Act apply? (S104–107)

The Act applies to:

- ❖ contracts entered into on or after **1 May 1998;**
- ❖ **contracts in writing.** It is sufficient if the contract is evidenced in writing;
- ❖ contracts for **construction operations** which include the construction, alteration, repair, maintenance, decoration, demolition and installation in buildings forming or to form part of the land and also architectural, design, surveying or engineering advice; and
- ❖ the carrying out of construction operations in England, Wales or Scotland whatever the applicable law of the contract.

The Act does not apply to:

- ❖ contracts with **residential occupiers** for work on their property where they intend to occupy the property as their residence;
- ❖ certain mining, drilling and extraction operations;
- ❖ installation or demolition of plant or machinery or steelwork to support or provide access to plant or machinery on a site where the primary activity is nuclear processing, power generation, water or effluent treatment, or the production processing of chemicals pharmaceuticals, oil, gas, steel, food or drink;
- ❖ manufacture and delivery of materials not involving installation; and
- ❖ artistic works.

Letters of intent may be subject to the Act where they are sufficient to amount to a legally binding contract in their own right.

Adjudication (S108)

The contract must:

- ❖ allow either party to refer a dispute to adjudication at any time;
- ❖ provide for the appointment of an adjudicator within seven days;
- ❖ require the adjudicator to reach a decision within 28 days **after** the dispute has been referred to the adjudicator (or a longer period if agreed by the parties);
- ❖ allow the adjudicator and the party who referred the dispute to the adjudicator to extend the period for the decision by up to 14 days;
- ❖ impose a duty on the adjudicator to act impartially;
- ❖ enable the adjudicator to take the initiative in ascertaining the facts and the law surrounding the dispute;
- ❖ provide for the decision of the adjudicator to be binding on the parties until the dispute is taken to arbitration or the courts; and
- ❖ provide that the adjudicator is not liable for anything he or she does unless he or she acts in bad faith.

If the contract does not comply with all eight elements in full, all the adjudication provisions of the contract will be set aside and the adjudication procedures under the Scheme for Construction Contracts will apply. The procedures under the Scheme cover the eight points listed above and introduce time limits.

Payment

The Act and the Scheme for Construction Contracts provide a 'menu' of payment provisions covering:

- ❖ payment by instalments;
- ❖ final payment;
- ❖ withholding payment; and
- ❖ conditional payment.

If a contract fails to comply with any one of the provisions from the 'menu' the relevant provisions from the Scheme will apply. The remainder of the contractual provisions that do comply with the Act will remain intact. It is therefore possible to end up with a contract where the payment provisions are a mixture of express terms agreed between the parties and implied terms from the Scheme.

Payment by instalments (S109–110)

A party to a construction contract is entitled to payment by instalments, stage payments or other periodic payments unless:

- ❖ the contract specifies that the duration of the work is less than 45 days; or
- ❖ the parties agree that the work is estimated to take less than 45 days.

Where the work falls within the 45-day limit, the right to instalment payments is excluded but all other payment provisions (notice of withholding payment, set-off, etc.) will apply as will the adjudication provisions outlined above.

Where a contract falls below the 45-day limit, payment of the contract price falls due 30 days after completion of the work (or 30 days after the contractor's claim if later) and payment must be made within 17 days.

In all other cases, the parties can agree between themselves:

❖ the amounts of each payment;
❖ the intervals between each payment;
❖ the date each payment becomes due; and
❖ the final date by which each payment must be made.

If the contract does not contain a clear mechanism for determining each of these four elements they will be determined by the Scheme for Construction Contracts, namely:

❖ The amount of each payment will be based on the value of the work and other costs to which the contractor is entitled during the payment interval.
❖ There will be 28-day payment cycles.
❖ Payment is due seven days after each 28-day period (or seven days after the contractor's claim for payment if later).
❖ The final date for each payment is 24 days after each 28 day period (or 24 days after the contractor's claim for payment if later).

The contract must provide for the paying party to give notice within five days of the date on which each instalment becomes due, specifying the amount proposed to be paid and the basis on which it is calculated. Any attempt in the contract to vary or exclude this requirement will be ineffective and this provision will be implied by the Scheme for Construction Contracts.

Final payment

The contract must contain a clear mechanism for determining when the final payment due under the contract becomes payable and the final date by which that payment must be made.

The parties are free to agree the dates or periods within which the final payment is due and is payable but if there is no such mechanism, in accordance with the Scheme the final payment:

❖ is due 30 days after completion of the work (or 30 days after the contractor's claim for payment if later); and
❖ the final date for making the final payment is 47 days after completion of the work (or 47 days after the contractor's claim for payment if later).

Withholding payment (S111)

❖ No payment can be withheld unless a 'notice of intention to withhold payment' has been given, specifying the amount to be withheld and the grounds for withholding payment.
❖ The notice must be given before the final date for payment.
❖ The contract can specify how long before the final date of payment, the notice must be given (even if it is just one day) but if this notice period is not specified, the Scheme applies and at least seven days notice must be given.

Conditional payment (S113)

Any provision in a contract which makes payment conditional upon the paying party receiving payment from someone else is ineffective and the payment provisions of the Scheme outlined above will apply.

The only exception is where the contract provides that payment may be withheld if the reason for non-payment is the insolvency of someone else in the payment chain.

Suspending performance (S112)

If any payment is not received by the final date for payment and a notice of withholding payment has not been served, the contractor may suspend work after giving seven days notice of his intention. The right to suspend performance ceases when the relevant payment is received. The period in which to complete the works is automatically extended by the number of days of the suspension.

This brief summary of the provisions of Part II of the *Housing Grants, Construction and Regeneration Act* 1996 is not intended to be a detailed explanation of the provisions of the Act and we recommend that legal advice is sought on any specific issues.

Adjudication under the Scheme for Construction Contracts – how to get started

Adjudication under the *Housing Grants, Construction and Regeneration Act* 1996 (the Act) allows for a quick fix method of dispute resolution. The right to refer a dispute to adjudication is available to a party to a construction contract within the meaning of the Act at any time.

Below is a brief explanation of the steps required to commence an adjudication under the Scheme for Construction Contracts, i.e. **where there are no contractual adjudication provisions.**

Where adjudication is your chosen method of dispute resolution, it is essential that you comply with the strict time limits laid down by the scheme and any timetable imposed by the adjudicator. The adjudicator is under an obligation to reach a decision within 28 days of referral unless the parties agree otherwise.

It is not possible to contract out of the time constraints laid down for adjudication by the Act.

Procedure

To commence adjudication you must take three steps:

- ❖ give notice of adjudication;
- ❖ request an adjudicator to act; and
- ❖ serve a Referral Notice.

Notice of Adjudication

This must be in writing, be given to every other party to the contract and contain:

- ❖ details of the parties involved;
- ❖ a brief description of the dispute;
- ❖ details of when and where the dispute arose;
- ❖ what you are seeking from the adjudicator, for example, an award for a specific sum; and
- ❖ names and addresses of the parties to the contract (including the addresses which the parties have specified for the giving of notices, if any).

Note: In view of the very tight timescale for adjudication you should ensure that your claim is fully prepared before issuing the Notice of Adjudication.

Appointing an adjudicator

After giving notice of adjudication you must make a request for an adjudicator to act. The timescale for the appointment of an adjudicator is extremely tight and a request for the appointment of an adjudicator should be made at the same time as giving the Notice of Adjudication. In order to determine who to appoint you should consider the following:

- ❖ If your contract names an adjudicator, contact that person to ensure that he or she is ready and willing to act.
- ❖ If an Adjudicator Nominating Body (ANB) is named in your contract, contact that body and ask for an appointment to be made.
- ❖ If no adjudicator or ANB has been named in your contract you can contact any ANB such as:
  - – The Association of Independent Construction Adjudicators, 0870 429 6353.
  - – The Royal Institution of Chartered Surveyors, Dispute Resolution Service, 020 7334 3806.
  - – The Chartered Institute of Arbitrators, 020 7421 7444.
  - – The Royal Institute of British Architects, 020 7580 5533.
  - – The Technology and Construction Solicitors Association, 020 7367 2000.
  - – The Construction Industry Council, 020 7637 8692.
- ❖ Contact the most appropriate ANB depending upon the nature of the dispute and the issues involved. Some ANBs will be able to offer a greater diversity and breadth of experience.
- ❖ If an ANB is used: The ANB has five days to inform you of the nominated Adjudicator. The nominated adjudicator then has up to two days to confirm his or her appointment.

Caution: If a named or nominated adjudicator refuses to act, another adjudicator can be agreed or nominated by any ANB, but beware the time limit for issuing the Referral Notice. If an alternative adjudicator cannot be appointed within seven days of the Notice of Adjudication the safest course is to issue a fresh Notice of Adjudication.

Referral Notice

Within seven days of the Notice of Adjudication you must send the Referral Notice to the adjudicator formally referring the dispute to him or her. The Referral Notice must be in writing, be given to the adjudicator and every other party to the dispute and:

- ❖ contain the basis of your claim, including an explanation of how the dispute arose and identifying the issues in dispute;
- ❖ be accompanied by copies of (or relevant extracts from) your contract (whether this is a standard printed form or evidenced in correspondence);
- ❖ include any documents upon which you wish to rely in support of your case;
- ❖ contain the remedies and award you are seeking; and
- ❖ give the adjudicator wide jurisdiction by giving him or her an alternative, for example, 'such other sum as the adjudicator may determine'.

It is important that the Referral Notice clearly sets out the issues in dispute which the adjudicator is being asked to determine including the history of the case and any arguments raised by the other party as well as identifying the remedies sought. Claims not identified in the Notice of Adjudication cannot be introduced later in the same adjudication.

Following service of the Referral Notice the adjudicator should set a timetable for dealing with the adjudication including a response from the opposing party and request any further information or evidence in order to reach his or her decision.

Landlord and tenant

Legislation

Dilapidations

The principle

'Dilapidations' refers to breaches of obligations either express or implied within a lease relating to: reinstatement of alterations; repair; decoration; breaches of statute, other specific requirements; and associated costs.

The fundamental purpose of a 'Schedule of Dilapidations' is to identify these breaches of covenant. The allegation of a breach of contract is the first step in the legal process. Consequently, for a Schedule of Dilapidations to have worth and perform the function for which it is drafted, it is necessary that the schedule is enforceable in a court of law. The legal remedy for breach of dilapidations obligations is typically a claim for damages. The Schedule of Dilapidations is usually prepared as part of a claim which itself should represent the damage actually suffered by the landlord. This might not equate to the cost of the works set out in the Schedule of Dilapidations as a consequence of section 18(1) of the *Landlord and Tenant Act* 1927 and common law principles. (See Section 18(1) of the *Landlord and Tenant Act* 1927 on page 180.)

Schedules can be prepared on behalf of a tenant, where there are alleged breaches by the landlord of its obligations to the tenant. However, the more common approach is for the document to be prepared on behalf of a landlord in relation to tenants' alleged breaches.

There are three types of landlords' Schedule of Dilapidations: Interim, Terminal and Final. An Interim Schedule relates to breaches during the lease term; the Terminal Schedule to breaches identified towards the end of the term; and the Final Schedule is one published after the end of the term. By far the most common is the Terminal Schedule of Dilapidations and it is this document that we focus on here. By virtue of its pre-eminence, guidance on practice and procedure associated with Terminal Schedules has been published by the Property Litigation Association, in the form of a Protocol.

The PLA Protocol and RICS guidance note

In 2006, the Property Litigation Association (PLA) published a revised version of their Dilapidations Protocol. The revised document made some minor changes to the original version including:

❖ a formal diminution valuation is not now required at an early stage (if the landlord has not yet or does not intend to carry out the works) but it is still required prior to legal proceedings being issued. Instead, the landlord's claim should now contain a written endorsement that the overall figure claimed is a fair assessment of the loss;

❖ the importance of considering Alternative Dispute Resolution methods is reinforced;

❖ the distinction between the Schedule of Dilapidations and the landlord's Claim is clarified;

❖ a requirement for the landlord to confirm to the tenant whether an earlier Schedule is still being relied upon at the lease end date is introduced; and

❖ the anticipated timescales for actions by the parties are slightly revised.

Although the Lord Chancellor's department has not yet approved the Protocol, the courts may treat it as the normal and reasonable approach to pre-action conduct, and non-compliance might bring sanctions against the party concerned. Indeed, the RICS appended a copy of the previous Protocol to its own guidance note on dilapidations (4th edition), and it is probable that the revised version will be endorsed in similar fashion when the guidance note is next updated.

The 5th edition of the RICS Guidance Note is in draft form for consultation at the time of writing this 2008 Watts Pocket Handbook. It is expected that the 5th edition will be published in time for comment within the 2009 Handbook.

Stages in the dilapidations process

Stage 1 – preparation
Obtain and appraise all relevant documentation including:

- leases;
- licences to alter;
- schedules of condition;
- side letters;
- photographs;
- fit out specifications;
- agent's letting brochures;
- any statutory notices served;
- deeds of variation;
- schedules of landlord and tenant's fixtures and fittings;
- details of outstanding service charges; and
- any rent deposit agreements.

This list is by no means exhaustive.

Stage 2 – the inspection
This must be comprehensive and thorough and include specialist professions if deemed necessary, such as a structural engineer or mechanical or electrical consultant.

Establish the original condition at the beginning of the term, the standard of repair that the tenant has covenanted to achieve, and identify the remedial work. Take into account the age, character and locality of the premises when let (*Proudfoot v Hart* 1890).

Include all measurements to aid calculation of the cost of the remedial works and use as proof as required at a later date.

Stage 3 – preparation of the Schedule of Dilapidations and Claim
The Schedule should contain the information shown in the first five columns below. The additional columns relating to the tenant's and landlord's comments turn the Schedule of Dilapidations into a Scott Schedule, used as a negotiating tool between respective surveyors.

ITEM	CLAUSE No.	BREACH	REMEDIAL WORK REQUIRED	LANDLORD COST (£)	TENANT'S COMMENTS ON		LANDLORD'S COMMENTS ON	
					BREACH & REMEDY	COST (£)	BREACH & REMEDY	COST (£)

The Schedule of Dilapidations should be accompanied by a claim letter, which must include:

- ❖ landlord's and tenant's names and addresses;
- ❖ a clear summary of the facts on which the claim is based;
- ❖ the Schedule of Dilapidations (a separate document);
- ❖ any documents relied upon, such as invoices and evidence of costs and losses;
- ❖ confirmation that the landlord and advisors will attend meetings;
- ❖ a date by which the tenant should respond; and
- ❖ a summary of the claim including:
  - – cost of works;
  - – preliminaries;
  - – overheads and loss of profit;
  - – surveyors' fees for preparing the Schedule (quantified and substantiated);
  - – loss of rent;
  - – loss of service charge;
  - – surveyors' fees for negotiating a settlement (projected); and
  - – any sums paid to a superior landlord.

The Schedule of Dilapidations should be served within a reasonable time before the termination of the tenancy and typically not more than 56 days afterwards.

If a notice from the landlord has to be given to the tenant for reinstatement of alterations then this must be served within a reasonable period before the end of the tenancy so that the tenant is still able to start these works in time.

Electronic copies of the Schedule of Dilapidations should be provided to facilitate easier negotiation, preferably in a Scott Schedule format as shown in the diagram above.

Stage 4 – the response and negotiations

Following submission of the claim, the tenant must respond within a reasonable period, usually 56 days.

In order to establish the facts, surveyors should meet, preferably on site and on a without prejudice basis, before the tenant is required to respond to the Claim. If further meetings are necessary a strict timetable should be adopted. In any case it is expected that experts of the respective parties in their like disciplines should also meet within 28 days of the tenant's response.

Final dilapidations claims

The approach to a Final Schedule of Dilapidations will be similar to that adopted for a Terminal Schedule. However, the Final Schedule is served after the end of the term, so care should be taken to ensure that a suitable notice requiring the tenant to reinstate alterations is served before the term date, if so required.

Interim dilapidations claims

These claims are made during the continuance of the lease term and are typically as a consequence of more significant breaches of obligations. This is a complicated area of law so legal advice should always be taken on the appropriate service of notices and counter-notices. Interim dilapidations claims are in pursuance of one, or a combination of more than one, of three remedies: determination of the lease; damages; or specific performance.

To be successful, a landlord would need to satisfy one or more of five grounds (summarised below):

- ❖ that immediate remedying is necessary to protect the value of the landlord's interest in the property, or that the value has already been affected;
- ❖ that the work is necessary to comply with legislation;
- ❖ that where the tenant does not occupy the whole building, the work is necessary in the interests of other occupiers;
- ❖ that immediate remedying of the defect will be substantially cheaper than would be the case if the work was delayed; or
- ❖ special circumstances exist.

Jervis v Harris Notices (Repairs Notices)

Where the lease allows, landlords do have the option of entering the tenant's demise and completing the works themselves, at the cost of the tenant. This cost to the tenant is calculated as a debt, rather than as damages, so avoids the complications of capped damages claims as a consequence of section 18(1) of the *Landlord and Tenant Act* 1927 and common law. However, the lease will set out a series of events that the landlord must comply with before this opportunity is available to him or her. Typically these are:

- ❖ that a notice must be served on the tenant setting out exactly the alleged breaches;
- ❖ that the tenant is given a reasonable time to comply with the notice; and
- ❖ only then can the landlord enter and carry out the works.

However, carrying out work within a tenant's demise is complicated. Significant problems could be encountered such as: trespass by the contractor, access to power and water, disruption of the tenant's business and the effect on the relationships between the parties. For these reasons this is a little-used remedy and it is most commonly employed for external works only.

Break clauses

Sometimes, covenants within a lease give the option for the landlord or the tenant to bring the lease to an end before the contractual expiry date. It is important to establish whether the break clause is 'condition precedent' or not.

Where the clause is conditional, the party exercising the break may be required to comply with a variety of conditions before the break can be deemed effective. At its most severe this may include absolute compliance with all obligations within the lease, or may just require that vacant possession is provided at the break date.

The risk of non-compliance with a conditional break clause is often substantially greater than the cost of the works necessary to comply. It is therefore essential to commence planning of these works in advance to avoid the possibility of the lease continuing for the remainder of the contractual term.

A recent case has assisted practitioners in understanding the extent of work that may be necessary to comply with a break clause that required the tenant to comply 'materially' with its obligations *(Fitzroy House Epworth Street (No 1) Ltd v The Financial Times Ltd)*. The tenant undertook approximately £900,000 worth of works, but approximately £20,000 worth of works remained incomplete at the relevant date. The court held that, because there had been no consequential delay to the landlord in reletting or selling the property, the tenant had indeed complied materially. However, a consequence of the Appeal Court ruling is that there was no disadvantage to the landlord's case as a consequence of the landlord and its advisors declining to assist the tenant in determining the extent of works that would be required to comply with the obligations.

Dilapidations and the Disability Discrimination Act 1995 (DDA)

The tenant is free to decide, as a Service Provider or Employer, how to comply with its obligations and duties under the DDA. It is the Service Provider or Employer who has the obligations to take reasonable steps to ensure that they are complying with their duties under the DDA. Consequently, it follows that a landlord is unable to require a tenant to undertake works to comply with the duties imposed by the DDA during the term of a lease. Neither can it impose this as a part of a dilapidations claim at the end of, or during, a lease.

Under the terms of a lease it is likely that the tenant will be obliged to comply with statutory requirements. Under the DDA, the Service Provider or Employer has a duty to disabled people, not a statutory requirement to the landlord. At the end of the lease term the demised premises are vacated and subsequently there is no longer a Service Provider or Employer of any disabled people. It follows then that the demise at the end of the lease would not, at this point in time, be in breach of any duty imposed by the DDA.

Where a tenant has undertaken works to comply, there are implications under the *Disability Discrimination (Providers of Services) (Adjustments of Premises) Regulations* 2001. If a landlord wishes to remove the alteration, there is nothing to prevent him or her doing this after the outgoing tenant has vacated, but all reinstatement of these elements might be at the landlord's own cost. Any requirement on the outgoing tenant to remove these alterations may be considered unreasonable and could be challenged in the courts. This is as yet untested, and it remains to be seen whether a tenant will be able to use this in defence against a reinstatement claim.

VAT and dilapidations

The PLA Protocol, Clause 4.5, requires that the VAT status of the landlord should be stated. VAT in respect of dilapidations is a complex subject with its own set of rules, regulations and case law. Where a tenant is making a payment to a landlord in full and final settlement of its dilapidation liabilities, under Customs and Excise rules, the payment is not a 'taxable supply' for the purposes of VAT. This is because HM Revenue and Customs deem the payment to be one of damages and not a supply. VAT may be payable if the landlord passes the payment on to an incoming VAT registered tenant.

Complying with European Community Law, the *Finance Act* 1989 introduced major changes that included giving UK payers of VAT the option to pay VAT on supplies relating to an interest in commercial land. Where a person or company is registered for VAT there is a special statutory exemption to the charging of VAT on such supplies. Taxpayers can waive this exemption if they desire. To do this they must notify HM Revenue and Customs. For clarity, if a landlord has elected to waive its exemption on a building, it must charge VAT on such items as rent received. In this instance, it will not be appropriate to include VAT as part of a dilapidations claim. If the VAT exemption has not been waived then VAT need not be charged by the landlord on supplies, and VAT may form part of a dilapidations claim.

So the first issue to establish is whether the landlord is registered for VAT, i.e. is the landlord required by VAT law to charge VAT on its normal business transactions, such as rent receipts. If so, has it elected to waive its exemption to VAT on the specific building that is subject to the dilapidations claim? Once this has been established, a simplified VAT analysis might follow the steps shown in the diagram below. The Protocol requires that the Claim establishes what the landlord's intentions are and states the landlord's and/or the demised property's VAT status.

Dilapidations VAT Analysis

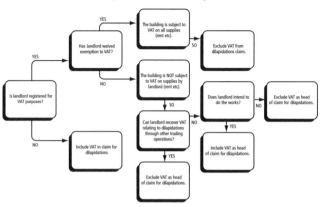

Valuation – diminution in value

See Section 18(1) of the *Landlord and Tenant Act* 1927 on page 180.

Summary of important statutes

Landlord and Tenant Act 1927, section 18(1)
Limits the cost of a claim for breach of covenant.

Law of Property Act 1925, section 146
Prescribes the form of notice for re-entry for forfeiture.

Law of Property Act 1925, section 147
Provides relief for tenants on long leases in respect of internal redecorations.

Leasehold Property (Repairs) Act 1938
Gives protection to certain tenants in respect of section 146 notice (ii) above.

Defective Premises Act 1972
Provides that a landlord shall be liable for lack of repair in cases where he or she knew or ought to have known of the defect.

The Civil Procedure Rules 1998
Introduced by Lord Woolf, they provide rules and practice directions for dispute procedures.

Summary of important case law

There have been a number of leading decisions relating to dilapidations law in the last few years. The following cases give an indication of developing areas of law.

Scottish and Mutual Assurance Society Limited v British Telecommunications plc (1994) (unreported)
Section 18(1) of the *Landlord and Tenant Act* 1927 Part II.

Loss of rent.

Notice for reinstatement of alterations.

Shortlands Investments Limited v Cargill plc (1995) (EGLR 51)

Section 18(1) of the *Landlord and Tenant Act* 1927 Part II.

Trane (UK) Limited v Provident Mutual Life Assurance Co Limited (1995) (WGLR 78)

Compliance with conditions of break clauses.

Jervis v Harris (1996) (EGLR 78)

Use of provision for landlord's re-entry.

Extent of recovery of expenditure.

Mannai Investments Co. Limited v Eagle Star Life Assurance Co Limited (1997) (EGLR 69)

Accuracy of notice showing intent to break tenancy.

Credit Suisse v Beegas Nominees Limited (1994) (4 All ER 803)

Establishing the interpretation of the repairing covenants and the different types of obligation placed on the tenant.

Fitzroy House Epworth Street (No 1) Ltd and Fitzroy House Epworth Street (No 2) Ltd v The Financial Times Ltd (2006) (CA1 2207)

Test of 'material compliance' of a conditional break clause.

Requirements of landlords and their advisors to assist tenants under conditional break clause circumstances.

Section 18(1) of the Landlord and Tenant Act 1927

Section 18(1) of the *Landlord and Tenant Act* 1927 is divided into two limbs.

Crown copyright material is reproduced with the permission of the Controller of HMSO and the Queen's Printer for Scotland.

> Limb 1 provides that 'damages for a breach of a covenant . . . to keep or put premises in repair . . . shall in no case exceed the amount . . . by which the value of . . . the premises is diminished owing to the breach . . .'.

Limb 1 of section 18(1) applies in all dilapidations cases. The common law claim in dilapidations, usually comprises the following components:

1. Cost of works.
2. Fees for preparation and service of the Schedule.
3. Fees for carrying out of the works.
4. Fees for negotiating the claim.
5. Loss of rent, loss of empty rates and service charge.
6. Loss of insurance.
7. VAT.

Limb 1 of section 18(1) provides that whatever the amount of the common law claim, the landlord's entitlement in damages is limited to the amount by which the value of his or her interest has been diminished owing to the breach of the covenant to repair. (This is not the same as the covenant to redecorate or to reinstate.)

The operation of the Act requires comparison to be made between two valuations:

> Valuation A – Assuming compliance.
>
> Valuation B – Assuming actual condition.

The difference between Valuation A and Valuation B assesses the statutory cap on the amount of damages payable.

It has been held that where Valuation A is a negative figure and Valuation B is a greater negative figure the difference, amounting to the landlord's loss, is payable (*Shortlands Investments Plc v Cargill Plc*).

> Limb 2 of section 18(1) further provides 'no damage shall be recovered . . . if it is shown that the premises, in whatever state of repair they might be, would at or shortly after the termination of the tenancy have been or be pulled down, or such structural alterations made therein as would render valueless the repairs . . .'.

Limb 2 of section 18(1) would operate, for example, where it could be demonstrated that the landlord of an unmodernised 1960s office building intended, as at the expiry of the lease, to carry out refurbishment works to install a suspended ceiling, a raised floor and air conditioning.

In such a case, the landlord's proposals would significantly impact upon the repairs required to the interior of the building, rendering the benefit of the required repair valueless. As a consequence, to the extent that this work is rendered valueless, it will fall out of the claim.

However, unless the landlord intends to carry out works to the exterior of the building that will render valueless the exterior disrepair, the repairs required will remain a valid part of the claim.

The critical date upon which to establish the landlord's intention is at the expiry of the lease (see *Salisbury v Gilmore* (1948) and *Cunliffe v Goodman* (1950)).

The fact that the landlord is contemplating a number of options, including a potential refurbishment as at the expiry of the lease is not a sufficient basis itself to render the value of the repairs nugatory. A clear and fixed intention must be demonstrated.

Section 18(1) relates to repair only. It does not relate to the reinstatement or decoration content of the claim. However, these elements of the claim are governed by common law principles under which the landlord's entitlement is to be reimbursed for his or her financial loss, and the same principles apply. It will be relevant however, in assessing the loss, whether the landlord truly intends to reinstate tenant's alterations, for example, a mezzanine floor in a warehouse.

The introduction of the Dilapidations Protocol, a second edition of which was published in 2006, has confirmed that valuations under section 18(1) are required when a claim is made in virtually all cases. The exceptions to this rule are when the landlord has either carried out the works or can demonstrate intention to do the works.

As a consequence, both landlords and tenants should obtain advice as to the likely impact of section 18(1) on their claim at an early stage.

Tenant fit out and licences to alter

The following comments are intended as an overview as to how licences for alteration are addressed in property and construction matters generally. These comments offer an overview only and professional advice should be sought to ensure any application for landlord approval is administered correctly.

What are they and how are they used?

A licence is a form of permission, a legally enforceable document, which is granted by a landlord to a tenant enabling the latter to exercise a right within a formal lease agreement.

There are many forms and types of licence relating to property such as change of use, assignment of a lease or subletting for example, but this section refers specifically to licences for alteration. These are most often used where a tenant seeks the landlord's formal approval to carry out alterations, fitting-out works and similar within the demised premises.

An application for formal approval is normally prepared when a tenant wishes to make significant changes, structural or otherwise, to a premises. Typically this may include subdivision works, provision of mezzanine floors, changing shop fronts, extending or other alterations.

It is important to review the lease obligations with regard to proposed alterations. The lease may prevent any changes or activities being undertaken at all. Such prohibitions may take the form of two types:

- ❖ **absolute**: where the landlord is not obliged to grant any consent or approval to an application; and
- ❖ **qualified**: where the landlord's approval is required but such approval should not be unreasonably withheld.

Whilst the lease may already permit the tenant to carry out minor or internal cosmetic works, the licence affords the landlord the opportunity of retaining a degree of control as to how more substantial work is carried out, mainly to ensure the landlord's interests and objectives for the premises are not compromised or reduced. For example, the licence may require that noisy work is done out of hours, to reduce the likelihood of other tenants alleging a breach of their right to quiet enjoyment of their own demise.

Licences for alteration are also used in some dilapidations claims. If there is no licence in place for works undertaken the landlord would probably have the right to insist on removal and reinstatement to the former condition and layout. However, if the licence is worded to avoid any form of reinstatement the changes made may be left in situ at the expiration of the tenure period. There are some exceptions to this, and the issue of reinstatement is considered elsewhere in this handbook.

There are occasions when an application may be required to satisfy certain legal and statutory requirements, for example to comply with the *Disability Discrimination Act*. In such situations the landlord's consent must not be unreasonably withheld.

The application and appraisal process

There are occasions where a tenant may have already formally agreed with the landlord that works can commence to an agreed scope. In such situations an application for formal approval may not necessarily be required, but the lease terms should clarify this. If an application is not considered necessary, the tenant should offer the professional courtesy of notifying the landlord when the work is to be carried out.

If the landlord is itself a tenant, then additional superior landlord approvals may be necessary. Be wary, however, that the superior landlord's interests may not necessarily be the same as the tenant-landlord's. All respective interests and requirements should be contained in the licence for alteration.

On the assumption, however, that the landlord is indeed the freeholder and the application is a straightforward procedure this should be acknowledged by the landlord and/or the landlord's adviser promptly. More often than not, tenants seek approval in order to improve their premises to improve business performance, and this should be considered in a pragmatic manner by the landlord.

There is no benchmark or minimum requirement governing the information to be submitted as part of the application. Clearly, it is advisable for the landlord (or the landlord's property adviser) and the tenant to discuss the extent of works to establish what information is expected as early as possible in the process, to avoid any delays in the application. Indeed, the parties may establish or agree that an application may not even be necessary.

In all application procedures the landlord should behave reasonably as to turnaround time, the level of information and detail needed, and whether any amendments or conditions would be necessary. It can be prudent to make use of a standard template checklist to ensure the basic and critical information is provided, thus allowing for further communication if more detail is needed.

In order for an efficient and prompt appraisal and response from the landlord, the tenant should ensure full details of the proposals are forwarded to the landlord. Unless the lease comments, there is no hard and fast rule to what level of information is deemed necessary. However, it is not unreasonable for an application to include the following technical information:

❖ complete set of architectural, structural and building services plans, specifications and scope of work;

❖ typical programme with commencement and completion dates;

❖ details of tenant project team for ease of communication; and

❖ copy of applications for statutory consents, and subsequent consent/discharge confirmation.

The landlord and/or the landlord's adviser would usually be able to form an opinion on the proposals fairly quickly and advise if any further information is needed. Similarly, advice can be obtained as to whether any ongoing inspection of the works is needed, and the procedure for final inspection and sign off.

Factors to consider

Clearly, there are a number of factors which may need to be determined when a landlord assesses an application. This may be reported on by external advisers from various professional disciplines depending on the scope, magnitude and complexity of the proposals.

Examples of factors to be considered may include the following:

❖ Is the applicant the current tenant, are they the sole occupier of the property, or will other tenants be disturbed or inconvenienced by the works?

❖ Are the proposals sensible for the property and the tenant's business objectives?

❖ If the proposals increase the rental value, the landlord should consider financing the works pursuant to the *Landlord and Tenant Act* 1927, in exchange for additional rent.

❖ Will the proposals have any bearing on changes to floor areas, service charge agreements, rateable values and similar?

❖ How will the work be carried out – in a single contract, or phased over time?

❖ Will building services installations be affected temporarily or permanently?

❖ Will the structural integrity of the property be compromised temporarily or permanently? Is phasing of the works needed which may affect third parties?

- ❖ Will the building work or the completed alterations affect the landlord's building insurance cover?
- ❖ Will any fire precautions be affected during or after the work? How will fire security be maintained?
- ❖ Who will be responsible for settling the landlord's costs and professional fees?
- ❖ Identify the need for any additional enabling or remedial work after the proposals are complete.
- ❖ Consider responsibility and liability for all design, construction work and the securing of all appropriate consents.
- ❖ Consider any landlord's obligation to provide additional parking areas, refuse collection point and similar.
- ❖ Consider the need and frequency for landlord work inspections, to ensure compliance with the agreed documents.

Form of consent

In many commercial property situations, the landlord's solicitor will draft a licence for alteration and agree this with the applicant's solicitor. It is usually the case that each party will have technical consultants and their agreed version of the plans and proposals would be appended to the main licence. Similarly, if the landlord wishes to insert specific conditions, such as sequencing of work to prevent disconnection in working hours, then these can be agreed and incorporated into the licence.

A signed and certified copy of the agreed licence is normally held with the lease for cross reference purposes.

It is normal practice that once the work has been completed, the tenant submits final copies of all statutory consents secured for the works, and permits the landlord to inspect the completed activity to ensure these are fully signed off and agreed, to complete the licence conditions. This should always be formalised in written form promptly.

Occasionally, some tenants carry out alterations without any form of approval or licence in place. Normally, the landlord could insist on reinstatement of an unlicensed alteration. However, the landlord's position may be reduced if the alterations are left unchallenged for a period of time. Similarly, if an unlicensed alteration has been undertaken but not discovered within 12 years (England and Wales), then it is possible the *Limitation Act* 1980 may apply.

Further information

Further reading on licence for alterations can be found in the RICS guidance note *Handling Tenant's Applications for Approval to Alterations*.

There is also extensive case law on this matter.

Neighbourly matters

Rights to light

The subject of rights to light usually concerns the assessment of whether proposed obstructions (for example, new developments) are likely to interfere materially with neighbours' easements of light. Interpretation of whether a material right to light issue is likely to arise requires knowledge of the law, particularly easements and nuisance, and an understanding of the technical measurements of skylight entering a room. It is then possible to assess the risk of injunction and, where appropriate, the likely level of damages that could be awarded. It is also possible to determine how to modify a proposed scheme in order to reduce or overcome potential problems.

Legal background

Rights to light problems bring together two distinct but different areas of English law namely private nuisance – a subdivision of the law of torts; and easements – a subdivision of land law.

Private nuisance

The tort of private nuisance, like the tort of public nuisance, regulates activities affecting individual rights in or rights over real property (land).

A private nuisance may be defined as:

An unreasonable interference with a person's use or enjoyment of land itself, or some right over or in connection with land (i.e. a right to light).

The law of nuisance tries to balance the legitimate activities of neighbours – a give and take approach. Interference with a right to light must be objectively unreasonable in its extent and severity if it is to be sufficient to constitute a nuisance in the eyes of the courts. Only when the courts are satisfied that the interference is unreasonable will they remedy the situation by awarding an injunction and/or damages. It should be appreciated that levels of natural light can often be interfered with to a marginal extent and this will not necessarily constitute an infringement of a proprietary right that will be recognised as a nuisance.

Easements

An easement may be defined as a right annexed to land to use or to restrict use of neighbouring land in some way. For an easement to be valid, four essential characteristics must be satisfied:

- ❖ There must be a dominant tenement and a servient tenement.
- ❖ The right must accommodate (benefit) the dominant tenement.
- ❖ The dominant tenement and the servient tenement must be owned or occupied by different persons.
- ❖ The right concerned must be capable of forming the subject matter of a grant.

Rights to light have been recognised as a valid easement for centuries. The general rights to light principles set out below have been distilled from the large body of case law that exists.

A right to light can be defined generally as:

A negative easement providing a right for a building to receive sufficient natural light through a defined aperture (usually a window), over the land of another, in perpetuity or for a term of years.

Nature of a right to light

A right to light is not personal – it runs with property/buildings.

A right benefits the dominant tenement and burdens the servient tenement. A right to light is for 'sufficient' natural light only and this is taken to mean enough light, 'according to the ordinary notions of mankind' for:

❖ comfortable use and enjoyment of a dwelling house; or

❖ beneficial use of and occupation of a warehouse, shop or other place (office, etc.).

The test for 'sufficiency' is whether or not the dominant tenement will be left with enough light according to the ordinary requirements of mankind. Sufficiency is not based on the measure of light lost. See *Colls v Home & Colonial Stores* [1904] AC 179.

Actionable injury and measurement of light

No specific rule has been developed by the courts to define exactly when a reduction in natural light becomes actionable. The test for injury is uncertain but flexible. The court will have regard, in all cases, to the specific facts and circumstances and it will usually hear objective technical evidence from a rights to light expert, as well as more subjective evidence from the injured party.

A form of technical evidence has evolved that entails analysis of the amount of the notional sky dome that can be seen from a series of points in an affected room at table level. At any given point on the working plane there is a minimum amount of sky area below which the level of daylight at that point will be inadequate. Adequacy is considered to be just enough for undertaking work that requires visual discrimination, such as reading, drawing or sewing. In technical terms this is one lumen or 1/500th of a standard uniform dome of overcast sky in December (i.e. 0.2% sky factor).

It is possible to plot the 0.2% sky factor contour in the subject room and measure the area of the room that will receive more than adequate light both before and after development. Today, leading rights to light experts tend to do this with the aid of 3D computer modelling and specialist software, which is more accurate and efficient than the laborious manual Waldram method.

Having measured the area that will be adequately illuminated, it is possible to assess whether an actionable injury will arise. Very generally, for day-to-day practical purposes, light specialists have adopted the general conventions that:

❖ A commercial property may be considered actionably damaged when less than 50% of an office floor area is lit to the critical one lumen (0.2% sky factor) level, i.e. the so-called 50/50 rule.

❖ A residential/domestic property should be considered actionably damaged when less than 55% of a room area is lit to the critical one lumen (0.2% sky factor) level.

It must be understood that the percentages mentioned above are not strongly founded in specific legal authority, although courts will make reference to previously decided cases where the facts are similar. The courts regard the so-called 50/50 rule as a 'convenient rule of thumb'.

Acquisition of a right to light

A right to light may be created by:

❖ express grant or reservation (sometimes encountered);

❖ implied grant or reservation (rarely encountered); or

❖ prescription (very common and often called 'ancient lights').

Prescription means the procuring of a right on the basis of a long established custom and three methods of prescription exist, namely:

- ❖ time immemorial (right enjoyed since before 1189);
- ❖ doctrine of lost modern grant (right enjoyed continuously for minimum 20 years); and
- ❖ *Prescription Act* 1832: sections 3 and 4 (right enjoyed continuously for 20 years).

(Note: In the City of London, because of the 'Custom of London', the acquisition of a right by the doctrine of lost modern grant is not available – see *Bowring Services Ltd v Scottish Widows* 1995.)

Defeating a right to light

Prescription through the doctrines of lost modern grant or time immemorial can be defeated if it can be shown that the easement has not been enjoyed, 'as of right', i.e. through force, secrecy or with permission.

Statutory prescription, under the *Prescription Act* 1832, may be defeated if the servient party can show that:

- ❖ at some time within the last 19 years, they have prevented the entry of natural daylight through the subject apertures by erecting an opaque physical obstruction for a continuous period of at least one year;
- ❖ at some time in the last 19 years, they registered a light obstruction notice under the *Rights of Light Act* 1959 for a whole year (see below); or
- ❖ the right has been enjoyed under some consent or agreement expressly given for that purpose by deed or in writing.

Defending your right to light

A prescriptive right to light may be lost if it is not defended in the face of development. A neighbour who acquiesces in or submits to an interruption of light for one year or more will lose a claim to a prescriptive right under section 4 of the *Prescription Act* 1832. See *Dance v Triplow and Another* [1992] 17 EG 103.

Successful defence of a prescriptive right to light relies much on eternal vigilance and prompt protestation in writing to the obstructor. The protestations should also be repeated at regular intervals. Ultimately legal proceedings will need to be brought against a developer who ignores the objections and the timing of this may considerably affect the chances of obtaining an injunction.

Remedies

The current legal system permits the awarding of:

- ❖ prohibitory or mandatory injunctions; and/or
- ❖ common law damages.

Injunctions

The courts are reluctant to sanction a wrong doing by a servient party in allowing that party to purchase his or her neighbour's rights. Generally, an injunction is regarded as the normal remedy, with damages the exception. The court of Appeal has recently reminded all of this principle in their decision in *Regan v Paul Properties Ltd and Others* [2006] EWCA Civ 1319.

The court may award damages in lieu of an injunction if all the four requirements below can be answered in the affirmative:

- ❖ Is the injury small?
- ❖ Would a small money payment be an adequate remedy?

❖ Would it be oppressive to the defendant to grant an injunction?

❖ Is the injury one that can be estimated in money terms?

These requirements are derived from *Shelfer v City of London Electric Lighting Co* [1895] 1 Ch 287 31, however, the courts have departed from a strict application of the test and it is not necessarily applicable to every rights to light situation.

The conduct of parties will also have a significant bearing on the matter. If a developer ignores the communicated protestations from his or her neighbour and continues developing regardless then once a nuisance is proved an injunction should be the default remedy.

Damages (compensation)

Compensation for injury to a right to light may be assessed using one of two methods:

❖ the traditional valuation approach; or

❖ the share of developer's profit approach.

Compensation/damages based on a share of the developer's profit is the method more likely to be used since the case of *Tamares (Vincent Square) Ltd v Fairpoint Properties (Vincent Square) Ltd* [2007] All ER(D) 1034 (assessment of damages). This method will often derive a significantly larger sum in compensation than will the traditional valuation approach. In *Tamares*, the court set out eight principles, derived from previous cases, to give guidance on how damages should be assessed.

Whichever method is adopted, the valuation approach is based on a freeholder in possession. With a traditional valuation approach, a 'base book value' is calculated for the light loss, which may then be enhanced by a multiplier of up to three or four times, having regard to the case of *Carr Saunders v Dick McNeil Associates Ltd and Others* [1986]. Any compensation will be appropriately apportioned between the various interests in the dominant tenement. For leases, this is generally dependent upon the number of years remaining until the next rent review. For residential property, however, the assessment of compensation is more subjective.

Compensation based on a share of the developer's profit requires an (often complicated) assessment to be made of the amount of profit that a developer will be expected to realise if construction of the infringing part of a proposed development actually occurs. The owner(s) of the injured building will then expect a share of that element of profit, which share could be anything between 5% and 50% depending on the circumstances. This approach essentially considers the possibility of sharing the profit that a developer will make from floor space that could not be built if the adjoining owner obtained an injunction.

Dos and don'ts

❖ Do establish whether surrounding properties enjoy rights to light, including other tenanted parts of the client's property, and identify all parties with an interest.

❖ Do establish whether development proposals are likely to leave the surrounding buildings with inadequate light.

❖ Do take specialist advice from a rights to light consultant at an early stage.

❖ Do obtain copies of all leases, deeds, transfers, restrictive covenants, and so on, that could have a bearing on the legal position.

❖ Don't be fooled by buildings that look less than 20 years old or have blocked-up windows: case law is complex and there could still be a right to light.

- ❖ Do consider whether the Crown has ever had an interest in the development site: the surrounding buildings may not be entitled to rights to light.
- ❖ Do consider whether the development site has ever been acquired or appropriated by the local authority for planning purposes under section 237 of the *Town and Country Planning Act* 1990, as this affects the potential for injunctions.
- ❖ Do obtain copies (if available) showing the massing and profile of the existing building on the development site, and the proposed building or extension, and also up to date floor layout plans for the surrounding buildings.
- ❖ Do establish the extent of a right (i.e. the number, size and location of apertures).
- ❖ Do consider whether transferred or 'incorporated' rights to light exist.
- ❖ Do seek the advice of lawyers if the legal position is complicated beyond your experience by any controlling deeds or similar documents.
- ❖ Do ensure that your client understands that the law relating to rights to light, and the valuation techniques, are not an exact science.
- ❖ Do remember that recent case law has reminded all that the primary remedy of interference with a right to light is an injunction – not damages.
- ❖ Do remember that you cannot rely on a neighbour, particularly a residential owner, settling for compensation.
- ❖ Do explain to your client that there are no general statutory procedures for dealing with rights to light issues and that there are no prescribed periods and deadlines during or by which parties are obliged to settle issues.
- ❖ Don't allow a 'dominant' party to be pressured into early agreement of compensation.

Light obstruction notices

Light obstruction notices can be used to either defeat an existing right to light that has been acquired by statutory prescription or prevent such a right from being acquired. They are a useful tool for preserving the development potential of a site and can also be used to 'flush out' potential claims.

Under section 2(1) of the *Rights of Light Act* 1959 a light obstruction notice can be registered with the local authority as a local land charge for a period of one year.

Further information

The two main statutes that are relevant to rights to light are:

- ❖ the *Prescription Act* 1832; and
- ❖ the *Rights of Light Act* 1959.

There exists a large body of rights to light case law. The selection of case reports listed below includes the more recent and more important decisions.

- ❖ *Allen and Another v Greenwood and Another* [1975] 1 All ER 819 6, 35-6.
- ❖ *Bowring Services Ltd v Scottish Widows Fund & Life Assurance Society* [1995] 16 EG 206.
- ❖ *Carr Saunders v Dick McNeil Associates Ltd and Others* [1986] 1 WLR 992 37, 43.

- *Charles Semon & Co v Bradford Corporation* [1922] 2 Ch 737.
- *Colls v Home & Colonial Stores* [1904] AC 179 4, 9, 10, 29, 31-2, 34.
- *Dance v Triplow and Another* [1992] 17 EG 103.
- *Deakins v Hookings* [1994] 14 EG 133.
- *Ecclesiastical Commissioners for England v Kino* [1880] 14 ChD 213 40.
- *Fishenden v Higgs and Hill Ltd* [1935] 153 LT 128 33.
- *Lyme Valley Squash Club Ltd v Newcastle under Lyme Borough Council and Another* [1985] 2 All ER 405 28-9.
- *Marine and General Mutual Life Assurance Society v St. James Real Estate Co Limited* [1991] 2 EGLR 178.
- *Midtown Ltd v City of London Real Property Co Ltd* [2005] 14 EG 130.
- *Ough v King* [1967] 3 All ER 859 34.
- *Price v Hilditch* [1930] I Ch 500 5, 37, 43.
- *Pugh and Another v Howels and Another* [1984] 48 PCR 298 36-7.
- *Regan v Paul Properties Ltd and Others* [2006] EWCA Civ 1319.
- *RHJ Limited v (1) FT Patten (Holdings) Limited and (2) FT Patten Properties (Liverpool) Limited* [2007] EWHC 1655 (Ch).
- *Scott v Pape* [1886] 31 ChD 554 6, 80.
- *Sheffield Masonic Hall Co v Sheffield Corporation* [1932] 2 Ch 17 43.
- *Shelfer v City of London Electric Lighting Co* [1895] 1 Ch 287 31.
- *Tamares (Vincent Square) Ltd v Fairpoint Properties (Vincent Square) Ltd* [2006] EG41 226 (injunction v damages ruling).
- *Tamares (Vincent Square) Ltd v Fairpoint Properties (Vincent Square) Ltd* [2007] ALL ER(D) 1034 (assessment of damages).
- *Wheeldon v Burrows* [1879] 12 ChD 31 78.
- *Wrotham Park Estate Co v Parkside Homes Limited* [1973] ChD 321.

Daylight and sunlight amenity

As greater emphasis is placed on environmental issues, local planning authorities are increasingly concerning themselves with the effect of developments on the daylight and sunlight enjoyed by neighbouring properties. The local authority's Unitary Development Plan or Local Plan should always be consulted, as it will give an indication of what they expect in this regard.

The Building Research Establishment (BRE) published Report 209 in 1991 titled *Site layout planning for daylight and sunlight: A guide to good practice* written by P J Littlefair. It was intended to give guidance on how to ensure good daylight and sunlight to proposed new development through good design, while avoiding detrimentally affecting neighbours' daylight and sunlight amenity. It sets out various tests that can be undertaken to establish if a problem is likely to be created.

The BRE report was not intended to be mandatory. However, it is not uncommon for planning authorities to require a developer to submit a daylighting and sunlighting study in support of a planning application and some may expect compliance with the recommendations given in the guidelines.

It is important to note that even if a scheme is granted planning consent this will not override the private rights of individuals, and therefore, rights to light may still be an issue. See *Brewer and another v Secretary of State for the Environment and others* [1988] 2 PLR 13.

Daylight

The BRE report states that if any part of a new building or extension, measured in a vertical section perpendicular to a main window wall of an existing building, from the centre of the lowest window, subtends an angle of more than 25° to the horizontal, then the diffuse daylighting of the existing building may be adversely affected. This will be the case if either:

❖ the vertical sky component measured at the centre of an existing main window is less than 27%, and less than 0.8 times its former value; or

❖ the area of the working plane in a room which can receive direct skylight is reduced to less than 0.8 times its former value.

In such circumstances the occupants of the existing building will notice the reduction in the amount of skylight and more of the room will appear poorly lit.

The BRE report also presents another method of assessing the interior daylight levels within a room, called the average daylight factor (ADF), which it takes from British Standard BS 8206 Part 2. There are recommended minimum ADF values for dwellings, namely 1% for bedrooms, 1.5% for living rooms and 2% for kitchens.

Sunlight

The BRE report advises that new development should take care to safeguard access to sunlight for existing dwellings and any non-domestic buildings where there is a particular requirement for sunlight. If a living room of an existing dwelling has a main window facing within 90° of due south, and any part of a new development subtends an angle of more than 25° to the horizontal measured from a point two metres above ground in a vertical section, perpendicular to the window, then the sunlighting of the existing dwelling may be adversely affected.

The sunlight amenity of the existing dwelling will be considered to be adversely affected if the window reference point:

❖ receives less than one quarter of annual probable sunlight hours, and/or less than 5% of annual probable sunlight hours during the winter months between 21 September and 21 March, and the available sunlight hours in either period is reduced to less than 0.8 times its former value.

Analysis

The BRE report sets out the methods by which the effect of a development on existing neighbouring buildings may be calculated. If the local planning authority requires an assessment to be undertaken and submitted in support of a planning application, it is usual for the analysis to follow the tests in BRE Report 209.

The target values recommended in BRE Report 209 are quite demanding and can be difficult to achieve, particularly in dense urban environments. Care may need to be taken when applying the guidance and interpreting the results of analyses.

Further information

BRE Report 209, *Site layout planning for daylight and sunlight: A guide to good practice.*

BS 8206-2: 1992, *Lighting for buildings: Code of practice for daylighting.*

Brewer and another v Secretary of State for the Environment and others [1988] 2 PLR 13.

Planning appeal by St George Central London, decided 20 April 2004.

Malster v Ipswich Borough Council [2001] EWHC ADMIN 711.

Planning appeal by West End Green (Properties) Limited, decided 10 October 2005.

Planning appeal by Inner Circle Limited, decided 16 March 2007.

High hedges

The current position

The *Anti-social Behaviour Act* 2003 came into operation in England on 1 June 2005. Part 8 of the Act provides Local Authorities with powers to deal with complaints about high hedges.

The legislation means that neighbours who are in dispute over a high hedge can now go to their Local Authority for resolution. Note that 'in dispute' does not mean one neighbour can simply bypass the other and expect a favourable response from the Local Authority. The legislation provides a vehicle for neighbours who have discussed the matter and have tried, but exhausted, all other possibilities for resolving their dispute.

Note also that the Local Authority is not expected, nor empowered, to mediate between the neighbours or to assist or progress negotiations. Its role is simply to adjudicate on whether 'the hedge is adversely affecting the complainant's reasonable enjoyment of their property'.

In its deliberations the Local Authority must consider all the relevant factors and must try to strike the right balance between the interests of the two neighbours. It may also consider the interests of the wider community if it considers this may be adversely affected.

Once it has considered all the relevant issues (not the neighbours' arguments), the Local Authority will either dismiss the matter and write to the neighbours telling them its reasons, or it will write to the hedge owner in a formal notice setting out what he or she must do (and by what date they must do it) to the hedge in order to remedy the problem.

A hedge owner who fails to comply with the notice or in any way fails to carry out the works which are required by the Local Authority will be guilty of an offence. Upon summary prosecution the failing hedge owner could receive a fine of up to £1,000 and continuing fines which will accumulate on a daily basis whilst the owner remains in breach of the order.

Tall stories and the truth of the matter

High hedges are all those which are over two metres tall.

Not true: The legislation does not apply to all hedges, only to those which are evergreen or 'semi-evergreen'. It does not cover single or deciduous trees. For clarification this means a hedge which has two or more consecutive trees or shrubs which are evergreen, or one which is predominantly evergreen. Furthermore, some hedges over two metres do not block light, do not cause a nuisance and do not prevent anyone from enjoying their own land. Therefore, they are not going to be the subject of a dispute and can safely be allowed to grow as high as they will.

You need permission to grow a garden hedge over two metres tall.

Not true: A hedge owner can grow a hedge as high as he or she likes in the first instance. Permission is not required and the Local Authority will take no automatic action unless a dispute is referred to it. If both neighbours want a tall hedge and are not in dispute over it then it is very unlikely that a Local Authority will become involved.

If the Local Authority receives a complaint it will order the hedge to be cut down to two metres.

Not true: If a Local Authority receives a complaint it will weigh up all the relevant matters and consider the merits of each case in isolation. It may order a reduction in height, either in one cut or in stages if a single cut could be drastic enough to kill the hedge. The Local Authority may stipulate a greater height than two metres if it considers that this height will abate the nuisance sufficiently. The confusion seems to stem from the fact that the Local Authority may not order a reduction to less than two metres. Additionally, the Local Authority cannot require the hedge to be removed completely.

The hedge will be a nuisance if it blocks light to a neighbouring property.

Not true: Whilst a hedge which is blocking a neighbouring owner's light may be interpreted as a nuisance this is not unequivocal. Each case will be considered individually and an appropriate order will be made, but the legislation does not guarantee an adjoining property access to uninterrupted light.

Anyone served with an order under Part 8 of the Anti-social Behaviour Act 2003 will be the subject of an ASBO.

Not true: There is no provision in the Act to serve an Anti-social Behaviour Order in respect of high hedge complaints.

Further information

There is, of course, a lot more to high hedges and their problems than has been outlined above. Much of the information is somewhat confusing and needs to be interpreted carefully.

Be aware, also, that a number of organisations exist purely to complain about high hedges. Some of these organisations can be really helpful, however they do not all consider the interests of fair play and some may offer confusing, if not misleading, information.

It is better, then, to get information from an official source.

The department for Communities and Local Government (CLG), formerly the Office of the Deputy Prime Minister, has more information, including guidance from the Building Research Establishment on calculating light loss and appropriate hedge height. Their website can be found at www.communities.gov.uk/planningandbuilding/planning/treeshighhedges/highhedges/

Although the Act applies in Wales, the situation is slightly different. Further information can be found on its application in Wales at:

❖ www.wales.gov.uk/consultations/closed/plancloscons/1208212/?lang=en

Party wall procedure

The *Party Wall etc. Act* 1996 came into force throughout England and Wales on 1 July 1997. All previous local enactments, including the *London Building Acts (Amendment) Act* 1939 Part VI and the *Bristol Improvement Act* 1847, have now been repealed.

The general principle of the Act is to enable an owner to undertake certain specific works on, or adjacent to, adjoining properties while giving protection to potentially affected neighbours. As suggested by the word 'etc.' in its title, the Act relates not just to party walls.

The parties

The owner of the property where the work is to be undertaken is the 'building owner'. The owner of the adjoining property is the 'adjoining owner'. There can be many adjoining owners including freeholder, leaseholder and anyone with an interest greater than from year to year. Under the Act, the word 'owner' can also include people with a contract to purchase or an agreement for lease; this arrangement allows a prospective owner to serve notice, and even commence work, before completion of the contract.

Party structures

A party wall is one that stands on the land of two owners, by more than its footings, or one which separates buildings of different owners. In the first case, the whole wall is a party wall whereas in the second, it is only a party wall for the extent to which the two buildings are using it and the whole of the rest of the wall belongs to the person on whose land it stands. Other types of party structure are party fence walls (i.e. shared garden walls) and party floors (e.g. separating different flats).

In the case of a party wall, each owner owns the part of the wall that stands on their own land, but also has rights over the remainder of the wall. The Act allows owners to treat the whole of the party wall as if it were their own, and debars them from dealing with their half on its own without informing their neighbours.

Before exercising any of the rights bestowed upon them, owners must follow the procedures set down in the *Party Wall etc. Act* 1996. If an owner wishes to underpin, raise, cut into, thicken or demolish and rebuild a party wall, they must give notice of their intention to do so. In the event that the adjoining owner disagrees, each party must appoint a surveyor and a formal agreement known as a party wall award must be entered into.

An adjoining owner may respond to a party structure notice by serving a counter notice requiring certain specified works to be undertaken to the party wall for his or her future purposes. However the notice must be served within one month of the original notice and the adjoining owner will be responsible for the cost of the additional work.

Excavations adjacent to structures

The *Party Wall etc. Act* 1996 requires notice to be served on adjoining owners of certain intended excavations within three metres or six metres of adjacent buildings or structures.

Refer to figure below for details of these notifiable excavations.

The excavations could be for any purpose, not just for a building or its foundations.

New walls at boundaries

Where it is proposed to build at the 'line of junction' (i.e. the boundary) notice may need to be given to the adjoining owners. This will be the case where the boundary is not already built upon, or is built upon only to the extent of a boundary wall (not being a party fence wall or external wall of a building). In return, a right to construct projecting mass concrete footings work may be claimed.

Three metre notice

Six metre notice

General rights and obligations

The *Party Wall etc. Act* 1996 grants various general rights and obligations in relation to work undertaken in pursuance of the Act. The key ones are as follows:

- ❖ obligation to serve notice on adjoining owners before undertaking the work;
- ❖ obligation to execute the work in compliance with other statutory requirements and in accordance with details agreed either by the parties or by appointed party wall surveyors in an Award;
- ❖ ability to enter and remain on adjoining owners' land so far as is reasonably necessary to facilitate the work;
- ❖ duty not to cause unnecessary inconvenience;
- ❖ duty to compensate adjoining owners for loss or damage arising as a consequence of the work; and
- ❖ obligation to make good damage caused by work to party structures.

Agreeing the works

The building owner and adjoining owner may agree the details of the works between them. Where disagreements occur, either deemed or actual, the Act provides a mechanism for resolving them through the appointment of party wall surveyors. The appointed surveyors have a duty to settle the matter by making an award and they must act expediently and impartially, having regard to the interests and rights of both parties.

Entry to adjoining land

There are differing views on whether a building owner may enter adjoining land for all work covered by the Act or only where the Act expressly grants a right to do work, such as raising a party wall. The Act is ambiguous, which may potentially create difficulties for building owners who wish to build a new wall wholly on the line of junction and who need to erect scaffolding on adjoining land. For such work it is important to establish the views of the surveyors and adjoining owners concerned at an early stage.

Dos and don'ts

- ❖ Do consider whether proposed excavations and building works require the serving of notices under the Act.
- ❖ Do allow adequate time in the project programme for identifying and resolving all party wall issues. Time periods stated in the Act are statutory minimums, and often longer periods should be allowed.
- ❖ Do establish which party will act as the 'building owner' and verify his or her legal interest in the property.
- ❖ Do remember that if the building owner parts with his or her interest in the property part-way through proceedings, matters will have to start afresh.
- ❖ Do remember that the interests of all relevant adjoining owners will have to be identified with certainty and each owner notified separately.
- ❖ Do remember that each adjoining owner has a right to disagree with the proposals and to appoint a surveyor.
- ❖ Don't let unreasonable or unresponsive adjoining owners or surveyors hinder progress: use the mechanisms in the Act to force matters along.
- ❖ Do make allowance within the cost plan for the reasonable fees of the adjoining owners' surveyors and any necessary subconsultants (typically structural engineers).
- ❖ Do ensure that the design team and contractors cooperate and produce all necessary drawings, method statements, calculations, etc. in good time.
- ❖ Do ensure that the proposed time and manner of carrying out the work is reasonable and that no unnecessary inconvenience will be caused.
- ❖ Do consider making provision within tender documents for restrictions on working hours and/or methods of working for noisy elements of work falling within the scope of the Act.
- ❖ Do consider whether access will be required onto adjoining land to build a wall at the line of junction and bear in mind that differing views exist as to whether a right of entry exists for such work.
- ❖ Do ensure that the procedures required by the Act are followed meticulously; otherwise, notices and awards could be invalidated.
- ❖ Do remember that the party wall surveyors are administering the Act impartially and not representing clients.
- ❖ Do ensure that awards are agreed prior to starting the relevant work.
- ❖ Don't confuse common law and rights to light matters as being part of party wall procedures.
- ❖ Do establish a line of communication between adjoining owners and contractors for dealing with day-to-day issues of noise, dust, and so on.

❖ Do ensure that any variations in the agreed works are agreed between the parties, or by their appointed surveyors.

❖ Finally, do ensure that all parties fulfil their obligations.

References

Party Wall Legislation and Procedure, RICS guidance note (5th edition), RICS Books, 2002.

The Party Wall Act Explained – A Commentary on The Party Wall etc. Act 1996 (The Green Book), Pyramus and Thisbe Club, 2nd edition, 1997.

Party Walls – The New Law, S. Bickford-Smith and C. Sydenham, 2nd edition, Jordans, 2003.

A Practical Manual for Party Wall Surveyors, J. Anstey, RICS Books, 2000.

Anstey's Party Walls and What to Do with Them, G. North, 6th edition, RICS Books, 2005.

An Introduction to the Party Wall etc. Act 1996, J. Anstey and V. Vegoda, Lark Productions, 1997.

The Party Wall Casebook, P. Chynoweth, Blackwell Science, 2003.

Party Wall etc. Act 1996, audio cassette, Owlion.

Party Walls – Best Practice Roadshow, audio CD, Owlion, 2002.

Party Wall etc. Act, 1996: explanatory booklet, Department for Communities and Local Government.

Practical Neighbour Law Handbook, A. Redler, RICS Books, 2006.

Useful websites

Party Wall etc. Act 1996 – Office of Public Section Information:
www.opsi.gov.uk/acts/acts1996/1996040.htm

Royal Institution of Chartered Surveyors:
www.rics.org/Services/Usefulguides/Consumerguides/party_walls.htm

Pyramus and Thisbe Club:
www.partywalls.org.uk

Department for Communities and Local Government (CLG):
www.communities.gov.uk

Party Wall and Rights to Light Discussion Forum:
www.partywallforum.co.uk

Access agreements

Access to Neighbouring Land Act 1992

Under the *Access to Neighbouring Land Act* 1992 a court may grant an order for access to land where such access is required to enable the execution of basic preservation works and where access has been refused by the neighbour. Such works include:

❖ maintenance, repair or renewal of any part of a building or structure;

❖ clearance, repair or renewal of drains, sewers, pipes and cables;

❖ cutting back or felling trees and hedges in certain circumstances; and

❖ filling in or clearing any ditch.

The Act contains provisions for the preparation of schedules of condition and for overseeing of the work by surveyors. Surveyors can also be called upon to provide evidence where claims for damage under the Act are made.

The access order made by the court may require the payment of consideration, having regard to the likely financial advantage to the applicant and the degree of inconvenience, except where the works are to residential land.

Often the knowledge that rights exist under the Act will prompt neighbours to be accommodating, but, even then, it is still sensible to enter into an informal access agreement in the form of a licence with accompanying schedule of condition.

The Act is available online at:
www.opsi.gov.uk/acts/acts1992/ukpga_19920023_en_1.htm

Rights of way and fire escape agreements

More intense use of an existing right of way often requires re-negotiation of the right altogether. One type of right commonly encountered relates to fire escape routes benefiting properties that adjoin a development. The rights are often disrupted by large-scale redevelopment and negotiations for both temporary escape rights during the redevelopment and for revised escape rights over the new permanent development will be required.

Oversailing cranes and encroaching scaffolds

Most large developments necessitate the use of at least one crane. There are benefits to the developer or contractor of using fixed-jib tower cranes, as opposed to luffing-jib or folding-jib cranes, such as reduced cost and increased speed and load capacity. However, where the jib of a crane will oversail adjoining land, the agreement of the adjoining land owner, and any other party with an interest in the air space above it, will be needed.

Without such agreement the developer will be committing a trespass on every oversailing occasion.

The law on this matter comes from the tort of trespass. The position was clarified in the case of *Anchor Brewhouse Developments Ltd and others v Berkeley House (Docklands Developments) Ltd* [1987], in which the plaintiffs sought, and were granted, injunctive relief in relation to an unauthorised oversailing crane.

While some developers manage to place oversailing risks on their contractors, when work is abundant contractors will often not accept such risks or, if they do, their tender prices are significantly enhanced.

Similar trespass issues often arise in relation to temporary independent scaffolding, although, wherever possible, rights granted by the *Party Wall etc. Act* 1996 and emanating from the *Access to Neighbouring Land Act* 1992 should be exercised.

Developers and/or their contractors should give consideration at an early stage to the issue of access onto or over adjoining land or the airspace above it. Neighbours should be approached in advance for consent and the terms of such consent will be the subject of negotiation by the parties. It is sensible to enter into an access agreement or licence and the developer may be expected to pay a sum of money in consideration or grant reciprocal oversailing rights. Typically such agreements will provide for indemnities, insurance arrangements, schedules of condition, payment of fees and costs and so on.

Construction noise and vibration

The law relating to construction noise and vibration is controlled by the common law of nuisance and a number of statutes, in particular the *Control of Pollution Act* 1974. A range of guidance is available, including BS 5228, Part 1 (1997), Part 2 (1997) and Part 4 (1992).

Nuisance

A private nuisance is 'an unreasonable interference with a person's use or enjoyment of the land'. If a neighbour can demonstrate that a nuisance exists and that he or she has suffered substantial damage as a result, then he or she may be successful in bringing an action against the parties creating the nuisance.

The remedies available are injunctions and/or damages. The courts have, however, traditionally regarded demolition and construction sites as a special case as far as noise is concerned. It would appear that as long as the works are carried out with proper skill and care, and all reasonable precautions are taken to minimise disturbance to neighbouring occupiers, no action in nuisance will arise.

Developers and contractors have to ensure that they take 'reasonable means'. They must be aware of the definition of 'best practicable means' in the *Environmental Protection Act* 1990. This includes considering local conditions and circumstances, the current state of technical knowledge and financial implications.

A leading case on construction noise and nuisance is *Andreae v Selfridge* [1938] 3 All ER 264 where the judge held that provided demolition and building operations are 'reasonably carried on, and all proper and reasonable steps are taken to ensure that no undue inconvenience is caused to neighbours, whether from noise, dust or other reasons, the neighbours must put up with it'.

Control of Pollution Act 1974

The *Control of Pollution Act* 1974 deals, in part, with the control of noise on construction sites. Section 60 empowers a local authority to serve notice imposing certain limitations. These limitations include specifying the hours of work, permitted noise levels and the particular plant and machinery that may be used. The recipient may appeal against the notice within 21 days. Contravention of the notice is an offence under the Act. Section 61 provides an opportunity for a developer or contractor to apply to the local authority in advance of the works and seek agreement to such matters as the method of carrying out the work and the steps that will be taken to minimise noise. The local authority is not obliged to give its consent and, even if it does, it may attach conditions to it. It may also change the conditions if it sees fit.

The local authority will often specify that 'best practicable means' are used. The developer/contractor will be expected to adopt the quietest viable method of working within reasonable cost limits. The local authority may also require continuous noise and vibration monitoring and regular liaison meetings with neighbours.

Architectural and design criteria

Design

Basic design data

Typical design data for different building types

Internal circulation
Space allowances: (minimum areas per person)

Building type	m²
Offices (excluding cores)	9.3
Retail	4.6–7.0
Factories	7.0
Restaurants	0.9–1.1

Typical design values for internal environment

Lighting (maintained illuminance) requirements
Circulation: 100 Lux
Casual work: 200 Lux
Routine work: 300 Lux
Offices: 500 Lux
Drawing office: 750 Lux
Fine work: 1000 Lux
Very fine work: 1500 Lux
Minute work: 2000 Lux

Acoustics requirements
Auditoria: 20–30 NR
Bedroom: 25 NR
Small office: 30–35 NR
Open plan office: 35 NR
Light industrial: 40–55 NR

Temperature requirements

Flats and residences
Living rooms	22–23°C
Bedrooms	17–19°C
Bathrooms	20–22°C
Staircases and circulation	19–24°C

Offices
General	21–23°C
Circulation	19–21°C

Retail
Small	19–21°C
Large	19–25°C
Supermarkets	19–23°C
Restaurants	21–23°C

Factories
Sedentary work	19–21°C
Light work	16–19°C
Heavy work	11–14°C

Hotels
Bedrooms	19–21°C
Bathrooms	20–22°C

Vehicle car parking/circulation

Car parking	Standard bay 2.4 x 4.8m	Area per car 18.8m²
Ramps	Car parking garages Pedestrian	max. gradient 10% 5–8.5%
Carriageway widths	One-way four lanes One-way two lanes	14.6m 7.3m
Vehicle movement Turning circles	Standard articulated truck Fire engine	18m long: 12m radius 6.80m long: 9.25m radius

Sources of information

Neufert, E. and Neufert, P., *Architects' Data* (3rd edition), Blackwell Science, 2000

Adler, D. (editor), *Metric Handbook: Planning and Design Data*, Architectural Press, 1999

CIBSE, *Environmental Design: CIBSE Guide A* (7th edition), CIBSE Publications, 2006

Building types

Housing

Typical housing equivalent densities:

(Note: hr/ha = habitable rooms per hectare.)

c125 hr/ha: low-density layout (e.g. 4+-bed detached houses with gardens)

c200hr/ha: high-density 2-storey housing with traditional street pattern

c250 hr/ha: 3-storey flats, street pattern still possible

c250+ hr/ha: block of flats, no street pattern

Recommended planning grid – 300mm

Recommended minimum floor to ceiling – 2300mm

Minimum floor to floor – 2600mm

English Partnership (EP), the national regeneration agency, has recently launched new minimum space standards that apply to all EP schemes from 1 November 2007, although detailed guidance is still in preparation.

The agency's requirement for minimum internal floor areas (MIFA), calculated in line with the RICS Gross Internal Floor Area, are:

Unit type	Space standard (m²)
1 Bed / 2 person dwellings	51
2 Bed / 3 person dwellings	66
2 Bed / 4 person dwellings	77
3 Bed / 5 person dwellings	93
4 Bed / 6 person dwellings	106

EP has announced additional standards relating to space and usage, including the demand that all dwellings provide access to private outdoor space 'of sufficient size to enhance the use of the dwelling' (winter gardens/conservatories, used in addition to MIFA, can count as outdoor space).

For further guidance, watch for announcements on EP's website at: www.englishpartnerships.co.uk

For more information on the Carbon Challenge, please see: www.englishpartnerships.co.uk/publications.htm#ccstandardbrief

Hotels

Types
- ❖ city centre hotels
- ❖ motor hotels
- ❖ airport hotels
- ❖ resort hotels
- ❖ motels

Typical space allocation (m²/room gross) by star rating

2*	20–22m²
3*	25–27m²
4*	30–34m²
5*/exclusive	36m²
Family run	<25 rooms (typically)
Independent hotels, country houses	50–80 rooms (typically)
Budget inns, lodges	80–120 rooms (typically)

Fire precautions
BS 5588 deals with fire precautions for the design of buildings along with Part B of the Building Regulations.

Car parking
- ❖ resident guests: 1.2–1.3 spaces per room
- ❖ conference facilities: 1 car space per delegate

Required provision must be agreed with the local authority.

Recreational

Typical dimensions of a number of particular sports facilities are listed below.

Outdoor sport facilities

Olympic standard swimming pools	length width	50m 25m
Running tracks	200m 400m	86.79 x 61.78m 176.91 x 92.52m
Association Football pitch		100m–110m x 64m–75m
Rugby Union pitch		144m x 69m (max.)
Hockey pitch		90m x 55m
Tennis court		10.97m x 23.77m

Not including circulation areas.

Indoor sport facilities

Netball court		30.50m x 15.25m
Badminton court		13.4m x 6.1m

The above are based on ancillary halls (practice halls).

An indoor space 32m x 26m can typically contain the following sports:	Two badminton courts, karate, fencing, table tennis, basketball, archery, volleyball, soccer and hockey. (This is only one arrangement.)

Industrial

Typical design data for industrial property are identified in the following table.

Site coverage:	Plot ratio normally maximum of 1:1 including office content. Site coverage should not normally exceed 75% (normally approx. 50–60%)	
Car parking (factories):	Staff:	1 car/50m² of gross floor area
	Visitors:	Typically 10% of parking
Car parking (warehouses):	Staff:	1 car/200m² of gross floor area
Factory building types:	(Light duty) industrial:	Spans min. 9m max. 12m Ht. to eaves 4.5m Floor loading 16kN/m²
	(Medium duty) industrial:	Spans 12m–18m Ht. to eaves 6.5m Floor loading 25kN/m²
	(Heavy duty) industrial:	Spans 12m–20m Ht. to eaves 7m–12m Floor loading 15–30kN/m²
Warehouses:	General purpose:	Spans 12–18m Ht. to eaves 8m Floor loading 25kN/m²
	Intermediate high bay:	Spans 11.1–20.5m Ht. to eaves 14m Floor loading 50kN/m²
	High bay:	Ht. to eaves 30m Floor loading 60kN/m²

Offices

Methods of calculating areas

- ❖ For planning purposes, gross total area measured over external walls.
- ❖ For cost purposes, gross total area measured inside external walls.
- ❖ The RICS guidance note, *Code of Measuring Practice* (6th edition, 2007), gives further detail.

Definition of space

❖ deep plan (triple zone): 20m+
❖ medium depth (double zone): 15–20m
❖ shallow plan (double zone): 12–15m
❖ shallow plan (single zone): 8–12m

Dimensional criteria

❖ planning grids: 1500 x 1500mm, 3000 x 3000mm
❖ floor-to-floor heights: 4000–4500mm
❖ floor-to-ceiling heights: 2600–3000mm
❖ raised floor zone: typically 150mm–450mm

Means of escape

As a general guide:

❖ maximum travel distance with escape in only one direction is 18m (note: shopping complexes have more stringent distances as noted in BS 5588-10); and
❖ maximum travel distance with escape possible in alternative direction is 45m.

Sanitary provision

Regulation 20 of the *Workplace (Health, Safety and Welfare) Regulations 1992* requires employers to provide sanitary conveniences in sufficient numbers.

Car parking

❖ staff: 1 car/25m² of gross floor area
❖ visitors: 10% of parking provision.

Required provision must be agreed with the local authority.

Sources of information

Adler, D. (editor), *Metric Handbook: Planning and Design Data*, Architectural Press, 1999

Pickard, Q. (editor), *The Architects' Handbook*, Blackwell Science, 2005

BCO best practice for new offices and fitting out works

It has long been recognised that good design can help improve the workplace environment and contribute to business performance. The British Council for Offices (BCO) research and develop best practice in the specification of commercial offices.

The BCO launched their first guide to the specification of offices in 1994 and their latest guide, *The British Council for Offices Guide 2005 Best Practice in the Specification of Offices* (the BCO Guide), sets out guidance on current best practice for shell and core developments.

The BCO Guide considers:

❖ **Site issues** – The location of the development and proximity to local amenities, the density of the development to the site (plot ratio), the orientation of the development to surrounding buildings and the design of landscaping.
❖ **Building form** – Design issues such as the plan shape and floor plate efficiency, the coordination of building elements and services (the planning grid), requirements for circulation space and the design of the building core, lifts and toilet accommodation.

❖ **Engineering design** – Design criteria and objectives for the structure and envelope, building services and security considerations.

Throughout the BCO Guide reference is made to good practice published by recognised organisations such as Centre for Window and Cladding Technology (CWCT), Building Research Establishment (BRE) and Chartered Institution of Building Services Engineers (CIBSE).

Recent legislative changes have focused designers' attention on environmental and sustainability issues and this is reflected in the latest edition of the BCO Guide.

Examples of BCO design criteria include:

❖ net floor area (per person) = $12m^2$–$17m^2$

❖ floor plan efficiency (net internal area / gross internal area) = 80–85%

❖ finished floor to underside of ceiling = 2600mm–3300mm

❖ plan depth (window to window or atrium, not core) = 13.5m–21.0m

❖ column grid = 7.5m–9m

❖ raised floor void = minimum 150mm (300mm for computer floors)

❖ live load (general) = minimum $2.5kN/m^2$ (for 95% of the lettable floor area)

❖ live load (high) = minimum $7.5kN/m^2$ (for 5% of the lettable floor area for filing and paper storage)

❖ office lighting = 300–500 Lux minimum average maintained illuminance

❖ comfort (summer air conditioned space) = 22°C +/– 2°C

❖ comfort (winter) = 20°C +/– 2°C

❖ fresh air standard = 12–16 litres per person per second

❖ noise criteria (open plan offices) = NR 38

❖ noise criteria (cellular offices and meeting rooms) = NR 35

The above specification data is based on data from the BCO Guide, and is reproduced with permission from the British Council for Offices.

The BCO also produce the *Office Fit-out Guide* which complements the BCO Guide. Last published in 2003, this describes the key decisions that face clients and their project team when undertaking a typical fit-out project. It recommends the use of management checklists and goes on to describe the processes that need to be considered at pre- and post project stage. It ends with a section on move management and operational issues.

Whilst every development will have its own set of requirements and objectives, the BCO guides provide a useful source of benchmark information and guidance on processes for successful execution.

Specifications

The specification is the hub around which the various documents forming a modern day building contract are assembled.

The specification will incorporate a complex array of information, which will include design, testing, procedural, legislative and quality requirements.

The specification should form part of the contract documents and will typically be supported by the preliminaries and either work schedules, bills of quantities or contract sum analysis. It will schedule the drawings to which it refers, and which should form the contract drawings.

Types of specification

Prescriptive specification

This form of specification will be used where the author wishes to prescribe the project in as much detail as possible. Specific products or materials will be named and the assembly of the building will be described and supported with drawn information. Where materials are not named, reference will be made to published standards governing their composition.

The form of contract employed here will be a traditional one, which will not carry a design responsibility for the contractor.

Performance specification

A performance specification describes the requirements of a product, process or service to meet stated criteria.

The key difference to a prescriptive specification is related to design responsibility. With a performance specification, the contractor is responsible for the design development of the specification to meet the performance requirements.

The client will not need to advance the design as far before inviting tenders from interested contractors. This is a more economic approach since pre-contract design costs are usually less at the early stages of procurement.

The form of contract must be carefully considered to ensure that the contractor's design proposals can be incorporated.

Specification writing

The accurate collection and recording of information is essential when preparing a specification in order to convey information from one party to another. Sufficient time must be allowed at the design stage to survey, inspect, test, and research relevant data sources. Insufficient or poorly described information can mislead contractors resulting in contract variations and potential claims for loss and/or expense.

For projects involving multidisciplinary design services, great care must be taken to ensure that the various aspects of design are well coordinated and integrated into a seamless set of specification documents. For complex projects, the design is usually coordinated through 'design team meetings' at regular stages during the design period.

Construction consultants have established standardised data at their disposal to assist and form the basis on which to prepare their documents. Online specification writers are available by subscription, such as:

❖ www.thenbs.co.uk – provides a comprehensive specification for most conceivable products and materials, which may be adapted, added to or modified according to a particular project;

❖ www.nbsplus.co.uk – a library of building product manufacturer information linked to NBS clauses; and

❖ www.barbour-index.co.uk – a specification tool designed to create, edit and manage specification documents, and it offers a comprehensive library of all major specification clauses.

Other useful websites include:

❖ www.greenspec.co.uk – guide to 'green' building design, products, specification and construction; and

❖ www.productioninformation.org – project specification – a code of practice for building works.

Site archaeology

While the British Government, including associated Scottish Parliament, Welsh Assembly and Northern Irish Authorities, are consulting on changes to Heritage, Scheduled Ancient Monuments and Archaeological Protection legislation, including the production of Unified Lists covering all categories, no final decisions have yet been made. Accordingly, the following procedures remain currently in place. The White Paper of March 2007 covering England and Wales *Heritage Protection in the 21st Century* has now completed the consultation period but no legislative changes are presently anticipated until 2009/2010 at the earliest. No other dates are yet confirmed as at the time of writing.

Traditional dictionary definitions focus on the study of history through excavation (usually implicitly below ground) and the analysis of the remains.

Not everyone will realise that in the construction world we have to deal with two types of archaeology:

❖   the traditional excavation of what lies hidden below ground; and

❖   the archaeology of standing buildings or above-ground archaeology.

How does archaeology affect construction?

Archaeology affects construction primarily through the way that the planning process limits and controls development. Both above and below ground archaeology can easily be applicable to the same site.

The present key government reference document is Planning Policy Guidance Document 16, published in November 1990 (PPG16). The government was consulting for the replacement for PPG16 with the first of the new Planning Policy Statements (PPS), in this case the Planning Policy Statement on *Planning for the Historic Environment*.

Scotland has the most useful NPPG5 – *Archaeology and Planning*, which can be found at www.scotland.gov.uk/Publications/1998/10/nppg5

Northern Ireland has the equally useful PPS6 – *Planning, Archaeology and the Built Heritage* – March 1999, which can be found at www.doeni.gov.uk and search under 'Planning' for PPS6. (Alternatively try www.planningni.gov.uk/AreaPlans_Policy/PPS/PPS.htm or www.planning ni.gov.uk/AreaPlans_Policy/PPS/pps6/pps06_master.pdf.) PPS6 and the Scottish NPPG5 are recent integrated documents of the type that England and Wales are moving towards.

However PPG16 for England and Wales is still current and the ministerial statement (CLG having replaced ODPM) of 5 May 2006 stated that the review and replacement of PPG16 (amongst others) will only take place as and when necessary.

PPG16 sets out the Secretary of State's policy on archaeological remains on land and how they should be preserved or recorded, both in an urban setting and in the countryside.

Planning permission is required for works of development – the carrying out of building, engineering, mining or other operations in, on, over or under land or the making of any material change in the use of any buildings or other land.

The first port of call for any planning application is the local planning office and the published documentation in either the Development Plan or the Unitary Development Plan.

If the Local Development Plan and/or the local planning office identifies a site as one with Scheduled Ancient Monuments or locations where archaeological remains are believed to exist then it is vital to engage in the earliest possible consultation with the county archaeologists or their equivalents at English Heritage, Historic Scotland, CADW (Welsh Heritage) and the Environment and Heritage Service in Northern Ireland.

This consultation will identify the archaeological sensitivity of the site.

Following discussions with the county or national archaeologists the next step for the developer is to have researched exactly what is or might be there and how it will or could impinge on the proposed development.

This is a cost for the developer and will have to be paid for by the developer in the same way as any other site investigation exercise is paid for prior to a development being undertaken.

Options for archaeological investigations are potentially twofold.

Desktop studies

These draw on the archaeological records of the site itself and those of neighbouring sites. They are relatively quick and easy. Crucially they must be done by a trained archaeologist. The handbook of the Institute of Field Archaeologists will help in locating the right archaeologist or archaeological unit to undertake the study. The IFA website at www.archaeologists.net gives excellent advice. Contact by email can be made on admin@archaeologists.net or by telephone on 0118 378 6446.

Discussions may however indicate that the next level of investigation is necessary.

Field evaluation

This is not a full archaeological elevation or 'dig' but a ground survey and small scale trial trenching.

The results from the desktop study and/or the field evaluation will inform the developer, the county archaeologist and the local planning officers, especially the conservation officer, as to the importance of the site in archaeological terms.

Draft model agreements (December 1986 editions) between developers and the appropriate archaeological body regulating archaeological site investigations and excavations can be obtained from the British Property Federation, www.bpf.org.uk search under 'Who we are' and 'Publications' or telephone 020 7828 0111.

Statutory protection for archaeological sites

Where Scheduled Ancient Monuments have been identified under the *Ancient Monuments and Archaeological Areas Act* 1979, these are sites of national importance and as such rank as the equivalent of Grade I (Grade A in Scotland) or Grade II* (Grade B in Scotland) buildings of special architectural or historic interest.

The protection of Scheduled Ancient Monuments is based on the requirement that scheduled monument consent has to be obtained from the Secretary of State (of the Department for Culture, Media and Sport whose website is www.culture.gov.uk or CADW, Historic Scotland or DoE Northern Ireland).

Application has to be made to the Secretary of State for any works that would have the effect of demolishing, destroying, damaging, removing, repairing, altering, adding to, flooding or covering up a monument.

If you find a Scheduled Ancient Monument standing on or laying below your site take great care. Ensure your professional advisors fully appreciate the implications before application is made. If in doubt, enter into the earliest possible discussions with the relevant heritage and conservation authorities covering the site. These will include the local authorities conservation officer, the county archaeologist, and the Inspectors of Ancient Monuments at English Heritage, Historic Scotland, CADW and the Environment and Heritage Service in Northern Ireland.

Above-ground archaeology

A Scheduled Ancient Monument is usually, although not exclusively, an unoccupied structure and can be either remains below ground and/or a standing structure above ground.

Above-ground Scheduled Ancient Monuments will require Scheduled Ancient Monuments Consent for works to the structure. To fully understand what is important in this structure in understanding 'ancient peoples by the study of their physical remains' was borne the concept of above-ground archaeology. This can involve the physical digging in to the structure above ground. This can equally involve the 'desktop study' approach of bringing together the known archive or history of the structure to fully understand what is important in the remains and what is less important.

This is because as structures are added to and/or changed over time there may well be pieces or parts of what is now extant that can well be removed or modified or changed and benefit the scheduled monument.

The final use of archaeology in standing structures is the extrapolation of the 'desktop study' for above-ground Scheduled Ancient Monuments into the 'Conservation Plan' for all types of listed historic buildings.

Conservation Plans are increasingly required by Heritage and Listed Building authorities, particularly for the more important Grade I (Scottish A) and Grade II* (Scottish B) buildings as listed as being of Special Architectural and Historic Interest. This is as part of the application process for Listed Building Consent for works that will affect the special architectural or historic interest of these Listed Buildings.

Conservation plans have a number of practical and financial advantages for the developer/renovator of historic buildings. The key ones are:

- ❖ certainty for the design team in formulating in what can or cannot be done to the building and site before they formulate details for the Listed Building Consent and Planning Permission applications; and
- ❖ certainty for the developer/renovator that the scheme will not be stopped in its tracks by the heritage authorities discovering that the building contains important previously unknown historic elements in the structure that precludes all or part of the development going forward. The worst case would be the stopping of the scheme or at least making it less viable or completely unviable.

Project extranets as a method of coordinating project information

Some of the specific characteristics of the construction industry make the quality, quantity and timing of information flows difficult to administer. These include the following:

- ❖ large numbers of participating companies collaborating on projects of relatively short duration;
- ❖ diverse locations and working conditions related to the building site;
- ❖ comparatively low levels of management support; and
- ❖ diverse sources of information – CAD, Power Project, Microsoft Project, etc.

Despite this, the use of electronic systems for information management, 'project extranets', can have significant benefits including:

- ❖ direct 24-hour access to project-related material;
- ❖ enhanced communications, faster drawing/document approvals;

- ❖ reduced paper trails on labour intensive tasks;
- ❖ reduced distribution/production costs and associated time savings;
- ❖ improved management of information providing accountability and an audit trail;
- ❖ competitive differentiation;
- ❖ less chance of losing information;
- ❖ a platform to stimulate innovation; and
- ❖ the support of a green agenda.

As with any application there are also drawbacks which need to be considered:

- ❖ systems, no matter how secure, are threatened by malicious intrusion from a remote, often untraceable, source; and
- ❖ the sharing of information assumes all parties have access to the relevant software to view the files posted.

Research

Independent research commissioned by the Network for Construction Collaboration Technology Providers (NCCTP) in 2006 showed that 74% of clients favoured contractors/consultants who are experienced in using web based collaboration systems (project extranets). In addition the *Proving Collaboration Pays* study carried out by Benchmark Research also found that teams welcomed the greater control afforded through collaboration technologies.

A number of benefits were identified in the NCCTP survey, which are included within the above list. In particular, the research indicated that drawing approval times were reduced by 26% from an average of 9.3 days to 6.9 days.

Relevant legislation/best practice information

The British Standards Institution's section for delivering information solutions to customers (BSI-DISC) sets out five principles which should be the starting point for coordinating information in DISC PD 0010:1997. BSI consider that the key principles of good practice for information management are to:

- ❖ be aware of all information types and sources;
- ❖ recognise your responsibilities in the use of the information;
- ❖ find a procedural solution;
- ❖ resolve a support network/resource for the solution; and
- ❖ review the results and apply lessons learnt.

Other relevant legislation/best practice information includes:

- ❖ DTI Building Centre Trust and Phrontis Limited construction best practice report entitled *Effective Integration of IT in Construction*, June 2003;
- ❖ DTI/CCPI *A Code of Procedure for the Construction Industry on Production Information*, April 2003;
- ❖ BS7799, *Information Security Management*; and
- ❖ *Data Protection Act* 1998.

Examples of project document management systems

The following list summarises a small sample of project document management systems currently available:

- ❖ Asite: www.asite.com
- ❖ BIW Technology: www.biwtech.com

- ❖ Business Collaborator: www.groupbc.com
- ❖ Cadweb: www.cadweb.co.uk
- ❖ CTSpace: www.ctspace.com
- ❖ Meridian: www.meridiansystems.com
- ❖ Sarcophagus: www.sarcophagus.co.uk
- ❖ 4 Projects: www.4projects.com

Key issues

In order to ensure the successful adoption of a project extranet, a number of key issues need to be carefully considered and resolved, these include the following:

- ❖ Adopt document handling procedures within the project team that prevent double handling, e.g. the benefits of a project extranet system will only be realised if information is distributed electronically and not with simultaneous hard copy (perhaps because some members of the professional team are not IT literate or prepared to utilise the system).

- ❖ A principal barrier to entry is the selection of an appropriate system with appropriate pricing arrangements, reflecting the project particulars. The opportunities to purchase or procure project extranet systems appropriately scaled to project needs have greatly enhanced over recent years. Accordingly, further to appropriate research, it should be possible to identify a suitable system. System selection should include consideration of the following points:

  - ownership of data;

  - post project archive access;

  - procedures for recovery of information should a hosting company cease trading;

  - system redundancy;

  - numbers of users; and

  - other practical matters as set out in this section.

- ❖ A suitable policy or system feature is required to ensure that all required users are aware of and review new information when posted to the website. This can either be resolved through separate communication or an extranet site design that ensures all personnel are notified of new postings and are required to review them within a certain period, allowing the project manager to audit compliance.

- ❖ Policies are required concerning the information exchange format, e.g. are Autocad drawings to be posted in DWG format for design team use or in a finalised common exchange format such as Adobe PDFs. Perhaps both editable and fixed information is required.

- ❖ The system should provide different levels of ownership allowing data to be available to the whole project team, other stakeholders such as letting agents or tenants and to the contractor. However, full availability of data to all parties is unlikely to be appropriate.

- ❖ The system administration arrangements should be simple and clear as unlimited opportunity to amend the procedures and systems will inevitably generate a large barrier to the effective use of the system.

- ❖ Systems requiring a specialist appointed information coordinator may be less appropriate on all but the largest schemes, as this provides an additional workload to one particular team member and may delay information distribution. Of additional benefit can be a system allowing direct posting by all enrolled stakeholders, however, the notification points discussed above remain key.

❖ Team members experienced in utilising a project extranet should be a factor in the selection protocol for the team.

❖ Adopting a suitable framework to resolve the above matters throughout the team might most usefully be documented within the Project Execution Plan and matching provisions should be reflected in all appointments.

Web tendering

The most recent introduction to the online coordination of project information is web-based tendering, whereby construction project tender documents are posted by the client (otherwise known as the 'buyer') onto a website. 'Suppliers', i.e. contractors, are then able to access the tender documentation and submit a price online. The service is able to satisfy most types of procurement method including open (open to any contractors) and closed (restricted to a preferred tender list) tenders, as well as negotiation. One such provider of this service is the RICS: www.ricsetendering.com

In conclusion, a complete understanding of the project, the environment and an active commitment by the people involved is necessary to effectively coordinate project information through the use of a project extranet. However, the benefits of a well organised approach are significant and the barriers to entry are reducing; accordingly, a project extranet can offer a real benefit on many schemes.

Modern methods of construction

Modern Methods of Construction (MMC) is a term used to describe a wide range of techniques whereby buildings or parts of buildings are manufactured and assembled off site. Generally, these systems or components are produced in a factory environment and delivered to site ready for installation. The aim of MMC or 'off-site' is to improve the cost, speed, quality and reliability of the finished product, in line with the recommendations set out in the influential 1998 Construction Task Force report *Rethinking Construction*. MMC is also variously referred to as off-site manufacturing (OSM), modular construction, prefabrication, pre-assembly, standardisation, off-site production and off-site fabrication.

Off-site systems

These can be broadly divided into the following categories:

❖ **Panel systems** – Flat panel units are manufactured in a factory and assembled on site. Open panels consist of a frame only, with external cladding, services, insulation and internal finishes applied on site. Closed panels have some or all of these elements, including doors and windows, fitted in the factory. Panels are then simply assembled on site and services connected.

❖ **Volumetric systems** – Complete units, or pods, are factory assembled, with the resulting 3D modules delivered to site ready for installation. Modules may or may not have all their component parts and finishes installed prior to leaving the factory.

❖ **Sub-assemblies and components** – These are factory-fabricated parts used with otherwise traditional construction methods. For example, floor or roof cassettes, precast foundations and preformed wiring looms would fall into this category.

❖ **Hybrids** – This method of construction is sometimes known as semi-volumetric: both panel and volumetric systems are used. For example, kitchen or bathroom pods may be used in a building otherwise constructed using panels.

What are the benefits?

Generally accepted benefits of MMC include:

Cost – Initial costs may be more expensive but economies of scale apply. The more factory-assembled components you use, the cheaper they become, hence the popularity of MMC in the social housing sector and with major fast food chains such as Pizza Hut and McDonalds.

Cost advantages may also result from:

❖ reduced risk of cost overruns;

❖ fewer defects, leading to less time – and fewer materials – wasted on site; and

❖ reduced life cycle costs.

Off-site manufacturer Kingspan has benchmarked its own off-site products against conventional construction methods and costs and the company asserts that they are both capital and whole-life-cycle cost competitive.

Time – less build time on site; and more predictable completion dates.

The environment – Kingspan has also made environmental comparisons with traditional construction, using the ARUP SPeaR sustainability assessment method. From this Kingspan concludes that off-site techniques 'significantly enhance sustainable construction'. Other benefits include:

❖ reduced waste on site; and

❖ less noise and pollution from additional traffic.

Quality – consistent, quality-assured products manufactured in a controlled environment; and less accidental damage to or theft of construction components due to reduced on-site storage.

Safety issues – MMC has a major contribution to make in improving health and safety in the construction industry. By manufacturing large parts of a building in a controlled environment, fewer accidents are likely to occur on site. The necessity for site staff to work at height is also greatly reduced. Falling from a height continues to be the most common cause of accidents, accounting for 22% of fatal injuries to workers in 2005/06 (source: HSE).

In the light of existing skills shortages, another key benefit may be that off-site manufacturing reduces reliance on on-site 'wet trades' and other types of traditional skilled labour.

The market for MMC

Despite the advantages cited above, MMC only accounts for 2.1% of total UK construction output (source: Buildoffsite). However, this is set to change. A survey carried out in 2005 by market research company MSI forecast massive growth in the modular construction market during the next four years, particularly in the housing sector. Other sectors that MSI highlights for growth are:

❖ military buildings – up 193%;

❖ schools – up 103%;

❖ prisons – up 102%; and

❖ healthcare facilities – up 69%.

The biggest uptake of MMC in the UK to date has been in the social housing sector. As demand for housing continues to outstrip supply, MMC is increasingly gaining government support as a realistic solution to the problems of providing large numbers of homes quickly. Since 2004, the

Housing Corporation has made a commitment that at least 25% of the housing that it funds should be built using MMC methods, regarding it as part of effective supply chain management. English Partnerships too is leading major innovations in the use of MMC, including it in the development briefs for a number of high profile exemplar projects such as the London Wide Initiative and Oakgrove Millennium Community. Like the Housing Corporation, English Partnerships has a target of 25% MMC by number of dwellings on projects for which it supplies funding.

Initiatives such as the Design for Manufacture competition launched in 2005 and the launch of the BRE's LPS 2020 Standard for Innovative Systems, Elements and Components for Residential Buildings have helped promote greater use of off-site techniques. In addition, the government has allocated £1.3 billion more to housing spending in 2007–08 than in 2004–05 (source: 2004 Spending Review), which can only be good news for the MMC sector.

Commercial clients are also taking MMC seriously. Off-site manufacture has successfully thrown off the stigma attached to post-war 'prefab' construction. It is now regarded as a legitimate way of improving quality and site safety while at the same time minimising waste, reducing delivery times and addressing skills shortages.

Private sector house builders, particularly those like Urban Splash who specialise in developing high density, city apartment schemes, are increasingly using MMC. Moho was the first private housing scheme to use off-site manufacturing techniques to build 120 apartments in the centre of Manchester.

One of the major players in the off-site manufacturing market is the Shepherd Building Group. Its subsidiary, Yorkon, has produced more than 200 ready-made buildings around the UK for the McDonalds fast food chain and has developed a partnership with Pizza Hut to build a number of UK restaurants for the company. Companies such as Yorkon are now developing their own ranges of exemplar designs for different building types to give clients more choice and to combat the perception that greater uptake of MMC means producing bland buildings with no design values.

Further information

- ❖ www.bre.co.uk
- ❖ www.buildoffsite.com
- ❖ www.englishpartnerships.co.uk
- ❖ www.housingcorp.gov.uk
- ❖ www.homein.org

Building into the basement

At a government-sponsored conference held on 24 January 2005, the government called on the UK house building industry to increase the provision of domestic basements. This is a complete reversal of previous policies, based on the perception that a basement area as living, working or storage space represented a poor relation to housing the same functions above ground. It also represents considerable challenges for both new and adaptive construction in providing dry, warm and decent environments below ground level.

Basements for Dwellings Approved Document 2005

The conference was the launch pad for the private sector *Basements for Dwellings Approved Document* 2005, published 17 January 2005. This was also approved by the Secretary of State, under section 6 of the *Building Act* 1984, as practical guidance on meeting the requirements of the relevant paragraphs in Schedule 1 to the *Building Regulations* 2000 (as amended 2001 and 2002) as they apply to the incorporation of basements to dwellings. It has the same standing as HMSO Approved Documents.

The Approved Document brings into one text all of the relevant Building Regulations for dwellings that are affected by the inclusion of a basement. The sections covered are:

Part A – Structure

Part B – Fire safety

Part C – Site preparation and resistance to contaminants and moisture

Part E – Resistance to the passage of sound

Part F – Ventilation

Part J – Heat producing appliances

Part K – Stairs, ramps and guards

Part L1 – Conservation of fuel and power

Part M – Access and facilities for disabled people

Part N – Drainage and waste disposal

The sections are laid out in order of construction, rather than in the strict alphabetic order of the Building Regulations.

An **Addendum** covering **Plain Basement Retaining Walls**, was submitted to the Department for Communities and Local Government (CLG) in 2007 and has been approved for production. The addendum will cover both plain concrete and plain masonry retaining walls of height up to 2.7m.

Keeping water out

Where basements are concerned, whether for new build or alterations and adaptations, the key issue is that of water resistance. The Approved Document details four grades of construction to achieve various levels of water resistance:

Grade 1 – which allows water seepage and is almost certainly going to be inappropriate for any dwelling use;

Grade 2 – which is the reasonable minimum for garages;

Grade 3 – which is the reasonable minimum for accommodation; and

Grade 4 – which is for totally dry conditions or for premises which require a very controlled environment. This is unlikely to be appropriate for housing except in very exceptional circumstances.

The Approved Document also details different types of wall construction. Typically, there are three:

Type A – which is geared around total reliance on waterproofing;

Type B – where the structure provides the main resistance; and

Type C – where the structure provides some resistance but the principal reliance is on an internal system which intercepts moisture ingress, controls it and carries it away so the internal environment is not affected. In simple terms, the moisture is intercepted by a drainage layer on the internal face of the wall directing the moisture downwards to gutters which, in turn, direct the water into a sump from which the water is pumped away into the drainage system to the outside.

Environmental exposure

On reading the Approved Document in detail, you will come across the phrase 'acceptability of construction types'. You start with the three forms of construction (A, B and C given above) and then you introduce different levels of severity, or environmental exposure, to the construction types. A key factor is where the water table lies in relation to the proposed, or existing, basement. This is referred to as 'low', 'variable' and 'high'. A pertinent observation here is that water tables are almost invariably 'variable' on a seasonal basis – higher in winter and lower in summer, unless you have water tables that are high all year round, particularly as a result of proximity to river or sea coasts.

Adapting existing basements

Without a doubt, the most complex cases will be where existing basements are being considered for refurbishment. Almost without exception, Georgian, Victorian and Edwardian houses had basements varying from limited storage and coal cellars to complete basements. These were either fully below ground level or semi-basements originally designed to provide storage, kitchens and servants' accommodation.

Houses built pre-1914 and some constructed pre-1939 should be dealt with cautiously. The brickwork of such properties will have been constructed using lime-based mortars rather than Portland or similar cements. Such mortars are hygroscopic and take up water readily, with the result that the mortars can decay and, in the worst conditions, can crumble away completely. Their ongoing stability and the retention of the strength of the mortars relies on their being able to release the moisture into the internal environment through plaster facings into the rooms. In other words, such construction has to be able to release moisture inwards. The last thing one would want to do in dwellings constructed in this way is to lock moisture into the brickwork by means of waterproof renders on the internal face of the walls.

Moisture ingress into basements of buildings such as these should primarily be dealt with by the Type C wall construction described above. Any use of Type A internal waterproofing to the building should be thought through very carefully to ensure the lime-based brickwork is not compromised.

Structural and civil engineering design

A basic introduction to structures

Whilst in many respects parallels can be drawn between the work of a structural engineer and the work of the building surveyor, the approach of each discipline to the appraisal of a building will be fundamentally different. Whilst a surveyor will inevitably concentrate upon the condition of the fabric (the areas where he or she is most comfortable), an appreciation of the way in which the building resists the forces applied to it will often be of secondary importance. Conversely, the engineer will be reviewing the load paths within the building and considering its stability first before worrying about the condition of the fabric. There is nothing wrong with either approach, but surveyors are often called upon to make judgements of the building that will be expected to include some assessment of its structural stability. If the stability has not been analysed, how accurately can that judgement be made? This section sets out some basic information on structures and structural mechanics: some generalisations must be permitted for the sake of brevity.

Essential terminology

❖ Force – an influence upon something measured in Newtons (N) or kiloNewtons (kN).

❖ Mass – the amount of matter in a body, measured in grams or kilograms.

❖ Weight – in engineering commonly expressed as force exerted on an area, i.e. mass x acceleration due to gravity ($9.8m/s^2$).

❖ Density – mass in kg/volume in m^3.

❖ Stress – the internal pressure that exists within the body of a structural member as a result of an external influence. Direct stress is expressed as force/area and measured in N/mm^2.

❖ Shear stress – the internal pressures resulting from shear (slicing) forces and expressed as shear force/area N/mm^2.

❖ Strain – the physical extension or shortening of a member as a result of stress. Strain is not expressed in units; it is the ratio of change in length to original length. This may be a very small number hence the use of the term 'microstrain'. Strain can be expressed as a percentage.

❖ Youngs Modulus (E) – a constant that expresses the ratio of stress to strain in any given material.

An object of mass 1kg dropped from height will fall 9.8m in the first second and 19.62m in the second – increasing until it reaches terminal velocity. 9.8 is conveniently rounded to 10, and so for engineering purposes the weight of an object is its mass multiplied by 10.

A mass of 1kg will have a weight of 10N, i.e. (1kg x 10).

❖ A 1kg bag of sugar will impose a force of 10N upon a table.

❖ Four 25kg bags of cement will impose a force of 1kN on a floor.

❖ An 80kg man will impose a force of 800N or 0.8kN on a bar stool.

❖ A 1000kg car will impose a force of 10kN on a car park.

❖ 1 litre of water = 1kg = 10N.

Types of load

- ❖ Dead load – a permanent load – the self weight of a structural element and the parts of the building that are supported by it.
- ❖ Live load – imposed load – variable loads that result from the use of the building – people and furniture, snow, stock, etc.
- ❖ Lateral load – a load (which may or may not be variable) acting horizontally or at an angle to the horizontal, e.g. a wind load or the load resulting from soil or water against a retaining wall.
- ❖ Point load or concentrated load – a load acting on a single point, e.g. the base of a storage racking system.
- ❖ Uniformly distributed load (UDL) – a load that is distributed equally over the length of a beam or over the area of a floor.
- ❖ Uniformly varying load – a load that is distributed continuously but not equally and in a linear manner, e.g. over the height of a retaining wall the force is greatest at the bottom and least at the top.

One of the fundamental engineering principles is Newton's third law:

'For every action there is an equal and opposite reaction'.

Effectively, for a structure to remain stable it must be capable of resisting the forces applied to it. Stability means that all of the forces are held in equilibrium. Structural members will be subjected to forces acting in different ways:

- ❖ In bending – a simply supported beam spanning between two points will, depending upon its span and the loads it carries, gradually bend. If the loads are increased, the bending will increase until failure occurs. Failure will not occur if the beam is able to provide equal resistance to the load imposed upon it. Floor slabs are effectively wide, shallow beams and, although they are often designed to span between two supports, they may also span in two directions between four supports.
- ❖ In compression – a column in a building may be supporting a floor slab or other structural elements. These loads act axially in a downward direction and must be resisted by an equal and opposite reaction – hence the column is in compression.
- ❖ In shear – a short beam with a heavy load close to one of the supports would be subjected to a slicing type force; rather than bending, the beam may fail as a result of this slicing action.
- ❖ In tension – the opposite of compression forces, occurring for example in the bottom tie member of a roof truss. The ends of the tie are resisted from moving outwards by an equal and opposite reaction within the tie.
- ❖ In torsion – a twisting or rotational force possibly caused by a load that does not pass through the centroid of a structural element.

A structural component will fail when the stress created by bending or shear exceeds the maximum permissible stress of a particular material.

The analysis of structures that are subjected to different forces is complex and for this reason engineers will often seek to simplify the design concept by making individual elements do specific tasks. Different structural elements can be designed to resist different forces. For example:

- ❖ An arch is held in compression throughout its span; thus materials that are weak in tension (brick, stone, etc.) can be made to span considerable distances.

❖ A truss is an assembly of components that are either held in compression or tension and so do not require an analysis for bending or shear.

The analysis of these elements and indeed the whole structure will depend upon an understanding of the routes that the loads must take. The sum of the live and dead loads will eventually be transferred via a load path down to foundation level. Here, the combined load must be resisted by an equal and opposite reaction otherwise the building would not stand up. However, the transmission of loads will depend to a large extent on how the individual members are jointed. Engineers use different types of joint to permit different load transfers:

❖ Pin joints (in reality these joints are rarely pins but the structure is analysed as if they were) – pin joints can be considered as pivot points: they can provide a reaction to horizontal or vertical loads but cannot resist rotation. Components in a pin jointed frame can thus be treated as if they have axial loads – either compression or tension.

❖ Roller joints – roller joints will provide a reaction to vertical loads but not to horizontal loads. So, for example, a bridge deck that is likely to expand and contract may have provision for movement in the form of a roller joint.

❖ Moment joints or connections – these joints are fixed in all axes, thus preventing vertical, horizontal or rotational movement at the joint.

Frames and bracing

If one were to consider a simple frame constructed of two members with a pivot joint it would be clear that the bottom ends of the frame would be free to move apart. However, if the two ends were to be joined by a third member, the frame would be rigid. Similarly, a square frame could easily be distorted into a parallelogram if a horizontal load were applied to one corner. If a diagonal member were to be inserted, the square would be rigid – in effect the insertion of a single diagonal 'brace' has created two triangular structures.

A framed building behaves in exactly the same way; unless it can be suitably braced it would be free to move under lateral load. Hence the provision of diagonal bracing to stiffen the structure and prevent lateral buckling. Steel framed structures, particularly large sheds, must be braced in this way. However, the provision of diagonal members may not be desirable for architectural reasons and so alternative forms of bracing are often employed. In buildings constructed during the 1960s and 1970s a very common form of bracing was the provision of a rigid core (e.g. a staircase or lift enclosure), or alternatively the provision of a reinforced concrete shear wall at the ends of a building as a means of providing resistance to lateral loads.

Today, the following forms of bracing are most common:

❖ cross or diagonal bracing to one bay of a series of steel frames;

❖ stiff cores or shear walls; and

❖ sway (or unbraced) frames. In a sway frame resistance to lateral loads is provided by very stiff joints or moment connections as described above. Such a system would be found in a large steel framed building with unobstructed internal spaces and 'lightweight' enclosures to staircases and lifts.

High-rise buildings may utilise a variety of structural techniques which are beyond the scope of this handbook.

Structural engineering

The Institution of Structural Engineers defines structural engineering as:

> 'The science and art of designing and making, with economy and elegance, buildings, bridges, frameworks and similar structures so that they can safely resist the forces to which they may be subjected.'

Structural engineers are involved with the design of new buildings, and with the assessment of existing buildings, including historical buildings, at times of repair, renovation and extension, and during change of use. Increasingly, structural engineers provide advice in connection with durability of materials and construction when buildings change ownership.

Over the next few years, significant changes to the design codes used in the design of buildings will occur as the construction industry changes over to the new Eurocodes. These are a set of unified international codes of practice for designing building and civil engineering structures, intended to replace national codes in the European Community.

The Eurocodes will be listed in the Approved Documents as a means of meeting requirements of the Building Regulations.

It is anticipated that all of the Eurocodes will be available by 2008, and fully operational by 2010.

The Eurocodes will comprise a base document together with a National Annexe. The National Annexe to each code will give specific parameters for those elements of design which can still be determined at national level, such as safety levels and issues relating to climatic conditions.

An assessment of ground conditions is usually essential to ensure the proper performance of the building superstructure.

Soils and foundation design

For very light residential building, a visual assessment of the soils with a minimum of physical testing may be sufficient, if local knowledge of the area is good. For larger buildings, a proper geotechnical investigation is usually recommended. This allows the measurement of relevant soils (geotechnical) data on which the foundation design will be based. Accurate testing of samples of soil obtained from boreholes usually leads to economies in foundation design. Samples are usually tested for consolidation, compressibility (both of these affect settlement) and shear strengths. In certain circumstances testing for chemicals, which could affect the structure, may be included.

Where soil conditions are good, and building loads are relatively light, a simple spread foundation is usually sufficient. This will be in the form either of simple strips or pad bases of non-reinforced concrete. As loads increase and soil conditions become more complex, foundations may need to be reinforced to allow loads to be spread sufficiently. Heavy building loads and poor ground often require piled foundations to take the foundation loads into suitable (deeper) soils.

Other features, such as trees (in shrinkable soils), groundwater, and basements, all require special consideration in foundation design.

Sources of further information

The relevant British Standard for site investigations was, for a long time, BS 5930:1990 *Code of Practice for Site Investigations*; this document is now partly superseded, although it remains current and is cited in the Building Regulations. Further detailed guidance is listed below.

BSI Standard	Title
BS EN ISO 22476-2:2005	*Geotechnical investigation and testing. Field testing. Dynamic probing (AMD Corrigendum 16932)*
BS EN ISO 22476-3:2005	*Geotechnical investigation and testing. Field testing. Standard penetration test (AMD Corrigendum 16931)*
BS EN ISO 14688-2:2004	*Geotechnical investigation and testing. Identification and classification of soil. Principles for a classification (AMD Corrigendum 16928)*
BS EN ISO 14689-1:2003	*Geotechnical investigation and testing. Identification and classification of rock. Identification and description (AMD Corrigendum 16929)*
BS EN ISO 14688-1:2002	*Geotechnical investigation and testing. Identification and classification of soil. Identification and description (AMD Corrigendum 14181) (AMD Corrigendum 16930)*
BS EN 1997-2:2007	*Eurocode 7: Geotechnical design. Ground investigation and testing*
BS EN ISO 22475-1:2006	*Geotechnical investigation and testing. Sampling methods and groundwater measurements. Technical principles for execution*

For preliminary design purposes only, the following table gives typical allowable bearing values under static loading for various types of soils and may be used to size strip or pad foundations.

Category	Soil type	Presumed allowable bearing pressure (kN/m²)
Unweathered rocks	Strong igneous rocks	10,000
	Strong sandstones and limestones	4,000
	Strong shales	2,000
Non-cohesive soils	Dense gravel	600
	Medium dense gravel or sand and gravel	200–500
	Loose gravel or loose sand and gravel	up to 200
	Loose sand	up to 100
Cohesive soils	Very stiff clay	300–600
	Stiff clay	150–300
	Firm clay	75–150
	Soft clay	75

Soil survey

Purpose

Soil surveys may be required to determine either, or both, of the following:

❖ geotechnical properties; and

❖ environmental contamination.

Geotechnical

The purpose of a geotechnical site investigation is to provide sufficient geotechnical information to enable design of foundations. Investigations will be designed specifically to suit the anticipated geology and development proposals. A geotechnical site investigation is intrusive and may include in-situ and laboratory tests. A geotechnical site investigation is often procured with an environmental site investigation given a significant overlap with the fieldwork requirements.

Environmental

An intrusive investigation may be required to establish the nature of any subsurface contaminated soil and/or groundwater. Site investigations are based upon site-specific factors such as the presence of likely contaminants, the anticipated subsurface geology and the location of the site. They are often referred to as Phase 2 investigations where they follow a non-intrusive Phase 1 audit. Samples of soil and groundwater are taken for laboratory analysis. The results are interpreted and a risk assessment undertaken for any contamination identified.

Fieldwork

The following methods of soil and groundwater sampling are common to both environmental and geotechnical investigations.

Trial pits

Trial pits are extremely valuable if the depth of investigation is less than about three metres. They allow a detailed examination of the ground conditions in situ with some indication of stability and groundwater conditions. Trial pitting is a relatively fast and efficient means of exploring subsurface conditions.

Auger holes

Auger holes are normally made by hand-turning a very light auger into the ground, or by using light power-auger equipment. However, while auger holes are effective in preliminary investigations they do not provide the depth or range of sampling and in-situ testing provided by conventional site investigation boreholes.

Window samplers

A window sampler is a steel tube, usually about one metre long, with a series of windows along the tube through which to view disturbed soil conditions or extract samples. A lightweight percussion hammer drives the sampler into the ground, which is then extracted with jacks. A depth of approximately ten metres can be achieved, depending on soil conditions, using a sequence of progressively smaller diameter samplers.

Boreholes

Light percussion drilling (shell and auger) is the most commonly used method in the UK. Samples are often unsuitable for soil description on the basis that the drilling process will have changed the strength of the soil by remoulding it and increased the moisture content of the soil through lubrication. For this reason U100 tube samples are often taken from boreholes at regular depths by driving a small diameter tube into the soil at the base of the borehole, thus extracting an undisturbed sample for laboratory analysis. Lubrication may be required if the subsurface is not cohesive making it unsuitable for some types of environmental site investigations.

Geotechnical in-situ testing

In-situ testing is typically undertaken on cohesionless soils where the strength characteristics may only be established on undisturbed in-situ samples.

Cone Penetration Test (CPT)

This technique involves hydraulically pushing a 10 or $15cm^2$ cone into the ground at a standard rate of penetration and measuring the penetration resistance. The equipment necessary for this type of investigation is housed in a large truck. The results from a CPT can be very valuable providing a soil profile, estimates of the soil types encountered, including consistency and density, and evidence of the presence of voids beneath the site.

Dynamic probing

Much less sophisticated than CPT, dynamic probing involves driving a steel rod into the ground by using repeated blows of a hammer of a specified mass falling through a fixed distance. The number of blows for each 100mm is recorded and plotted as a depth versus blow-count log. However, the information given by dynamic probing is very restricted and is difficult to interpret. Further investigations are usually necessary to supplement this test.

The Standard Penetration Test (SPT)

This test involves driving an open-drive sampler into the bottom of a borehole with repeated blows of a hammer falling a predetermined distance. The number of blows necessary to drive the sampler six increments of 75mm are counted and recorded, giving the penetration resistance value. The test is undertaken on cohesionless soils such as gravels.

Other methods of testing and sampling are used depending on the soil type and conditions on site.

Geotechnical laboratory testing

Laboratory testing is typically undertaken on cohesive soils, i.e. clays, where an undisturbed sample may be retrieved from the field. Such testing is not appropriate to cohesionless soils such as gravels. Tests include:

  ❖ Soil Classification: Particle Size Distribution, Plasticity Index, Moisture Content.
  ❖ Consolidation: To assess the settlement characteristics.
  ❖ Triaxial: To assess the compressive strength characteristics.

Geotechnical reporting

The results of the fieldwork and laboratory tests are assessed. For development purposes preliminary designs for foundations may be prepared. Sufficient information would be provided to enable design of building foundations. For diagnostic purposes the investigation would assist with identifying the cause of defects with a building superstructure allowing remedial solutions to be specified with confidence.

Environmental sampling and analysis

Information on soil, water and gas sampling for environmental information can be found in the sustainability chapter of this handbook.

Floor loadings in buildings

Guidance on the selection of appropriate imposed loads in new and existing buildings is set out in BS 6399-1:1996 (the Code). This standard does not include data on wind loadings, grandstands, bridges or stadia – which are covered by different codes. Over the years since publication, occupiers and investors have gradually changed their expectation for the use of buildings, methods of working and storage have in some cases changed and advances in technology have placed less demand on the need for fixed computer equipment or file storage. Reliance upon BS 6399 does not confer immunity from legal obligations, and strict adherence to the guidance may not necessarily provide a design that is suitable for a particular use – this is particularly the case in respect of industrial buildings where the code simply provides loadings that should be considered as a minimum.

Some useful definitions (see also the introduction to structures on page 220) include:

❖ **Dead load** – the self weight of all permanent partitions, walls, floors, roofs, finishes, etc. (in crude terms anything that would not fall out if you turned the building upside down). Dead loads are often calculated by reference to BS 648 or ascertained from other published data.

❖ **Imposed load** – the load that is produced by the occupants and use of the building, moveable equipment, impact loads, demountable partitions, furniture and the like. Imposed loads will in all probability vary from day to day or even moment to moment. Wind loads, whilst variable, are treated as a separate issue and are not classed as imposed loads for the purpose of BS 6399.

❖ **Storage height** – the height that is available for the storage of goods, extending from floor level to another physical obstruction such as a soffit, roof or element of structure. Usually measured to underside of the haunch in a portal framed industrial building.

❖ **Uniformly distributed load (UDL)** – the load per square metre of plan area measured in kN/m^2.

❖ **Concentrated load** – a load applied over a relatively small area of the structure.

❖ **Reduction in load** – given that the imposed design loads in some types of buildings are unlikely to be reached over all floors at all times, a design that is based simply upon the selection of a stated imposed load could result in an unnecessarily high calculation of total load – a factor that would be relevant say in the design of foundations or columns in multi-storey buildings. In certain cases therefore, a reduction in total loads can be factored into the calculations and permissible reductions are set out in the Code.

❖ $1kN/m^2$ = approx 20lbs per sq ft.

Typical minimum loadings

❖ For offices in general use, a UDL of $2.5kN/m^2$ is usually considered to be the minimum. A few years ago 'institutional standards' regularly dictated an imposed load of $5kN/m^2$ but this is generally considered to be over design. The British Council of Offices recommend as a minimum $2.5kN/m^2$ plus a further $1kN/m^2$ to allow for partitions and $0.85kN/m^2$ for raised access floors. They further recommend an allowance of $7.5kN/m^2$ for 5% of the floor area for heavy filing, safes, etc.

See also *Imposed floor loading for offices: a re-appraisal* (Stuart, J. – Archives of the Structural Engineer).

❖ Plant rooms are often designed to 7.5kN/m².

❖ For warehouses and storage buildings in general use, the Code recommends 2.4kN/m² for each metre of storage height or a concentrated load of 7kN. However, many engineers will argue that floor design calculations based upon these criteria are too simplistic as they do not take into account the effects, for example, of rolling loads. Point loads, i.e. concentrated loads, from storage racking systems can be very high, whilst the practice of block stacking will be punishing. For cold stores it is usual to allow 5kN/m² per metre of storage but with a minimum of 15kN/m². Over the years a number of different studies into methods of specifying floor loads in industrial and warehouse premises have supported the view that the Code allowance needs to be reviewed. See also BRE Report *Floor loading in warehouses: a review*, 1984, BRE IP 19/87: *Classes of imposed loads for warehouses*, Concrete Society TR34; and C&CA Technical Report 550:1982.

❖ Retail areas are recommended under the Code to have a minimum UDL for sale and display of 4kN/m² although again this may not be truly reflective of actual conditions. The British Council of Shopping Centres' *Survey of Tenants Requirements 1998* sets out more detailed guidance according to use. Under this guide, bookshops and food shops would be designed to 5kN/m², whilst some household stores and sports shops may be as high as 7kN/m².

❖ Residential uses are usually designed to 1.5kN/m² (for living and bedrooms in private dwellings) whilst hotel bedrooms are normally to 2kN/m².

❖ Car parks for vehicles not exceeding 2.5 metric tonnes would normally be designed to 2.5kN/m².

Historic buildings

The adaptive reuse of historic buildings often demands an analysis of floor loading capacity. The application of floor loadings in strict compliance with the Code will often be very difficult to achieve in practice – at least without substantial and intrusive work – itself contrary to the principles of minimum intervention set out in BS 7913. In its June 2001 paper *Floor loadings in historic buildings* (Hume, I.), the IHBC Technical Subcommittee argues for a more realistic approach to design, based upon a careful analysis of the actual proposed use rather than a generalised 'one size fits all' approach.

Specific dynamic loadings

Certain types of building use can generate enhanced vertical or horizontal loads on a structure or alternatively an amplification of the dynamic response to loadings. Dance floors, lightweight, long span structures or buildings containing certain types of machinery are examples of building types where this type of loading must be taken into account. Floors or balconies have been known to collapse under conditions of crowding accompanied by, for example, dancing to music with a heavy beat. Under such conditions, the building must be designed to avoid resonance by limiting the natural frequency of the building or by designing for dynamic loads. Such design will involve specialist techniques.

Floors in industrial and retail buildings

Use

In the UK, industrial buildings are being increasingly constructed for use as storage and distribution facilities rather than for production. In these buildings the floor forms a vital part of the operation of the facility, and the specification of the floor must suit the tolerances of the storage and materials handling equipment which is to be installed.

Specification

The main factors which need to be considered in the specification of a floor are:

- ❖ durability and suitability of floor finish for intended use;
- ❖ tolerance on finished levels across the floor;
- ❖ accommodation of movement due to constructional and in-service movements; and
- ❖ type and intensity of loading.

In bespoke facilities, where the use of the floor and the location of plant or storage racking and aisles are known, the specification of all of the above can be quite precise. Where the final use of the building and the layout of the facility is not known, as is the case for speculative development, assumptions must be made, but it may still be beneficial in terms of costs and usability to define as much as possible before design of the floor commences.

Support

Structurally, floors in industrial buildings may be either ground supported or suspended. Suspended construction is where the floor is supported on piles and not designed to bear directly onto the ground immediately below the building. The design of such slabs is not dissimilar to the design of concrete upper floors in multi-storey buildings, with the concrete section being reinforced to span between supports.

The more common arrangement, ground conditions allowing, is the use of a ground-bearing slab. With this type of construction, the load capacity of the floor is derived largely from the strength of the underlying ground and the imported capping (sub-base). Reinforcement is included in the slab but does not contribute to strength, being essentially there to control cracking which, in an un-reinforced concrete section, would result from shrinkage as water in the freshly placed concrete dries out. The rate of drying and resulting shrinkage depends on many things including the method of curing, the thickness of the slab, the concrete mix design and the presence of a membrane under the slab.

Loadings

Floor slabs are subject to distributed loads, for example from materials stored on the floor, and to concentrated loads from materials handling plant, storage racking, mezzanine floors and internal division walls. Of these, it is generally the concentrated loads which are more critical to the design of the slab and hence there are moves to specify floor capacities in these terms rather than in terms of distributed loadings.

In general, the weakest parts of a floor slab are the edges and the sections immediately adjacent to joints, particularly where joints intersect.

Construction methods

The proposed construction method will influence the design of the slab. Increasingly, large floor slabs are constructed using specialised plant which only trade contractors specialising in floor construction, rather than general contractors, are likely to have. With this type of procurement and construction much of the design and specification of materials is done by the contractor. In particular, the use of fibre reinforcement instead of conventional reinforcement is common for large bay construction.

Components

Concrete – the concrete mix will be specified by the structural engineer or specialist trade contractor to meet the requirements of the floor in terms of constructability, durability and finish. The concrete will include reinforcement in the form of either reinforcing bars or mesh, or fibres. Such fibres may be of steel or polypropylene.

Joints – joints are provided in a concrete floor slab to split it into easily constructed sections, and to cater for inevitable movement within the construction. This movement arises from shrinkage of the concrete soon after casting and from expansion and contraction due to changes in temperature over the life of the slab. Joints are expensive to provide and introduce weaknesses into the floor, and therefore, much design and specifying expertise has been expended into trying to reduce their number, or even to omit them entirely.

Membranes – the provision of a membrane immediately below the concrete slab can assist in reducing the friction which develops between the shrinking concrete as it dries out and the material below (sub-base). Good preparation of the sub-base and the inclusion of a membrane can reduce the amount of reinforcement required to control cracking. A membrane may also be used to minimise loss of fine particles from the concrete mix during placing and, if specified and laid appropriately, as a damp-proof membrane to protect against rising damp.

Sub-base – this is the imported material which forms the foundation of the floor slab and is necessary on all but the best natural ground (sub-grade).

Sub-grade – an investigation, undertaken on site with laboratory testing, to determine the nature of the ground on the site, is required to allow design of the floor slab. This investigation is normally undertaken by geotechnical firms to a specification that is usually drawn up by the structural engineer.

Flatness

Sophisticated materials handling equipment in warehouse and distribution facilities requires tight control of variation in level between different parts of the slab. In general terms, it is not economic to construct all concrete floor slabs to meet these requirements. Where tolerances are inappropriately specified, the slab may be unnecessarily expensive or unsuitable for certain uses.

Specialist surveying equipment is necessary to confirm compliance with the higher categories of level specification. Such surveys are usually undertaken soon after construction and records of survey results should be sought where flatness is important. Visual survey will not pick up failure of a floor slab to meet level tolerances unless the variation in level is extremely large.

Finish

In contrast to the majority of upper floors in buildings, the concrete often forms the finished surface of the floor in warehouse and retail buildings. Durability of the concrete surface against impact damage and wear, including tendency to form dust, is important.

Defects

Most defects in floor slabs affect the serviceability of the floor, but occasionally more fundamental structural defects occur.

The most common defects are:

- ❖ dusting or breakdown of surface, or finishes;
- ❖ lack of flatness;
- ❖ cracking;
- ❖ breakdown of joints; and
- ❖ structural defects due to slab or sub-base defects, or poorer than anticipated ground.

Increasingly, floor slabs will be considered as important components of buildings in the way that cladding and services are, and recorded information on aspects of their construction and performance will be required during the life of the building, particularly at times of change in use or ownership.

Further Information

Further information may be found in Technical Report No 34 *Concrete industrial ground floors – A guide to design and construction* (ISBN 1 904482 01 5) published by the Concrete Society.

Office floors

Suspended upper floors for modern office buildings are generally of some form of concrete construction, usually precast or cast in situ, but in some cases pre- or post-stressed concrete. Earlier buildings have a greater variety of floors, including some unusual or proprietary forms. Timber floors will be found in some older buildings. Modern concrete floors may take many forms, including solid, waffle or voided slabs. The concrete may have been cast on timber shuttering, subsequently removed, or on proprietary profiled metal decking, in which case the metal decking is incorporated into the final construction, providing part of the strength of the floor by acting as all or part of the tensile reinforcement to the combined steel and concrete floor construction.

Floor slabs are usually supported on a grid of beams which may be of steel or concrete construction, and which are normally visible below the soffite of the slab. The term 'flat slab construction' is used to describe concrete floor slabs supported directly off columns without the use of downstand beams. In these floors, bands of reinforcement within the slab perform a similar function to that of conventional beams.

Choice of floor construction normally includes consideration of issues such as cost, construction programme, proposed spans, column layout, and distribution of building services between and through floors, etc. Increasingly, environmental aspects of the building construction will also influence the type of construction chosen.

Service distribution through floor structures

Various structural systems are available which allow horizontal service distribution within the overall depth of the structure. Generally, with these systems, the overall depth of the floor structure is increased, but savings in overall floor depths are made because there is no need for a service distribution zone between the ceiling and the underside of the structure.

Small openings can often be formed through floors to allow distribution of building services between floors, but larger openings will normally require some form of trimming to avoid compromising the strength of the floor. The acceptability of forming openings in floors varies depending on the type of structure and on the location of the hole relative to spans and columns.

Environmental aspects

Environmental issues may influence the choice of floor structure used in a new building. In particular, the use of heavier reinforced concrete floors can be utilised as a heat sink to reduce fluctuations of temperature within a building.

Loading

Load on floors is commonly categorised as being either dead or live, with live load often being referred to simply as superimposed or imposed.

Dead load refers to the load arising from construction present at the time of construction and likely to be in place throughout the life of the building, and which can therefore be assessed relatively accurately by the designer. This normally includes the weight of the structure, any finishes (topping, screeds, raised floors, etc.) and the weight of floor coverings, ceilings, and building services, as well as any permanent partitions, such as those around cores.

Imposed load refers to loads arising from the occupation of the building which may vary substantially from user to user and cannot always be accurately assessed when the building is designed. This includes the load from people in the building, furniture, and de-mountable partitions and screens.

Occupiers are primarily interested in the capacity which the floor has to accommodate the latter of these two categories, i.e. the imposed load.

Imposed loadings in offices have not changed greatly over the years, with modern office equipment such as personal computers weighing no more than typewriters. BS 6399: Part 1, the current British Standard, sets out the statutory minimum requirement for different uses of building including offices and banks, and gives loadings for areas of general use and for filing and storage spaces, ranging from 2.5 kN/m² to 5.0 kN/m². These values have led to the blanket use of 5.0 kN/m² in many office buildings, although more recent research suggests that this leads to uneconomical construction: lower values are now more usually accepted. However, it should be noted that even the higher loading of 5 kN/m² will not accommodate proprietary rolling filing systems which can impose far greater loads on floors and need special consideration.

Sources of information on appropriate design loads for floors in office buildings are given below:

❖ BS 6399: Part 1 *Loading in buildings* – published by British Standards

❖ BCO Guide 2005 *Best practice in the specification for offices* – published by the British Council for Offices

❖ *Office floor loading in historic building* – published by English Heritage

Approximate equivalent loadings in metric and imperial units for common floor loadings in office buildings are as follows:

2.5 kN/m²	=	50lb / sq ft
3.5 kN/m²	=	70lb / sq ft
4.0 kN/m²	=	80lb / sq ft
5.0 kN/m²	=	100lb / sq ft

Floor dynamics

The perception of floor vibration due to pedestrian walking has become a growing issue in modern lightweight buildings, especially those with large floor spans.

Where walking pace matches the floor's natural frequency the energy from walking will be transferred into the floor structure, causing the floor to vibrate more strongly than would otherwise be the case. The perception of vibration in floors varies significantly between persons. Vibration of floors can also cause problems for users of large panel monitors or sensitive equipment.

Recommendations for the design of new buildings include guidance on design checks on the responses of structures to loading, which seek to minimise the likelihood of occupants being aware of floor vibration.

In existing buildings, testing can be carried out to assess the natural frequency of floors, and from this a comparison with other buildings can be made so that the probability of discernable vibration under footfall can be made.

Finishes

Office floors may be directly finished concrete, or finished with some form of sand-cement screed or concrete topping, or be finished by the addition of a raised floor system, usually a proprietary product, often supported on pedestals.

Whereas screeds are generally used solely to provide a level wearing surface to a floor, concrete toppings usually have a structural function as well, providing strength and lateral stiffness to the floor.

Defects

Some forms of floor construction have a higher incidence of defects in certain circumstances than others. Some defects may be common to all types of floors, whereas others are specific to certain types of construction. Defects may relate to structural or to serviceability aspects of the construction. Although not exhaustive, the following list comprises some of the more common defects:

❖ Requirement for strengthening, where particularly heavy equipment or storage is required, or where additional finishes are required, such as when kitchen facilities or shower rooms are to be installed, or where heavy acoustic or sliding partitions are added.

❖ Occupants being disturbed by vibration of the floor, as a result of people walking in open areas or corridors.

❖ Weakening of floor structures as a result of inappropriate alterations, overloading, removal of structural toppings, etc. or as a result of fire, or reduction in fire resistance following inappropriate work.

❖ Cracking of finishes, which sometimes occurs where brittle finishes are laid onto floors not designed specifically for them.

❖ Floor constructions containing high alumina cement (HAC). High alumina cement concrete has been found to lose strength over time, associated with a chemical process referred to as conversion. Concrete containing HAC can be identified by visual survey supplemented by the taking of samples on site for subsequent testing in the laboratory. Where HAC is found, further investigation and appraisal of the structure is necessary to assess its capacity.

❖ Defects in the original construction, such as inadequate concrete cover to reinforcement, poor compaction of concrete between pots or in narrow ribs, or in concrete cast on certain types of formwork, which may affect strength, reduce durability and/or fire resistance.

❖ Filler-joist floor constructions with clinker-aggregate concrete that may contain inclusions, which in damp conditions can create an acidic and therefore corrosive environment to the embedded steel sections.

- ❖ Floor construction which contains concrete with high levels of calcium chloride, which can lead to severe pitting corrosion of embedded steel sections or reinforcement.
- ❖ Floor constructions containing reinforced autoclaved aerated concrete planks which, in early designs before 1980, may have insufficient strength leading to excessive deflection.

Building services design

Design

Air-conditioning systems

Air-conditioning refers to a system or process for controlling within predetermined limits the temperature, humidity and sometimes the purity of the air in a building, accommodating the internal heat gains in conjunction with the external ambient conditions. The air, as well as being filtered, is heated or cooled as necessary and moisture is added or extracted to give a controlled humidity.

A comfort cooling system is essentially an air-conditioning system but without full control of the humidity.

The table overleaf provides a comparison of some of the more common floor/ceiling system type characteristics. Wall positioned systems may be utilised however, these have different features. The abbreviations used in the table relate to the following system configurations:

❖ **DX:** Direct expansion split type unit system operating with a minimum fresh air system.

❖ **VRV/VRF:** Variable refrigerant volume/flow system operating with a minimum fresh air system.

❖ **Heat Pump:** Unitary reverse cycle heat pump system operating with a minimum fresh air system.

❖ **FCU:** Four pipe fan coil unit system operating with a minimum fresh air system.

❖ **VAV:** All-air variable air volume system incorporating terminal reheater batteries.

❖ **Underfloor swirl:** All-air underfloor system with perimeter heating.

❖ **Displacement:** Underfloor displacement system with ceiling positioned chilled beams and perimeter heating.

Mixed mode ventilation systems

Mixed mode is a term used to describe engineering strategies that normally combine natural ventilation and/or mechanical ventilation and/or cooling in various combinations to achieve acceptable indoor environmental conditions in the most effective manner. It involves maximising the use of the building fabric and envelope to modify the internal climate/temperature swings, such as the use of night time pre-cooling of the building structure via the mechanical fresh air system. This approach has generally been used in offices; however, it is suitable for a wide range of building types.

Comparison of floor/ceiling based AC system type characteristics

	DX	VRV/VRF	Heat Pumps	FCU	VAV	Underfloor Swirl	Displacement
Installation costs	Low	Medium	Medium	Medium/high	High	Medium	Medium/high
Flexibility to change	Poor/average	Average/good	Poor	Good	Very good	Average	Average
Maintenance costs	Medium	Medium	Poor	Poor/medium	Good	Very good	Good
Operating costs	Medium	Low/medium	Low/medium	Poor	Very low	Low	Low
Ceiling void depth	Medium/low	Medium/low	Medium/high	Medium	High	Very low	Low
Floor void depth	Low	Low	Low	Low	Low	High	Medium
Suited to refurbishments	Average	Good	Average	Good/average	Poor	Poor	Poor
Resultant noise level	Average	Good	Poor	Average	Good	Good	Very Good
Plant space requirement	Medium	Medium	Medium	Low/medium	High	Medium	Low/medium
Riser space requirement	Low	Low	Low	Low/medium	High	Medium	Low/medium
Environmental control	Poor	Average	Poor	Good	Very Good	Good	Very Good

Plant and equipment

Boilers – (purpose is to heat water for distribution)

- ❖ Fuel can be gas, oil, coal, electric or dual fuel;
- ❖ air is required for combustion and cooling (not for electric);
- ❖ some form of flue is required (not for electric); and
- ❖ usually quiet in operation with insignificant vibration.

Water chillers – (purpose is to cool water for distribution)

- ❖ Normally electrically driven, but can be gas driven;
- ❖ conventionally air cooled to avoid the need for cooling towers that can be susceptible to bacteriological contamination (if near large body of water, water cooled chiller can be used);
- ❖ best externally located but can be internal and ducted to atmosphere;
- ❖ refrigeration machines are complex and expert maintenance is required;
- ❖ high noise and vibration levels can be generated; and
- ❖ old machines incorporated CFCs and HCFCs but new ones must not.

Air-handling units – (purpose is to deliver heated/cooled and filtered air to various spaces)

- ❖ Units incorporate fans, heaters, coolers, humidifiers and filters in various combinations;
- ❖ may be located externally or internally with fresh air ducts to outside;
- ❖ low tech equipment and easily maintained; and
- ❖ noise and vibration levels can be contained (but additional space required in plant room for silencers).

Diesel generators – (purpose is to provide a standby electrical supply to compensate for a breakdown in the main utility supply)

- ❖ Normally diesel oil fed for commercial developments;
- ❖ high fresh air and exhaust requirements demanding large louvred areas (for cooling);
- ❖ noise and vibration levels require special attention;
- ❖ oil storage facility – daily use and possibly long term storage; and
- ❖ flue is required.

Lift terminology

Power systems

Traction

- ❖ Ideally requires motor room above (possible planning problem);
- ❖ can be positioned at other levels, usually below or adjacent to lift pit – more expensive (doubles load on structure);
- ❖ machine room – less (MRL) models now available;
- ❖ incorporates counterbalance weight;
- ❖ high efficiency; and
- ❖ high speed available.

Types

- ❖ Single speed AC motor: up to 0.5m/sec jolt stop;
- ❖ dual speed AC motor: up to 1.0m/sec, more accurate levelling;
- ❖ geared variable voltage (VVAC and VVVF): smoother ride and greater speed (VVAC and VVVF); and
- ❖ gearless variable voltages above 2.0m/sec, very quiet, long travel.

Hydraulic

- ❖ Higher starting current, but not significant as compared to electric traction lifts;
- ❖ maximum travel 20m;
- ❖ less efficient, higher energy consumption;
- ❖ no counterbalance;
- ❖ limited starts per hour;
- ❖ motor and pump house can be remote from shaft (up to 10m from lift pit), ventilation important for cooling; and
- ❖ lower speed, up to 1.0m/sec.

Types

- ❖ Direct acting: ram and bore hole below car;
- ❖ side acting: usually 'fork lift' action ram and cylinder within shaft; and
- ❖ indirect: combined ram and ropes, ram raises and lowers pulley.

Control systems

Automatic push button

- ❖ Responds to first push – no calls stored; preference given to car button calls – flats and small offices.

Down collective

- ❖ Answers landing calls in down direction only – mainly used for flats.

Full collective

- ❖ Calls stored and answered in sequence in both up and down direction.

Destination despatch

- ❖ Requires passengers to enter their destination at the landing – can improve overall journey time.

Door arrangement

Manually operated

Power operated

- ❖ Single sliding: cheapest – larger shaft size required;
- ❖ two speed side opening: expensive – minimum shaft size; and
- ❖ centre opening: quickest to full opening position.

Safety provisions

- ❖ Retractable door safety edge – operating micro-switch;
- ❖ pressure sensitive doors – operating micro switch on door operating mechanism;
- ❖ electronic proximity detectors – detects presence of obstruction; and
- ❖ light ray or sonar.

For further information refer to BS EN 81 Parts 1 and 2.

Lighting design

Categories of lighting, their respective lux levels, and the areas for which they are typically suitable are identified in the following table.

Category	Lux	Typical areas
Casual	100–150	Storage areas, plant rooms, lifts, circulation areas, bathrooms
Casual rough work	200–300	Dining areas, lounging rooms, bars, sports halls, libraries, rough machining
Routine work	300–500	General office, retail areas, lecture rooms, laboratories, kitchens, medium machining, supermarkets
Demanding work	750	Drawing offices, inspection of medium machining
Detailed work	1,000	Colour discrimination, fine machining and assembly, inspection rooms
Very fine work	1,500–3,000	Hand engraving, precision works, inspection of fine works

Lighting design should generally comply with the recommendations as laid down in the CIBSE/SLL *Code for Lighting*.

Lighting in offices should comply with the requirements of CIBSE/SLL Lighting Guide LG7. The purpose of LG7 is to promote the overall visual environment (i.e. surface reflections, direct daylight, etc.) and its effect on display screens and their users. Emphasis is also placed on designing schemes that avoid very high luminance patches in a space and abrupt changes in luminance across a surface or between adjacent surfaces.

Data installations

Data installations and information technology require extensive cabling which, in turn, demands adequate access through the building. Therefore, it is important to consider access via risers, suspended floors or floor trunking in order to present the user with these services.

A raised floor is normally a basic pre-requisite to enable full flexibility of outlet positions. Minimum clear void typically 100–150mm depending upon floor plate size and riser arrangement.

Modern buildings are now usually block wired for voice and data using common telephone/data jack outlets.

Definitions

MER: Main equipment room – Typically houses: main servers, switches, patching frames, UPS equipment.

SER: Satellite or secondary equipment room – Typically houses: switching, patching frames.

Field wiring types:

❖ Backbone – typically fibre cabling – used to interconnect MERs to SERs.

❖ UTP – unshielded twisted pair – commonly used where low risk of electromagnetic interference.

❖ STP – shielded twisted pair – used where medium risk of electromagnetic interference.

❖ FSTP – fully shielded twisted pair – used where high risk of electromagnetic interference.

Cabling categories (to EIA/TIA 568 Standards):

❖ Cat-5e – up to 100 MHz bandwidth

❖ Cat-6 – up to 250 MHz bandwidth

❖ Cat-7 – up to 600 MHz bandwidth.

Field cable lengths are generally limited to 90m + 10m patch cords. Fibre cables are used for greater transmission distances.

Wireless LAN (to IEEE 802.11) utilising Wi-Fi technology:

❖ 802.11a – up to 20 Mbit/s raw data rate (line of sight only)

❖ 802.11b – up to 11 Mbit/s raw data rate

❖ 802.11g – up to 54 Mbit/s raw data rate

❖ 802.11n – latest standard under development.

Range typically restricted to tens of metres. Repeaters or access points are required to extend coverage. Can have data security issues.

Geomatics

243

Geomatics

What is meant by the term Geomatics?

Geomatics is an umbrella term covering all the activities undertaken by land surveyors, e.g. land surveying, photogrammetry, measured building surveys, engineering surveys, utility mapping, laser scanning, etc. The word geomatics was first adopted by universities and is now increasingly used to describe the activities of commercial companies. It is now used by the RICS to describe the relevant Faculty but, interestingly, members must use the description 'Chartered Land Surveyor'.

What are the essential techniques of producing measured survey information?

Any measured survey **must** incorporate distances and angles. Familiarity with trigonometry is a must, use of which will enable most angles and distances to be calculated, if not possible to measure directly. All distances must be related to the 'horizontal' plane for presentation purposes. Corrections to slope distances are applied.

The 'dumpy' level, more commonly referred to as a 'level' or 'spirit level', enables a precise 'horizontal' line to be viewed and transferred around a site using a 'level staff' or graduated pole. This is still the most precise method of establishing ground or floor levels. But it is also the most common source of errors; therefore level loops **must** be started and closed onto points of known height.

Theodolites are instruments for measuring horizontal and vertical angles, now usually incorporating laser electronic distance measuring (EDM) devices and an 'on board' computer. This enables on site computation of co-ordinates, distances or angles. It is important to ensure that regular calibration takes place and to purchase or hire from an agent who can advise on its use.

Lasers can range from hand-held 'disto' instruments to state-of-the-art laser/lidar scanners. The hand-held devices are a quick and potentially accurate way of obtaining discrete measurements. Be sure to keep the laser horizontal.

Lidar scanners, which can capture up to 60,000 3D points a second, are expensive and their use is complex so experts in this field should be consulted.

Basic measurement principles for the surveyor

- ❖ You can never take too many measurements.
- ❖ Checks are essential.
- ❖ If in doubt, measure twice.
- ❖ Ensure measurements are taken horizontally – use a builder's spirit level if necessary.
- ❖ The old survey principle still applies, start from the 'whole to the part', i.e. take the long critical distance first, add detail later.
- ❖ Never 'assume' corners are 90° or walls are vertical.
- ❖ Always check inherited data.

How has GPS helped?

The benefits of GPS are enormous, however, the technology must be understood and it is important to recognise that a digital display of co-ordinates is not an indication of accuracy. With some of the most sophisticated equipment, methods and post processing, you can achieve accuracy in plan position to a few centimetres (with 'height' a little less accurate).

Many factors come into play, including the length of time an instrument observes orbiting satellites at a static point and the extent of the field of view to the horizon.

Hand-held GPS instruments will give accuracy to metres and are fine if 'fit for purpose'.

What information does the surveyor need to know to produce a quotation for a measured survey?

- ❖ details of project, site location, extent and condition;
- ❖ reasons for the survey;
- ❖ what accuracy is needed;
- ❖ health and safety/risk factors;
- ❖ desired completion date;
- ❖ what the data will be used for;
- ❖ what the deliverables are;
- ❖ who will pay for the survey;
- ❖ access details;
- ❖ CAD details;
- ❖ what features need measuring;
- ❖ what underground utilities are required;
- ❖ whether or not permanent survey markers need to be established; and
- ❖ who else is likely to be using the survey.

Further information

RICS – see www.rics.org

TSA – see www.tsa-uk.org.uk

English Heritage – see www.english-heritage.org.uk

Flooding

Design

Flooding and its impact on property

Around five million people in two million properties live in flood risk areas in England and Wales and these figures are set to rise. The government's Foresight Future Flooding report, released in April 2004 by the Department of Trade and Industry (DTI) is the most wide-ranging analysis of flood risk carried out to date in the UK. The report predicts that climate change will be an important factor in increasing flood risk, and that both the number of people in danger from flooding and the costs of damage from floods will rise significantly. It uses scenarios of potential social and economic change, as well as information on climate change, to identify future risks and to inform both public and government bodies about what will need to be done to mitigate these risks.

The report concludes that:

- ❖ the amount of carbon we burn must be reduced in order to help slow down the rate of climate change;
- ❖ more must be spent on flood and coastal defences to protect against the impacts of climate change;
- ❖ tougher restrictions are needed on building on flood plains; and
- ❖ new developments must be resilient to flooding.

Who is responsible?

Defra has overall policy responsibility for flood and coastal erosion risk in England and the Environment Agency has statutory responsibility for flood management and defence. The Environment Agency, Internal Drainage Boards and local authorities are responsible for maintaining, operating and improving flood defences. Defra funds most of the Environment Agency's flood management activities in England, it does not build defences, nor direct the authorities on which specific projects to undertake. The works programme to manage risk is driven by the operating authorities.

Since 1 April 2006, Defra's Flood Management Division has been reorganised into a programme-led structure. In future, the Environment Agency is expected to take on responsibility for operating the national capital investment prioritisation system across all operating authorities, approving the various authorities' capital improvement projects and distributing grants to them.

Managing the risk

One of the main goals of the Environment Agency, through its Flood Defence Committee, is to reduce flood risk. Defra's 2004 national assessment of defence needs and costs report estimated the capital value of assets at risk from flooding to be approximately £250 billion at 2004 prices. Average annual damages from flooding were estimated at some £1 billion per year and may be £3 billion in 2007. Average damages that would occur if nothing were done to manage the risk were estimated at more than £3 billion per year. The British Government now spends more than £300 million each year on flood defences: since 2000, 70km of defences have been built, reducing flood risk to more than 25,000 people. And around 80 new flood defences were approved in the two years to 2006.

The government now believes that the most effective way to reduce flood risk is to adopt a portfolio of measures tailored to conditions in each location. These measures include the way in which land is used, what flood defences are built and the way in which flood warnings are given.

This is being achieved by:

- ❖ ensuring more residents in flood risk areas know they are at risk and are aware of the action they need to take to protect themselves;

- ❖ improving the coverage of flood warning services to reduce the number of properties exposed to a high risk of flooding;
- ❖ planning flood defences based on how a whole area is affected, rather than individual locations; and
- ❖ preventing all inappropriate development inside flood plains.

Longer term, as set out in *Making space for water*, published by Defra in July 2004, the government will continue to implement 'a more holistic approach' to managing flood and coastal erosion risks in England. Its stated aim is 'to manage risks by employing an integrated portfolio of approaches which reflect both national and local priorities so as to reduce the threat to people and their property and deliver the greatest environmental, social and economic benefit consistent with the government's sustainable development principles'.

The quotes above are Crown copyright and are reproduced from the report *Making space for water*, published by Defra.

Forecasting floods

According to the Meteorological Office, the ability to accurately forecast floods depends on the nature of the events which trigger them. Short periods of intense rainfall can cause flash flooding; longer periods of widespread heavy rain can cause rivers to overflow and storm surges can cause coastal flooding. The severity and extent of flooding depends to a large degree on the state of the underlying ground – if the soil moisture content is already high, flooding occurs much more quickly because surface water cannot soak away.

The Met Office is currently addressing this issue by developing tools and services to help combat the problem, including working closely with the Environment Agency and other experts in hydrology, and development of the National Severe Weather Warning Service (NSWWS). Using a wide range of technologies, it provides local authorities and the public with warnings of potentially dangerous weather events. In addition, a high-resolution rainfall forecasting and warning system, which has been developed in partnership with the Environment Agency, uses radar, satellite and Met Office numerical weather prediction model data to forecast rainfall rate and accumulation over England and Wales.

Rising groundwater

During the latter part of the 20th century, the level of groundwater beneath major UK cities rose rapidly, leading to increasing concern that huge costs could be incurred from damage to buildings and infrastructure if preventative measures are not taken. The problem stems from the city-centre industries that populated the areas during the industrial revolution and their demand for water. Beneath London this led to a reduction in the level of up to 90m. The usage has declined significantly since the late 1960s as the industries relocated and without this extraction levels have recovered, rising by 1.5m a year initially and by as much as 3m a year recently. By the late 1990s, water levels in central London had recovered by 35m, close to the 1900 level.

It was therefore realised that action to minimise the damage was needed urgently to allow time for planning and implementation. A group was formed from interested parties and in March 1999 it announced that a five-stage plan had been developed to safeguard London from the effects of rising groundwater. The plan involved controlled increased abstraction from 50 or more existing and new boreholes, with the amount that could be used for drinking water maximised and the remainder to be used for industrial or agricultural processes. The five phases of the strategy are:

- ❖ Utilise four existing licensed water supply boreholes on the outskirts of London.

❖ Equip three proven borehole sites near central London with the latest filtration technology to provide further water for drinking purposes.

❖ Encourage the use of existing and new private boreholes, in and around central London where the water quality is lower, for non-potable uses.

❖ Identify locations for new control boreholes in central London, initially to be pumped to waste until end uses can be determined.

❖ New control boreholes in outer London to intercept the flow of water towards the central basin.

The plan has the backing of government and is being managed by Thames Water, working in conjunction with the Environment Agency. Although the threat to London is the most immediate, other cities are at risk and it is likely that similar strategies will be implemented as required.

Flood plans

Predicting flooding is only the first part of the equation. When flooding occurs, by managing excess water as effectively as possible, the Environment Agency aims to save money, spare the environment as much as possible from catastrophic and often extremely damaging events, and keep greater numbers of people safe. Catchment Flood Management Plans (CFMPs) and Shoreline Management Plans (SMPs) have a key role to play in this strategy.

Instead of simply building flood defences, CFMPs look at land use across a larger area – or 'catchment' – seeing if the water can be moved to where it will do least harm to people and the environment. A catchment is an area that serves a river with rainwater and every part of land where the rainfall drains to a single river is in the same catchment. For this reason, hills and high ground are often the boundaries between catchments – rain falling on one side of the hill drains to one river; rain falling on the other side drains to another river.

The main aims of Catchment Flood Management Plans are to:

❖ understand the factors that contribute to flood risk within a catchment, such as how the land is used; and

❖ recommend the best ways of managing that risk during the next 50 to 100 years.

All land use changes will be decided in full consultation with those affected, such as local authorities that have responsibility for planning permission, land owners and conservation and marine organisations. It is anticipated that the majority of CFMPs will be written and ready for consultation by 2008.

Planning to avoid flooding

Planning has a vital role to play in flood risk management. The department for Communities and Local Government (CLG), formerly the ODPM, is responsible for the planning system, which aims to prevent inappropriate new developments in flood risk areas, and to direct development away from areas at highest risk.

The CLG estimates that around 10% of the total land in England lies within areas of flood risk, including large areas of Eastern England and much of London, Hull and York. The government is committed to continuing development in these areas and so in order to manage flood risk so that new development is safe and sustainable, former planning guidance detailed in PPG25 was superseded in December 2006 by a new Planning Policy Statement: PPS25.

This new planning policy statement aims to:

- ❖ ensure flood risk is taken into account at all stages in the planning process;
- ❖ avoid inappropriate development in areas at risk of flooding; and
- ❖ direct development away from high risk areas.

It will:

- ❖ focus on core policies that are clearer and easier to understand;
- ❖ provide a more strategic approach, emphasising the need to consider flood risk as early as possible in the planning process;
- ❖ clarify the sequential test that matches types of development to degrees of flood risk; and
- ❖ strengthen guidance on the need to include Flood Risk Assessments at all levels of the planning process.

Flood risk assessments

It is vital that checks are carried out at an early stage of all new developments to determine whether or not they are located in areas that fall within the Environment Agency's flood plain map. This map does not, however, take into account any mitigating effects of planned or existing flood defences or site specific features and therefore it is important to carry out a site specific flood risk assessment (FRA) at an early stage on those projects considered to be at risk.

A flood risk assessment (FRA) must include:

- ❖ the location of the development or redevelopment, showing streets, water courses, etc. with property clearly marked;
- ❖ site plan showing existing and future floor levels;
- ❖ cross section of the site showing floor levels and river banks;
- ❖ details of proposed Flood Alleviation Measures;
- ❖ sources of possible flooding;
- ❖ existing information on flooding;
- ❖ assessment of the probability of flooding and the expected impact of climate change;
- ❖ assessment of rate and duration of flooding;
- ❖ assessment of the likely rate and speed with which flooding might occur;
- ❖ assessment of the potential impact of any development on fluvial morphology (ground movement as a result of the action of water);
- ❖ assessment of the need for preventative measures, such as internal flood barriers, raising of threshold levels, flood attenuation using SUDS (sustainable urban drainage);
- ❖ assessment of the impact of the development on drainage, i.e. will there be increased run-off and if so, how this could be remedied; and
- ❖ assessment of escape routes and evacuation procedures.

Protecting property from floods

Research carried out by the Environment Agency in 2006 states that '2.3 million of 25 million homes in England and Wales were in flood risk areas, with property, land and assets worth £237 billion in danger of ending up under water'. Many of those homeowners and businesses most at risk in England and Wales are still denying that flooding could happen to them. Environment Agency research shows that, while 95% of people at risk agree flooding is a serious issue, less than half believe that it relates to them. And only one person in 20 takes any advance action to prepare for floods. The Agency thinks this could be due not only to apathy but also to public fears that acknowledging the risks and taking steps to protect against flooding could in some way have a negative effect on property values.

Although it is not possible to avoid floods occurring, there are a number of ways in which property owners can help safeguard their property from water damage. Sand bags have now largely been replaced by a range of more sophisticated flood protection products, such as flood boards and air brick covers. The Environment Agency in conjunction with CIRIA has published a leaflet outlining some of the many products on offer and giving advice on protecting premises against flooding. *Flood Product Advice Guide – using flood protection products* helps homeowners assess the risk to their property from flooding and understand the routes of flood water entry. It also introduces the range of flood protection products available, the level of protection that can be expected and other measures that can be applied to reduce the entry of flood water. Both organisations are also supporting the British Standards Institution's new Kitemark scheme for flood protection products.

In addition to using specialist flood protection products, property owners living in high risk areas should take the following precautions if flooding is likely:

❖ Check that all buildings insurance policies include cover for flood damage and inform insurers as soon as possible after the event so that a claim can be made immediately.

❖ Protect people, data and equipment – make sure that records and other business information are archived and stored off the premises.

❖ Businesses could consider investing in a generator to maintain emergency power supplies.

❖ Move valuable items away from lower floors where possible.

After a flood:

❖ Open doors and windows to ventilate the building.

❖ Don't heat the building to more than 4 degrees centigrade until all the water is removed and expose as much damp timber as possible to accelerate the drying out process.

❖ Don't forget about security. Burglar alarms may not be working if the electricity supply has been affected by the high water level: if necessary cover open or broken windows with security mesh.

❖ Never attempt to move back into a property that still contains standing water: it is a potential health hazard and should be pumped or baled out. Open up all the floor voids to check there is no water there.

Effects of flood water on building materials

Flood water can penetrate buildings rapidly, causing widespread damage to floors, walls, and finishes, with structural damage in more severe cases. The vulnerability of individual properties is dependent on building materials and construction methods.

Brickwork

Brickwork will inevitably allow some moisture penetration, so it is unlikely to remain waterproof if exposed to flood water for long periods. Generally, brickwork should be largely unaffected by flood water if it is allowed to properly dry out. However, as walls are wetter after a flood, there is a greater risk than normal that they will deteriorate from frost damage and may spall, flake or crack. The chemical action of salts in some flood water can also affect brickwork, particularly in older buildings, compromising the damp-proof course. This can cause long-term damp problems.

Walls are best dried by evaporation from the outer surface. The drying out process may take some time if the brickwork has been saturated. As a guide, the RICS recommends one month for every inch of wall thickness to dry out completely (see www.rics.org/Services/Usefulguides/Consumer guides/flood damage.htm).

If the brickwork fails to dry, then samples of the brickwork should be tested for moisture content. This will indicate if there is a rising damp problem, and if specialist advice is required.

Concrete

Depending on its quality, concrete can sometimes absorb large amounts of water and take a long time to dry out. This can cause ongoing problems such as chemical reactions and fungal growths, which can affect both the structure and contents until it is completely dry.

The construction of concrete floors may influence the length of drying time required. If the damp-proof membrane (dpm) is between the slab and the screed, generally there will be less damage than if it is located beneath the slab – because of relative drying times.

Where concrete floors are finished with timber-based flooring on battens, water retained under the flooring, or in any insulation, will not dry efficiently. In this situation, the insulation and battens must be removed and replaced.

If there is a high chloride content in the flood water, reinforced concrete could become contaminated allowing reinforcement bars to corrode.

Timber

Decay of timber is unlikely if the timber dries out within a few weeks, but the longer it remains wet, the greater the risk of swelling, distortion or decay. This can result in loss of strength and cohesion potential, and, in extreme cases, structural failure.

In timber-framed buildings, members that are immersed in water for prolonged periods could cause damage in other parts of the structure, for example, through stresses on external cladding.

Timber exposed in a well-ventilated space can dry to an acceptable moisture content of <20% in three weeks, although the bottom members may take longer. Concealed areas should be inspected for lingering moisture. Timber held at a moisture content of 20% and more is at risk of fungal decay.

Reducing moisture content will kill off rot, but if growth is rapid, replace any timber that shows signs of rot, and treat adjacent timber to reduce the risk of further damage.

Metals

Metals exposed to flood water will dry quickly, and a one-off flood event may not have any significant effect. Prolonged exposure can result in rusting. Powder-coated metal finishes are robust, and are unlikely to suffer long-term damage.

Render (external)

Undamaged renders containing cement are unlikely to suffer long-term damage, although they may be hard to clean and will be at risk from frost damage for several weeks.

Any significant damage (including cracking, spalled areas or hollowness) to an existing render finish should be repaired. The damaged render should be removed by hacking off to the masonry background. A consistent appearance between the original and repaired areas can be achieved by using a masonry paint finish.

Plaster and plasterboard

Gypsum plaster can be damaged in floods of significant duration, although very short-term duration floods are unlikely to cause significant damage. However, instances such as surface wetting, which may dry out relatively quickly, could still develop water stains or mould requiring remedial treatment/action at a later stage of the project.

If the flood stands for longer periods, gypsum-containing materials and components will absorb large quantities of water and begin to distort.

It is normal practice for gypsum plaster to be removed from the wall face after flood water has subsided to a level just above the flood tidemark.

Gypsum board that is exposed or in contact with water for longer than two hours will require replacement. This is necessary not only to remove the waterlogged and damaged gypsum board, but to open up the walls and expose the cavities of the walls so that the insides of the walls and the wood studs within can dry out. Delamination of the board can occur and damaged gypsum board may exhibit powder and mildew, causing unpleasant odours and an unacceptable base for paint if it is not removed. Furthermore, the risk of toxic moulds cannot be discounted.

Finishes

Internal decorations (e.g. wallpaper, paint, wall tiles) and floor coverings (e.g. linoleum and vinyl sheeting) may become debonded by wetting, as they will hold water and delay drying. The drying process can be speeded up by removing such coverings.

Gloss paint is fairly robust, however, it may bubble off and suffer from peeling after prolonged exposure to water.

Wash down and remove loose and flaking finishes. Remember also that moisture may be trapped beneath certain impervious finishes.

The drying of low permeability wall coverings such as vinyl wallpaper, gloss paint and tiling will slow down the drying of masonry, and could cause timber studs to rot.

The drying process can be speeded up if such coverings are removed from at least one side of the external walls.

Mould, blistering and peeling may occur if surfaces are painted or papered too soon. Once the repairs have finished, painted or papered should be left for at least three months to ensure the surface does not blister, mould or peel. Oil-based or stain block paint should be used before final painting to help stop emulsion staining from occurring.

The use of high permeability lime-based paints rather than oil-based paints or emulsion can allow walls to dry out more quickly following flooding.

Further information

❖ *Design Guidance on Flood Damage to Dwellings*, The Scottish Office, 1996

❖ *Improving the flood resistance of your home*, Series of 8 advice sheets, CIRIA, 2003, available at: www.ciria.org/flooding

❖ *Planning and Building Standards Advice on Flooding*, Planning Advice Note PAN 69, 2004, Scottish Government Publications

❖ *Preparing for floods: interim guidance for improving the flood resistance of domestic and small business properties* (2003 reprint with amendments), ODPM, 2003: see www.communities.gov.uk/publications/corporate/protectyourhome

❖ *Repairing flood damage*, BRE Good Repair Guide 11 (series of 4 booklets), BRE, 1997

❖ *Repairing flooded buildings – An industry guide to investigation and repair*, Flood repairs forum, BRE, 2006

- ❖ Garvin, S., Reid, J., Scott, M., *Standards for the repair of buildings following flooding*, C623, CIRIA, 2005
- ❖ www.ciria.org/flooding
- ❖ www.theconstructioncentre.co.uk/flood-advice

Help and support for flood victims

The National Flood Forum is a community-based network set up by people who have been through the experience of flooding and suffered the distress, losses and frustration that follow. The forum was established in 2002 to give communities and individuals who have been flooded or are at risk the support, knowledge and help they need to organise themselves, to manage the effects of flooding, to promote self-help and to campaign for flood alleviation.

The forum works closely with The Environment Agency, water companies, local authorities, the government, flood protection companies and the insurance industry.

It can provide information on all types of flooding, from main rivers, local watercourses, sewers, storm water and highway drains, tidal and coastal flooding, groundwater, to run-off from urban areas or agricultural land. The forum also offers free advice to individuals or groups on where to source flood protection products, specialist help or advice on insurance issues.

The surveyor's role in flooding

Construction professionals have an important role to play in advising clients about the impact of flooding. This applies both to those providing advice on proposed developments and those inspecting and reporting on existing buildings that may have suffered flood damage. However, according to recent research carried out for the Royal Institution of Chartered Surveyors (RICS), despite 'areas of good practice and pockets of experience in dealing with flooding and reinstatements … information remains uncoordinated and somewhat overgeneralised. There is little in the way of agreed professional procedures for dealing with flood risk and flood damage'. In response, RICS is developing guidance for chartered surveyors with the aim of enabling them to take a more active role in this area of work.

There is, however, already some useful guidance on renovation procedures published by other construction industry bodies. *Repairing Flood Damage*, BRE Good Repair Guide 11, offers guidance. The previous BRE publications, BRE Digest 152: *Repair and renovation of flood damaged buildings* and the BRE Guide: *Dealing with flood damage*, have now been withdrawn. Guidance includes:

- ❖ draining;
- ❖ cleaning – mud above damp-proof courses, under-floor spaces and cavity walls;
- ❖ drying – brickwork and plaster, masonry and timber;
- ❖ effect of water on materials – brick, stone and concrete, wall finishes, timber, floor finishes and metals;
- ❖ structural damage – foundations, walls, floors and roofs, paths, driveways and drains;
- ❖ renovation of interiors – walls and timbers;
- ❖ electrical installations – connections, ducts, cables and conduits, tests and future arrangements; and
- ❖ seawater flooding.

A new guide produced by the BRE's Flood Repairs Forum may also be useful. Titled *Repairing flooded buildings: an insurance industry guide to investigation and repair of flood damage to housing and small businesses,* it is available from the BRE bookshop.

CIRIA has produced a series of online advice sheets giving detailed technical information on assessing and inspecting properties and techniques for improving the flood resilience of a property. The advice sheets are designed to help home owners carry out any necessary work, but may also prove useful to surveyors and other construction professionals involved in repairs and refurbishment needed as a result of flooding. The advice sheets look at:

- ❖ identifying flood risk;
- ❖ how flood water enters a house above ground;
- ❖ how flood water enters a house below ground;
- ❖ flood-resilient walls;
- ❖ flood-resilient windows and doors;
- ❖ flood-resilient floors;
- ❖ flood-resilient services; and
- ❖ flood-resilient sewers and drains.

Another CIRIA publication, *Standards for the repair of buildings following flooding,* published in 2005, describes the causes of flooding and the impact it can have on buildings, gives advice on what to do in the immediate aftermath of flooding, sets out how to conduct post-flood surveys and future flood risk assessment and offers standards for repairing buildings that have been affected by flooding to improve their flood resistance. The guide is aimed primarily at building professionals and insurers experienced in flood damage and repair. However, it could also be used by general builders, surveyors and building owners needing advice when commissioning repair work.

Compensation for flooding

It has been the policy of successive governments that individuals should not be compensated for any flood loss except in exceptional circumstances. The thinking behind this is that, as flooding is generally an insurable risk, government compensation for flood losses would disrupt this private insurance market.

However, local authorities can apply for compensation under the Bellwin Scheme of Emergency Financial Assistance to Local Authorities. A Bellwin scheme can be brought into effect in any case where an emergency or disaster involving destruction of, or danger to, life or property occurs and, as a result, one or more local authorities incur expenditure in connection with the taking of immediate action to safeguard life or property in their area. It appears the scheme is designed to help local authorities and other government agencies with emergency repairs only, 'longer' term works of repair and restoration are not covered. The scheme does not provide financial assistance to individuals. There is no automatic entitlement to financial assistance and the government has discretion to decide whether or not to activate a scheme after considering the circumstances of individual cases.

The onus is therefore on individual home and business owners to ensure that, if their property is in an area susceptible to flooding, they have adequate insurance in place to cover the risk. Between October and November 2000, claims for flood and storm damage due to extreme weather conditions cost the insurance industry more than £750 million in total. However, despite the enormous cost to insurers, the Association of British Insurers (ABI) stresses that its members are committed to ensuring that flood insurance remains as widely available as possible. ABI members tend to deal with flooding risks as follows:

- ❖ for existing customers in higher risk flood areas, premiums may be higher or the customer may be asked to pay a higher excess to reflect the increased frequency of flood claims;

- ❖ for new customers in high risk areas, all cases are considered on an individual basis; and
- ❖ in exceptional cases, where flooding has occurred frequently and where no flood defences are planned 'within a reasonable timescale', flood cover may be withdrawn completely.

Further information

www.defra.gov.uk
www.environment-agency.gov.uk
www.abi.org.uk
www.norwichunion.com
www.devon.gov.uk
www.ciria.org.uk
www.communities.gov.uk
www.floodforum.org.uk
www.rics.org

Materials

Materials and defects

259

Deleterious materials

The presence of deleterious materials in a building may affect its market value and could, in severe cases, result in element failure or affect the health of persons working or living there.

The reaction of investing institutions to these materials depends on a number of factors and often the presence of a deleterious substance will not prevent a purchase. However, great care must be taken to assess the actual risks or consequences involved, so that a value judgement can be made.

Over the years a variety of building materials have been shown to perform in ways that are hazardous to people or, in the alternative, ways that were not anticipated. The property industry has, often unfairly, tagged these materials as deleterious – a concept that can be shown to be flawed in many cases. Without doubt, materials such as asbestos and lead can be hazardous, but other materials, when used in accordance with their known working parameters can perform perfectly well.

Materials hazardous to health

The more common hazardous materials, and associated risks, are identified in the following table.

Materials	Common use	Use risk
Lead	When used in water pipes and lead paint (lead roofing materials pose little or no risk).	Risk of contamination of drinking water in lead pipes, or from lead solder used in plumbing joints. Risk of inhalation of lead dust during maintenance of lead based paint. Risk to children of chewing lead painted surfaces (Pica). Concentration of lead in paint now generally much reduced. Beware of lead content in brass fittings.
Urea Formaldehyde foam	Cavity wall insulation. Some insulation boards but rare in UK.	There is some evidence that UF foam may be a carcinogenic material although this is not proven. Vapour can cause irritation. Poorly installed insulation can lead to passage of water from outer leaf of brick to inner leaf in cavity wall situation. There are some worries over formaldehyde used as an adhesive in medium density fibreboard and chipboard but this is likely to be a problem only in unventilated areas with large amounts of boarding.
Asbestos See also page 262	Commercial and residential buildings as boarding, sheet cladding, insulation and other uses particularly in the 1950s, 1960s and 1970s.	Airborne asbestos fibres may be inhaled and eventually lead to either asbestosis, lung cancer or mesothemelioma.

Materials damaging to buildings

Those materials which may affect building performance or structure are identified in the following table.

Materials	Common use	Use risk
Calcium silicate brickwork	Used in lieu of concrete or clay bricks, often as an inner leaf in cavity work. Often cited as deleterious but if used correctly will perform well.	Calcium silicate brickwork shrinks after construction with further movement due to wetting. Construction must provide measures of control to distribute cracking. Concrete bricks may display a similar propensity to shrinkage and again care must be taken in the design of movement joints, etc.
Calcium chloride concrete additive	Commonly used in in-situ concrete as an accelerator and often added in flake form. Often found in buildings constructed before 1977. (May also be present from atmospheric or traffic exposure).	Reduces passivity of concrete in damp conditions. Subsequent risk of corrosion of steel reinforcement.
High Alumina Cement (HAC) Further details on page 271	Mainly used in the manufacture of pre-cast X or I roof or floor beams together with some lintels, sill members, etc. between 1954 and 1974. HAC was first produced commercially in the UK in 1925.	Strength of concrete can decrease significantly often when high temperatures and/or high humidity is involved. Defects may be due to faulty manufacture.
Sea dredged aggregate	In-situ concrete or precast concrete.	May contain salts such as sodium chloride. If salts not properly washed out, risk of corrosion reinforcement. Provided the aggregates are properly washed and controlled in accordance with British Standard requirements the indications are that there are no greater risks involved than with the use of aggregates from inland sources. Risk of inclusion of reactive aggregates that could contribute to ASR, although this is unlikely with most UK-sourced aggregates.

Materials	Common use	Use risk
Mundic blocks and Mundic concrete	Concrete blocks and concrete manufactured from quarry shale commonly found in the West Country.	Loss of integrity in damp conditions. Further research required to identify level of risk across the country.
Woodwool slabs (also woodcrete and chipcrete)	Often used as (a) decking to flat roofs, or (b) as permanent shuttering.	Use in (a) may be considered acceptable providing material is kept dry. Use in (b) as a permanent shutter may result in grout loss (honeycombing) or voidage of concrete near to or surrounding reinforcement, particularly with ribbed floors. May result in reduced fire resistance, reinforcement corrosion or in extreme cases loss of structural strength. May be repaired by application of sprayed concrete. Condition investigated by cut-out removal of woodwool in many locations.
Brick slips	Typically 1970s and 1980s to conceal flow nibs in cavity walls.	Risk of poor adhesion, lack of soft joints can transfer load to slips and cause delamination.

For a fuller description refer to *Investigating Hazardous and Deleterious Building Materials*, Rushton, T., RICS Books, 2006 (see page 402).

Asbestos

Asbestos is the generic term for several mineral silicates occurring naturally in fibrous form. Because of its various useful properties (resistance to heat, acids and alkalis, and good thermal, electrical or acoustic insulator) it has been extensively used in the construction industry.

Three main types in the UK are Chrysotile (white), Amosite (brown) and Crocidolite (blue). It is used in a variety of forms varying from boards or corrugated sheets to loose coatings or laggings and, generally, the more friable the material, the greater the asbestos content.

Health risk

Inhalation of its microscopic fibres can constitute a serious health risk and is associated with several terminal diseases.

Not all asbestos, irrespective of its circumstances, constitutes an immediate risk, although the effects of possible future disturbance or deterioration must be considered. Factors to be taken into account are the type, form, friability, condition and location of the source material.

The (1987) Joint Central and Local Government Working Party on Asbestos concluded that 'Asbestos materials which are in good condition and not releasing dust should not be disturbed ... Materials that are damaged, deteriorating, releasing dust or which are likely to do so should be sealed, enclosed or removed as appropriate. Materials which are left in place should be managed and their condition periodically reassessed. The risk to the health of the public from asbestos materials which are in sound condition and which are undisturbed is very low indeed. Substitute materials should be used where possible, provided they perform adequately'.

The HSE actively discourages the unnecessary removal of sound asbestos materials and each case should be decided on its own merits following an assessment of the risks arising.

In the past the people most at risk have been workers in the asbestos industry involved in the importation, storage, manufacture and installation of materials or components containing this material.

These activities are now banned in the UK and the removal, treatment or intentional working with asbestos is strictly controlled and generally limited to specialists. The risk however continues for anyone who inadvertently disturbs the asbestos in the course of their routine business, including builders, maintenance workers, electricians and the like, and the most recent legislation is intended for their protection.

Legislation

The enabling act for asbestos legislation is the *Health and Safety at Work etc. Act* 1974 and failure to comply with its requirements is a criminal offence.

The principal Regulations that apply to works that could expose persons to the risk of respirable asbestos fibres are the *Control of Asbestos Regulations* 2006 (CAR 2006) which came into operation on 13 November 2006 and implement the 2003/18/EC amendment to the European *Asbestos Worker Protective Directive* 83/477/EEC.

These supersede the *Control of Asbestos at Work Regulations* 2002 (CAWR), the *Asbestos (Licensing) Regulations* 1983 (as amended) and the *Asbestos (Prohibition) Regulations* 1992.

In addition the HSE has produced various Approved Codes of Practice and Guidance:

   ❖   L143, *Work with materials containing asbestos, Control of Asbestos Regulations* 2006 (ISBN 0 7176 6206 3); and

   ❖   L127, *The management of asbestos in non-domestic premises*, Regulation 4 of the *Control of Asbestos Regulations* 2006 (ISBN 0 7176 6209 8).

In addition to legislation specifically focussed on asbestos, more general health and safety legislation that may also need to be taken into account includes:

   ❖   the *Management of Health and Safety at Work Regulations* 1999; and

   ❖   the *Construction (Design and Management) Regulations* 2007.

CAR 2006 has introduced fundamental changes to the previous legislation and these are set out below:

   ❖   The concept of 'action levels' is abandoned and a **single** 'control limit' is applicable to **all** types of asbestos.

   ❖   The applicability of specific regulations and methods of control are based on risk assessment, using the hierarchy of risk assessment of COSHH.

   ❖   In principle, CAR 2006 changes the concept of previous legislation by applying all of its many and varied regulatory requirements to **any** work involving **any** form of asbestos, subject to only a few limited and specific exceptions on a risk-based assessment basis.

These are known as the regulation 3(2) exceptions and in such cases the regulatory requirements relating to licensing, notification, arrangements to deal with accidents, incidents and emergencies, designation of asbestos areas and of health records and medical surveillance do **not** apply.

Control limit

This is a specific level of concentration of asbestos in the atmosphere, measured in accordance with the World Heath Organisation (WHO) recommended method, or approved equivalent. It is the trigger point for the application of specific regulations and/or controls. If the risk assessment for the works indicates it is liable to be exceeded, then regulation 18(1)(2) 'Designated areas' requires the establishment of 'respirator zones', where access is restricted to 'competent' persons and suitable respirators must be worn at all times. In addition, if it is **not** liable to be exceeded, then this is one of a number of circumstances set out in regulation 3(2) for which specific regulatory requirements may not necessarily apply.

The current control limit is 0.1 fibres per cubic centimetre of air averaged over a continuous period of four hours. This is more stringent than that contained in the *Control of Asbestos at Work Regulations* 2002, which was 0.3 fibres for White asbestos and 0.2 fibres for any other type or mixture of asbestos.

What are the regulation 3(2) exceptions?

The regulations in the table below do **NOT** apply to the circumstances set out in regulation 3(2) i.e. where:

a) 'the exposure of employees to asbestos is *sporadic and low intensity*;

b) it is clear from the risk assessment that the exposure of any employee to asbestos will not exceed the control limit; and

c) the work involves:

   i) *short, non-continuous maintenance activities*,

   ii) removal of *materials in which the asbestos fibres are firmly linked in a matrix*,

   iii) encapsulation or sealing of asbestos-containing materials which are in good condition, or

   iv) air monitoring and control, and the collection and analysis of samples to ascertain whether a specific material contains asbestos.'

Crown Copyright material is reproduced with the permission of the Controller of HMSO and the Queen's Printer for Scotland.

The phrases in italics are explained in the Approved Code of Practice (ACOP) and guidance accompanying the Regulations and should be referred to for detail.

Number	Title	Details
8	Licensing of work with asbestos	Licensed asbestos contractor
9	Notification of work with asbestos	Informing enforcement authority
15(1)	Accidents, incidents and emergencies	Arrangements in anticipation
18(1)(a)	Asbestos areas	Designated area where employee(s) liable to be exposed to asbestos
22	Health records and medical surveillance	

Generally this means that, subject always to the results of the risk assessment in the specific circumstances, work to asbestos-containing decorative coatings will fall into this exclusion category. Also, subject to the control limit not being likely to be exceeded, the definition of 'sporadic and low intensity' will also apply to:

❖ asbestos cement;

❖ bituminous, plastic, resin or rubber articles where thermal and acoustic properties are only incidental; and

❖ sundry products with no insulation purposes, including paper linings, cardboard, felt, textile, gaskets, washers and ropes;

effectively thus taking these low risk materials outside of the previous licensing requirements and allowing the works to be carried out by competent contractors, but who need not necessarily be licensed by the HSE.

Training

The list of training requirements is also augmented and the accompanying ACOP sets out the detailed requirements.

In addition to the general training requirements for any employee, set out in the *Management at Work Regulations*, regulation 10 of CAR 2006 requires every employer to ensure that adequate information, instruction and training is given to employees who:

❖ are, or are liable to be, exposed to asbestos, and to their supervisors; and

❖ carry out work in connection with the employer's duties under these Regulations so that they can carry out that work effectively.

The ACOP which accompanies CAR 2006 provides a full and detailed list of these training requirements.

There are three main types of information, instruction and training, namely:

Type	For
Awareness training	Those who are liable to be exposed to asbestos while carrying out their normal everyday work, e.g. maintenance staff; electricians; demolition and construction workers; installers of computers, fire or burglar alarms; and **'construction professionals'**.
For non-licensable asbestos work	For example, a roofer removing whole asbestos cement sheet in good condition.
For licensable asbestos work	For example, a contractor removing asbestos lagging or asbestos insulating board.

The topics which the training should cover are listed and should be given in appropriate detail by both written and oral presentation and by demonstration (as necessary). In particular, training is to be in a manner appropriate to the nature and degree of exposure identified by the employer's risk assessment giving the significant findings of the assessment and the results of any air monitoring carried out, together with an explanation of the findings.

The training should be given by a competent person and the procedures for providing the information, instruction and training should be clearly defined and documented and reviewed regularly, particularly when work methods change.

Records should be kept of the training undertaken by each individual. For licensable work copies should be given to each individual.

Refresher training should be given at least **every year** and more frequently if the work methods, equipment used or type of work changes.

Where **non-employees** are on the employer's premises, they should also be given adequate information, instruction and training as far as is reasonably practicable.

Management of asbestos

There is **no change** to the duty to manage asbestos, regulation 4.

Regulation 4 requires the dutyholder(s) to 'manage' asbestos in 'non-domestic premises' and also, for 'every person' to cooperate with the dutyholder so far as is necessary to enable him or her to comply with his or her duties.

Accredited personnel

Regulations 20 and 21 require, respectively, that only persons accredited as complying with ISO 17025 must be employed to measure the concentration of airborne asbestos fibres and analyse a bulk sample of material to determine whether it contains asbestos.

In addition, since 1 April 2007, anyone issuing a clearance certificate for reoccupation following asbestos removal work has been required to meet the relevant accreditation requirements of ISO 17025 and ISO 17020 extended to include all four stages of the clearance and not just the air testing part.

Distinguishing between asbestos insulating board and asbestos cement

Because of the relatively higher potential risks to health arising, working with asbestos insulating board (AIB) is subject to different and more stringent controls than working with asbestos cement.

As the two materials are very similar in physical appearance, depending upon the circumstances, it is necessary to distinguish between them.

The distinction is one of density, the general rule being that the greater the proportion of cementitious matrix to asbestos, the greater the density. Conversely, the more friable the material, the greater the asbestos content.

The ACOP that accompanies CAR 2006 defines asbestos cement as 'a material which is predominantly a mixture of cement and asbestos and which in a dry state absorbs less than 30% water by weight'. The guidance in the document includes a comprehensive description of the testing procedure.

Asbestos insulating board is defined as a flat sheet, tile or building board consisting of a mixture of asbestos and other material except asbestos cement or any article of bitumen, plastic, resin or rubber which contains asbestos, and the thermal or acoustic properties of which are incidental to its main purpose.

It is relatively easy to identify asbestos cement when it is used in preformed components such as corrugated sheeting, tanks or toilet cisterns, but when it is used in flat board form the only sure way of distinguishing the material from AIB is by laboratory analysis.

Where there is doubt, the regulations require that caution be taken, and the material is presumed to be AIB until proven otherwise.

Summary of CAR 2006

Regulation(s)	Title (in italics) plus explanatory notes
1	*Citation and commencement*
2	*Interpretation*
3	*Application of the Regulations* – see 'regulation 3(2) exceptions' on page 264
4	*Duty to manage asbestos in non-domestic premises* – see separate detailed explanation on the next page
5	*Identification of the presence of asbestos*
6	*Assessment of work which exposes employee to asbestos* – prior to the works, assess the likely level of risk, determine the nature and degree of exposure and set out steps to control it
7	*Plans of work* – produce a suitable written plan of the proposed works
8*	*Licensing of work with asbestos* – previously *Asbestos (Licensing) Regulations 1983* (as amended). All work except 'regulation 3(2) exceptions' must only be undertaken by licence holders
9*	*Notification of work with asbestos* – notify the enforcing authority of licensable work (min. 14 days notice)
10	*Information, instruction and training* – see 'Training' on page 265
11	*Prevention or reduction of exposure to asbestos* – prevent exposure to employees as far as is reasonably practicable, and where not reasonably practicable, reduce to lowest level reasonably practicable, both the exposure (without relying on use of respirators) and the number of employees exposed
12	*Use of control measures* – ensure that any control measures are properly used or applied
13	*Maintenance of control measures* – maintain control measures and equipment (keeping records of the latter)
14	*Provision and cleaning of protective clothing* – provide suitable PPE and ensure it is properly used and maintained
15*	*Arrangements to deal with accidents, incidents and emergencies*
16	*Duty to prevent or reduce the spread of asbestos* – where not reasonably practicable, reduce to lowest level reasonably practicable

Regulation(s)	Title (in italics) plus explanatory notes
17	*Cleanliness of premises and plant* – keep asbestos working areas and plant clean and thoroughly clean on completion; four-stage clearance procedure and certification for reoccupation
18*	*Designated areas for asbestos work* – 'asbestos areas' where any employee would be liable to be exposed to asbestos and 'respirator zones' where control limit liable to be exceeded
19	*Air monitoring* – monitor exposure of employees to asbestos
20	*Standards for air testing and site clearance certification* – see 'Accredited personnel' on page 266
21	*Standards for analysis* – of bulk samples, see 'Accredited personnel' on page 266
22*	*Health records and medical surveillance* – of employees liable to be exposed to asbestos
23	*Washing and changing facilities*
24	*Storage, distribution and labelling of raw asbestos and asbestos waste* – if received, despatched from, transported or distributed, waste must be in sealed, labelled, appropriate bags or containers
25–31	*Prohibitions and related provisions* – previously *Asbestos (Prohibition) Regulations* 1992
32–37	*Miscellaneous* – exemptions, etc. and defence 'must have taken all reasonable precautions and exercised all due diligence'

Regulations marked with an asterisk do **not** apply in whole or part where the work falls within any of the circumstances set out in 'regulation 3(2) exceptions'.

Duty to manage asbestos in non-domestic premises (regulation 4)

The dutyholder responsible for the management of asbestos in non-domestic premises as set out in regulation 4(1) is every person, who has by virtue of a contract or tenancy, an obligation for its repair or maintenance, or, in the absence of such, control of those premises or access thereto or egress therefrom.

This includes those persons with any responsibility for the maintenance, or control, of the whole or part of the premises.

When there is more than one dutyholder, the relative contribution required from each party in order to comply with the statutory duty, will be shared according to the nature and extent of the repair obligation owed by each.

This regulation does not apply to 'domestic premises', namely a private dwelling in which a person lives, but legal precedents have established that common parts of flats (in housing developments, blocks of flats and some conversions) are not part of a private dwelling.

The common parts, are classified as 'non-domestic' and therefore regulation 4 applies to them, but not to the individual flats or houses in which they are provided.

Typical examples of common parts are entrance foyers, corridors, lifts, their enclosures and lobbies, staircases, common toilets, boiler rooms, roof spaces, plant rooms, communal services, risers, ducts and external outhouses, canopies, gardens and yards.

The regulation does not however apply to kitchens, bathrooms or other rooms within a private residence, that are shared by more than one household, or communal rooms within sheltered accommodation.

The duties are identified in the following table.

Subject	Requirement
Cooperate (see also next page)	Cooperate with other dutyholders so far as is necessary to enable them to comply with their regulation 4 duties.
Find and assess condition of asbestos-containing materials (ACMs)	Ensure that a suitable and sufficient assessment is made as to whether asbestos is or is liable to be present in the premises and its condition, taking full account of building plans or other relevant information, the age of the building and inspecting those parts of the premises which are reasonably accessible. (Must presume that materials contain asbestos unless strong evidence to the contrary.) (See MDHS 100 *Methods for the determination of hazardous substances* for guidance on asbestos surveys.)
Review	Review assessment if significant change to premises or suspect that it is no longer valid and record conclusions of each review.
Records	Keep an up to date written record of the location, type (where known), form and condition of ACMs.
Risk assessment	Where asbestos is or is liable to be present assess the risk of exposure from known and presumed ACMs.
Management plan (see also next page)	Prepare and implement a written plan, identifying those parts of the premises concerned, specifying measures for managing the risk including adequate measures for properly maintaining asbestos or where necessary, its safe removal.
Provide information to others	Ensure the plan includes adequate measures to ensure that information about the location and condition of any asbestos is provided to every person likely to disturb it and is made available to the emergency services.
Review and monitor	Regularly review and monitor the plan to ensure it is valid and that the measures specified are implemented and that these are recorded.

Management plan

The management plan is an important legal document which in addition to its health and safety significance will be required to be made available to, and inspected by, a variety of interested parties.

The absence of such a document may thus have significant financial implications or affect the liquidity of the premises as an asset.

A plan is not required when the assessment whether asbestos is present or is liable to be present in the premises confirms that it is not. For example, the building is new and there is confirmation from the project team that asbestos has not been used in its construction.

Nevertheless a record must be kept of the assessment carried out and its conclusion to show to an inspector or prospective purchaser or occupant.

The dutyholder owns and is responsible for the safekeeping of the plan, however he is obliged to make the information available 'at a justifiable and reasonable cost' to anyone who is likely to disturb asbestos and this includes new owners or occupants.

(See HSE publication *A comprehensive guide to managing asbestos in premises* HSG227.)

Duty to cooperate

Every person has a duty to cooperate with the dutyholder so far as is necessary to enable the dutyholder to comply with his or her duties under regulation 4.

This includes the landlord, tenants, occupants, managing agent, contractors, designers and planning supervisor.

The possible scenarios envisaged by the ACOP include:

❖ anyone with relevant information on the presence (or absence) of asbestos; and

❖ anyone who controls parts of the premises to which access will be necessary to facilitate the survey and management of asbestos (i.e. its removal or treatment or periodic inspection).

Cooperation does not extend to paying the whole or even part of the costs associated with the management of the risks of asbestos by the dutyholder(s), who must meet these personally.

Where there is more than one dutyholder for premises, the costs of compliance will be apportioned according to the terms of any lease or contract determining the obligation to any extent for repair and maintenance of the premises.

If there is no such documentation then the apportionment of costs will be based on the extent to which parties exercise physical control over the premises.

In the final analysis, the courts will decide financial responsibility using the principles outlined above.

Guidance in the ACOP states that architects, surveyors or building contractors who were involved in the construction or maintenance of the building and who may have information that is relevant 'would be expected to make this available at a justifiable and reasonable cost'.

The duty to cooperate is not subject to any limitation or exclusion, thus there is an obligation to do whatever is necessary to cooperate with the dutyholder.

Short lease tenants, licensees or other occupants who control access, but do not have any contractual maintenance liabilities would be required to permit the landlord access to fulfil his duties.

In June 2003, RICS published a guidance note *Asbestos and its implications for members and their clients* (ISBN 1 84219 063 6).

High Alumina Cement concrete

Background

The manufacture of High Alumina Cement (HAC) commenced in the UK in 1925 to provide concrete that would resist chemical attack, particularly for marine applications. This cement developed high early strength, although its relatively high cost prevented extensive use.

During the late 1950s and 1960s the main use of HAC was for the manufacture of precast prestressed components which could be manufactured quickly, therefore offsetting the additional cost of the material.

The earliest UK failures were experienced during 1973–74 when several school roofs collapsed. There followed considerable investigation and testing. In 1975, the Building Regulations Advisory Committee (BRAC) Subcommittee P published design criteria to be used in checking the adequacy of buildings containing HAC structural members. The two main aspects of the investigation were, firstly, a strength assessment and, secondly, a durability assessment.

In 1976 HAC concrete was banned for structural use, although new uses are now becoming established under the name Calcium Aluminate Cement.

Problems with HAC

HAC concrete undergoes a mineralogical change known as conversion. During this process the concrete increases in porosity, which in turn results in a loss of strength and a reduction in resistance to chemical attack. The higher the temperature during the casting of the concrete, the more quickly conversion takes place.

The relationship between conversion and strength is complex, however the strength of highly converted concrete is very variable and is substantially less than its initial strength. Typically the original design strength of 60N/mm^2 may be reduced to 21N/mm^2.

Highly converted HAC concrete is vulnerable to acid, alkaline and sulphate attack. For this to take place water as well as the chemicals must have been present persistently over a long period of time at normal temperatures. Chemical attack is usually very localised in nature and the concrete typically degenerates to a chocolate brown colour and becomes very friable, often due to sulphate attack.

Given the sensitivity to moisture the greatest risk therefore lies in the use of HAC concrete in roof members. It is therefore important to appraise the condition of the concrete and any waterproof coverings before making any formal judgement as to the remedial work required.

In a warm and moist environment there is the possibility of alkaline hydrolosis occurring where high alkali levels may be present as a consequence of the use of certain types of aggregate or where alkalis may have ingressed from plasters, screeds and woodwool slabs.

Investigation

There are three generic stages in an investigation, namely:

- ❖ Stage 1 – identification.
- ❖ Stage 2 – strength assessment.
- ❖ Stage 3 – durability assessment.

A document known as the BRAC rules is often used in the assessment of HAC components of certain standard types. The rules were first produced in 1975 and were reviewed recently; they are now published by BRE, albeit the guidance is essentially the same.

A Stage 2 strength assessment is required to determine if the precast concrete members have sufficient structural capacity, even at the reduced fully converted strength, to safely withstand the applied loading. Subcommittee P sets out the guidelines for concrete strength based on 21N/mm². The strength assessment requires the section properties of the beam to be established. Thereafter the structural strength of the element can be calculated. In cases where the section properties are unknown, or cannot be determined by investigation, then assessments are limited to determining the concrete strength using near-to-surface tests.

A Stage 3 durability assessment is required to determine the long-term durability where affected by chemical attack and reinforcement corrosion. Testing can be undertaken to determine the presence of alkalis and sulphates. Laboratory testing may be supplemented by a detailed visual inspection and the removal of lump samples for petrographic examination. A durability assessment should also include a visual examination of the reinforcing steel where lump samples are removed. In recent years it has been found that HAC is less durable than members containing ordinary Portland cement.

Assessment

Putting all of this in context, however, there have been no recorded instances in this country of a failure of a floor incorporating HAC concrete. It is important to know that in the case of the original historic failures, manufacturing faults were eventually discovered. The greatest reduction in strength occurred where a high water content was present during the period of mixing and high temperatures took place during curing.

Of the five failures or new failures of roof constructions, two did not directly involve the quality of the concrete, one was aggravated by chemical attack and two were apparently due to defective concrete which should have been rejected at the time of casting. On no occasion has weakening of the concrete due to conversion been the sole cause of failure.

Chlorides

The presence of chlorides, whether added as calcium chloride or ingressed as de-icing salts, may result in 'chloride induced corrosion' and is less common than corrosion caused by low cover. When chloride corrosion does occur its effects may be wide ranging including a reduction in structural capacity.

Natural alkalinity of concrete

Steel does not corrode when embedded in highly alkaline concrete despite high moisture levels in the concrete because a passive film forms on the steel and remains intact as long as the concrete surrounding the bar remains highly alkaline.

Chloride induced corrosion

Corrosion may occur in concrete that contains sufficient chlorides even if it is not carbonated or showing visible signs of deterioration.

The presence of free chloride ions within the pore structure of the concrete interferes with the passive protective film formed naturally on reinforcing steel.

Chloride ions exist in two forms in concrete, namely free chloride ions, mainly found in the capillary pore water, and combined chloride ions which result from the reaction between chloride and the cement hydration process. These occur in proportions that depend on when the chloride entered the concrete. If chloride was introduced at mixing, for example, as calcium chloride, approximately 90% may form harmless complexes leaving only 10% as free chloride ions. If, on the other hand, seawater or de-icing salts penetrate the surface of the concrete, the ratio of free to combined chloride may be 50:50.

The corrosive effect of chlorides is significantly affected therefore by the presence of free chlorides. The effects of chlorides are classified in terms of risk of corrosion because in certain conditions even low levels of chloride may pose some risk. The permissible level of chloride added at mixing specified in BS 8110 is 0.4% by weight of cement. For pre-stressed concrete the level is lower at 0.06%. The overall effect of reinforcement corrosion caused by chlorides must therefore be considered with the depth of reinforcement and the depth of carbonation.

There are two methods by which chlorides can be the cause of corrosion in reinforced concrete:

❖ as cast-in chloride, usually calcium chloride added at the time of mixing or from sea-dredged aggregates; and

❖ as ingressed chloride, i.e. by the penetration of the outer surface of the concrete from de-icing salts.

Chloride induced corrosion results in localised breakdown of the passive film rather than the widespread deterioration that occurs with carbonation. The result is rapid corrosion of the metal at the anode leading to the formation of a 'pit' in the bar surface and significant loss of cross sectional area. This is known as 'pitting corrosion'. Occasionally a bar may be completely eaten through.

Chloride induced corrosion may occur even in apparently benign conditions where the concrete quality appears to be satisfactory. Even if there is poor oxygen supply reinforcement corrosion may still take place. Failure of reinforcement may therefore occur without any visual sign of cracking or spalling.

All aggregates used commonly for concrete mixing contain a background level of chlorides usually less than 0.06% by weight of cement. The use of calcium chloride as an accelerating additive at the time of mixing was popular during the 1950s and 1960s. It was used in precasting yards to speed up the reuse of expensive moulds and was used on site during cold weather to increase the rate of gain in strength. The use of calcium chloride additive was banned in 1977. The presence of calcium chloride cast-in within the mix usually attracts a chloride level significantly greater than 0.4% by weight of cement. Ingressed chlorides through the outer surface of the concrete are variable in nature. However the use of de-icing salts on, for example, external staircases and balconies is popular and may result in localised high concentrations of chlorides in excess of 1.0% by weight of cement. Concentrations of ingressed chlorides on the top surface of a car park deck may typically occur up to 3 or 4%.

The presence of calcium chloride is further exaggerated by the presence of deep carbonation. Carbonation releases combined chlorides into solution to form free chloride ions, thus increasing the likelihood of corrosion. For this reason many properties built approximately 20–30 years ago may only now start causing problems.

Risk assessment

Guidance on assessing the risk of reinforcement corrosion is provided by the BRE in Digest 444 Part 2. Here the risk of corrosion for structures of various ages is presented in the range negligible, to extremely high risk. Factors affecting the risk assessment are either a dry or damp environment, the depth of carbonation and of course the level of chlorides present. The digest includes risk assessment tables indicating the risk of corrosion activity according to the age of the building, whether in a wet or dry environment and whether the concrete is carbonated or uncarbonated.

Repair

The successful repair of chloride induced corrosion is notoriously difficult because of the tendency for new corrosion cells to form at the boundary of the repair. This mechanism is called 'incipient anode effect' and should be minimised by removing, wherever possible, all concrete with significant chloride contamination. In recent years the introduction of proprietary sacrificial zinc anodes embedded within the patch repair and attached to the reinforcement can help to reduce this effect. For high levels of chlorides and long-term protection this may not be sufficient.

For heavily chloride contaminated structures, particularly car parks, the only tried and tested long term solution is cathodic protection. The cost and complexity of installing cathodic protection is not usually warranted within building structures. A variation of cathodic protection is de-salination – a short-term process using higher current densities than cathodic protection. Migrating corrosion inhibitors have found some success; these are penetrating surface coatings applied under strict conditions.

Alkali aggregate reactions

ASR – the problem

Alkali aggregate reactions, of which alkali silica reactions (ASR) are only one variant, are relatively uncommon in building construction in this country and tend to occur in civil engineering structures rather than conventional buildings.

Concrete is a highly alkaline material: it follows that pore water contained within the concrete will also be highly alkaline, and can, given the correct combination of conditions, react with certain types of aggregate to produce a gel.

The gel imbibes water, expands and can cause the concrete to crack or disrupt. Sometimes a pattern of 'map' cracking occurs but in others small 'pop-outs' can occur – rather like concrete with acne. The durability of the concrete can thus be compromised and in extreme cases the tensile strength of the concrete component can be reduced.

For ASR to occur, three factors must be present. Remove one of the following three factors and ASR will not take place:

- ❖ critical silica in the aggregate;
- ❖ sufficient moisture; and
- ❖ high alkalinity.

Most of the aggregates used in the UK are considered to be of 'normal' reactivity rather than high reactivity, although there are some troublesome types in the South-West.

The Building Research Establishment (BRE) and the Concrete Society have prepared guidelines and flow charts to assist the designer in the selection of appropriate measures to reduce the risk of ASR. By adopting a 'sodium oxide equivalent' scale, cement can be classified according to low, moderate or high alkalinity. High alkalinity cement means an equivalent of 0.75% sodium oxide equivalent or greater. When dealing with the total alkali content of concrete it is usual to consider the equivalent sodium oxide in the concrete expressed as kilogrammes per cubic metre (kg/m^3).

However, the use of cement at high risk does not necessarily mean that ASR is inevitable. For the reasons given above, two other factors must be present. Where the aggregate is sea-dredged, marine flint classified in accordance with current guidelines as being of normal reactivity, it would present no particular concerns when used in combination with highly alkaline cement. A combination of normal reactivity aggregate with high alkalinity cement is permissible, if the total alkalinity of the concrete is kept within certain limits. However, good construction practice dictates that for normally reactive aggregates, the total alkali content of the concrete should not exceed 3.0kg/m³.

What if ASR occurs?

Concrete Society Report 30 and Part 4 of BRE Digest 330 are mainly concerned with the selection of materials to reduce the risk of ASR occurring. The available records seem to point to a low risk of the development of ASR, but it will be remembered that the third component necessary for the formation of a reaction is sufficient moisture.

If the concrete was reinforced, then any potentially expansive reactions in the concrete could be restrained (the degree of restraint depending upon the arrangement of the reinforcement).

A risk assessment based approach to analysis is advocated – taking into account whether the concrete is wet or dry, restrained with reinforcement or not and finally the consequences of failure – the structural significance of a component. The structural significance of an element is a function of the consequences of its failure. These are judged to be slight or significant as defined below:

- ❖ slight – the consequences of structural failure are either not serious or are localised to the extent that a serious situation is not anticipated; and

- ❖ significant – if there is risk to life and limb or a considerable risk of serious damage to property.

Further information

BRE Digest 330, *Alkali-silica reaction in concrete*

Structural effects of alkali-silica reaction: Technical guidance on the appraisal of existing structures, Institute of Structural Engineers, 1992

Concrete Society Report 30, *Alkali-silica reaction – Minimizing the risk of damage* (3rd edition), TR30, 1999

Investigating Hazardous and Deleterious Building Materials, Rushton, T., RICS Books, 2006

Corrosion of metals

Bimetallic corrosion

Corrosion will often occur when two different metals are immersed in water containing an electrolyte such as salt or acid. Similar problems can also exist when dissimilar metals may not be in contact but are connected electrically. The problem of bimetallic corrosion (sometimes called galvanic corrosion or dissimilar metal corrosion or contact corrosion) can be profound and must be taken into account during design. Metals submersed in seawater are particularly at risk. Detailed guidance on the subject may be found within BS PD 6484:1979 which contains a series of tables from which it is possible to identify the risk of additional corrosion of one metal in contact with another. However, the process of corrosion is complex and depends upon a number of variable factors and not just the presence of dissimilar metals; relative area, temperature and exposure to oxygen will all affect corrosion rates.

Some basic points

If a metal is immersed in a conducting liquid (the electrolyte), it will take up a conducting potential. Different metals assume a different potential – this is recorded in the electrolytic scale shown below.

Anodic end (corrosion) –ve, (less noble metal)

Magnesium

Aluminium

Duralumin

Zinc

Cadmium

Chromium iron (active)

Chromium-nickel-iron (active)

Soft solder

Tin

Lead

Nickel

Brasses

Bronze

Copper

Chromium iron (passive)

Chromium-nickel-iron (passive)

Silver solder

Silver

Gold

Platinum

Cathodic end (protected to the detriment of the anodic metal)
+ve, (more noble metal)

If two different metals are immersed in the electrolyte a current will flow from the more positive metal (the cathode) towards the more negative metal, the anode. This current flow arises because both metals have different electrical potentials. Standard texts often state that the further apart the metals are on the electrolytic scale, the greater risk of corrosion. The extent, or severity, of the corrosive action is proportional to the distance of separation of the metals in the list. This is of course true, but it is an oversimplification of the position when it comes to the selection of metals during the design of buildings and services, as corrosion rates will also depend upon a number of other factors. For example, even metals that are potentially highly reactive can be used successfully together given the correct precautions.

As noted above, seawater is highly conductive, and generally this will permit a greater electrical flow. A high flow produces more corrosion to the anode. By contrast, fresh water is generally less conductive. Rainwater, if polluted, can be moderately conductive and so exposure to a wet environment in an industrial area can be more damaging than in a rural area. Exposure to marine conditions can produce highly conductive conditions.

Surface contamination can absorb moisture from the atmosphere even when condensation does not form and so the fact that two metals are not immersed in water does not necessarily prevent corrosion from occurring. Metals buried in soil perform in much the same way as those that are immersed in water.

Corrosion rates can be affected by the area of the anode or cathode relative to the other. For example, a large cathode area and a small anodic area could result in a more severe condition.

Protection against bimetallic corrosion

Actions which may help prevent bimetallic corrosion include:

- ❖ insulating the metals from one another;
- ❖ applying a metallic coating;
- ❖ applying a non-metallic coating;
- ❖ using a jointing compound capable of excluding water;
- ❖ applying a paint coating; and
- ❖ applying sacrificial protection, e.g. cathodic protection.

The data within PD 6484 may be simplified and reproduced as in the following table. This table should be treated as a guide only; if a particular combination is critical it should be referenced to the more complete information in PD 6484. The table shows the performance of each metal in contact, so to determine whether or not corrosion is a problem, the performance of both metals must be checked. For example, to check the combination of cast iron with carbon steel, first check cast iron in the vertical columns – this shows no corrosion. However, now check carbon steel in the vertical column and it can be seen that in combination, the carbon steel will corrode in preference to the cast iron.

Step 1: Select metal from these columns										
Step 2: Select metal that is in contact with the metal selected in step 1	Zinc	Aluminium	Carbon steel	Cast iron	Tin	Lead	Brass	Phosphor bronze	Copper	Austenitic stainless steel
Zinc										
Aluminium	▨	▨								
Carbon steel	■	■								▨
Cast iron	■	▨	▨							▨
Tin	▨	▨	▥	▥						
Lead	▨	▨	▥	▥						
Brass	■	■	■	■	▥	▥				
Phosphor bronze	■	■	■	■	▥	▥				
Copper	■	■	■	■	▥	▥				
Austenitic stainless steel	■	▨	■	■	▥	▥				

Table derived from data in PD 6484:1979 and does not apply to metals that are immersed in fresh water or seawater.

■ Additional corrosion likely under all conditions

▥ Additional corrosion likely under marine exposure

▨ Additional corrosion likely under industrial or marine exposure

☐ Additional corrosion unlikely under all conditions

References

BS PD 6484:1979, *Commentary on corrosion at bimetallic contacts and its alleviation*

Guides to Good Practice in Corrosion Control – National Physical Laboratory (NPL)

Further information

For additional information refer to:

Lifetime Management of Materials Service
National Physical Laboratory
Hampton Road
Teddington
Middlesex
TW11 0LW
Tel: 020 8943 6142
Fax: 020 8943 7107
Web: www.npl.co.uk/lmm

Institute of Corrosion
Corrosion House
Vimy Court
Leighton Buzzard
Bedfordshire
LU7 1FG
Tel: 01525 851771
Fax: 01525 376690
Web: www.icorr.org

There are also a number of trade and development organisations for metals such as zinc, aluminium, lead, copper etc., who will provide information on the corrosion performance of metals.

Filiform corrosion (on coated aluminium)

This variety of corrosion can be found in the form of long filaments of growth between aluminium and its particular paint coating. The depth of penetration of this corrosion is generally found to be 10–20μm and is therefore considered to be cosmetic rather than structural. The deterioration process is primarily caused by a break or defect in the coating itself and is most commonly found in moist or wet environments (which may be internal or external) where sections of coated aluminium have been cut to form joints, or sections of cladding have been cut, drilled or damaged. Even the most microscopic of marks or breaks in the paint effectively cause the formation of a battery circuit between the exposed metal and adjoining sections which are protected from the air. The corrosion takes the appearance of a worm trail as the 'battery cell' moves along the surface of the aluminium underneath the paint.

Liquid waterproofing systems

Description

Advances in technology over the last 30 years or so have resulted in the development of many polymer-based roofing materials, offering favourable advantages to petroleum-based systems, which, since the 1970s oil crisis, have become increasingly expensive and in some cases of unpredictable quality. Furthermore, rising labour costs have resulted in a need to gain a competitive edge by providing materials that can be laid quickly and efficiently, without necessarily the intensive labour associated, for example, with built up felt (BUR) roofing applications.

But not only have materials had to cope with changes in the cost and nature of raw products, the method of forming buildings has changed: lightweight, highly insulated structures with increased propensities for movement place very onerous demands on roof membranes, which only some systems are capable of accommodating. Most of the new roofing materials are polymeric in nature, meaning that they are made up of many (poly) molecules (mer) that are linked together in a chain – in effect forming very large molecules of different chemicals, for example, poly(propylene) or poly(isoprene).

Broad categories

European Technical Approvals (ETAs) exist for the following:

- ❖ polymer modified bitumen emulsions and solutions;
- ❖ glass reinforced resilient unsaturated resins;
- ❖ flexible unsaturated polyester resins;
- ❖ hot applied polymer modified bitumen;
- ❖ polyurethanes;
- ❖ bitumen emulsions and solutions; and
- ❖ water dispersible polymers.

In addition, solvent-based acrylic roofing systems are available: these are not covered by ETAs and are often used for emergency repairs. Most of the above products are cold-applied, but polymer modified bitumens are very popular for new build applications whereas cold-applied materials are generally (but not exclusively) used for remedial works. Both have good performance characteristics and, if properly laid, a life expectancy in excess of 30 years would not be an unreasonable expectation, although as with most materials this is highly subject to workmanship, protection, maintenance, etc.

Hot-applied rubberised bitumen membranes

By dispersing virgin or reclaimed rubber in asphalt together with limestone powder, oil and styrene butadiene styrene (SBS) it is possible to manufacture a very flexible roofing membrane that can form a seamless membrane about 3–4.5mm thick. Some formulations include an additional spun bond polyester fabric interlayer with a further 3mm layer to form a roofing system. However, these materials are not usually resistant to UV light and so it is important to add a bonded membrane or alternatively a ballasted insulation layer to provide mechanical and solar protection.

The materials are usually supplied as cakes wrapped in polyethelene wrapping which are melted in a heater to around 200°C. The melt is discharged from the heater into a suitable container and applied to the roof using long-handled, rubber-bladed squeegees.

Prior to application, the roof surface must be free from contaminants. Liquid membranes depend upon a bond to the surface, so all traces of dust, grease and oil must be removed. Concrete surfaces are usually primed with a suitable asphaltic solution.

Cold-applied liquid membranes

These membranes are polymeric compositions with one or more ingredients, such as modified asphalt or coal tar pitch, or various resins or elastomers, such as polyurethane, dibromobutadiene, silicone or acrylic. The bitumen-based solutions are usually applied as emulsions, brushed or rolled in place.

Resin-based systems can often be supplied in different formulations to give 'guaranteed' life expectancies of up to 25 years. These materials can also be dressed with sand or mineral granules to provide slip resistance, and for this reason are often used for waterproofing car park decks where a degree of friction is desirable and where various colour pigments can be used to advantage.

Cold-applied systems tend to be used for remedial operations, with the clear advantage that heat producing appliances are not required, and the membrane can be sprayed over existing finishes without the need for a temporary roof. The ability to form complicated weathering details with the minimum effort places the materials at a distinct advantage over BUR systems. Like hot-applied systems, it is usual to reinforce the membrane with a polyester fleece sandwiched between two layers of waterproofing. Some coatings require periodic refresher coats.

Limitations

Whilst both hot- and cold-applied systems are relatively easy to lay, this does not mean that they are tolerant of lower levels of workmanship. Until recently, many systems could be supplied and laid only by licensed contractors using trained operatives. In recent years, the market has opened up and quality control standards have (in some cases) not met expectations. Most systems require trained operators for their proper installation whilst the European Liquid Waterproofing Association is working hard to introduce a skills card system to encourage appropriate levels of workmanship. Most systems require good substrate preparation – clear of sawdust, swarf, dirt, hydrocarbons or organic materials, whilst the maintenance of the correct dry-film thickness is important to ensuring future durability. Similarly, many products have only a limited shelf life before they deteriorate (six months or so).

From a designer's point of view, a failure to consider the usual principles of flat roofing design, rainwater disposal and the design of roof penetrations will lead to failure in much the same way as it would using more traditional methods. Similarly, because one of the great benefits of liquid membranes is their ability to bond to the substrate (and hence limit the propensity of water to travel through a sheathing layer) it is vital to ensure that the correct level of preparation is used and that the correct primers are employed. Compatibility with the substrate (and any likely contamination of the surface) must be established at the outset.

Generally speaking, all roofing materials must, for their service life, remain watertight, resist stresses arising from application and service and withstand weather factors such as rain, hail, thermal shocks, UV light, etc. In particular, when selecting a material, specifiers should consider:

- ❖ the ability of the material to deal with tensile stresses at places of concentrated movement, initiated, for example, by shrinkage in low temperature or creep during hot weather;

- ❖ ability to bridge cracks – particularly those that open and close cyclically as a result of changes in temperature or structural movements (if a membrane is fully bonded, the percentage elongation over say a 3mm crack is very high);

- ❖ ability to withstand heat and UV light;

- ❖ static and dynamic puncture resistance – the ability to withstand site damage due to an irregular substrate, construction traffic, falling loads (hail, dropped tools, etc.);

- ❖ compatibility with other materials; and

- ❖ risk of puncturing by plant growth (the roots of plants such as container grown bamboos can be highly invasive).

Health and safety

The generic precautions recommended in the *Health and Safety at Work etc. Act* and the *Control of Substances Hazardous to Health Regulations* (COSHH) apply to all liquid roofing materials. However, in some cases polyurethane resins can produce very unpleasant fumes, and if there is a danger of fumes being drawn into a building, one could well find that the occupants will protest volubly. In such circumstances, a solvent free membrane might be a safer option, although the life expectancy of these materials has yet to be proven by direct experience over, say, 30 years.

Where disposal is concerned, liquid waterproof systems must not be allowed to contaminate drains or water systems, or be buried where surface water may be affected.

Things to watch out for

Whilst the lack of obvious seams makes it easy to determine whether a liquid membrane has been installed, identifying the particular nature of the membrane is not always easy. Hot-applied systems are almost always protected against sunlight, whilst polyurethanes are usually of light, reflective colours with no additional protection. Look out for the following:

- ❖ adequacy of protection systems;
- ❖ evidence of chemical or biological attack – unusual colouring or mottling, softening and degradation;
- ❖ pinholing or mechanical damage;
- ❖ tearing;
- ❖ blistering;
- ❖ plant (root damage);
- ❖ adequacy of weathering details; and
- ❖ loss of adhesion.

Conclusions

Liquid applied systems offer real advantages over traditional asphalt membranes or built-up felt roofing. Good durability, flexibility and ease of detailing are attractive features, but in all cases they are no substitute for proper and considered good design.

Further information

The European Liquid Waterproofing Association publishes a series of useful guidance notes on the various types of liquid membrane, their application and workmanship (www.elwassociation.org.uk).

Canadian Building Digest 235, *Single ply membranes*, gives useful background information on performance characteristics and selection.

The National Federation of Roofing Contractors (www.nfrc.co.uk) publishes several guides to the safe use of liquid materials.

The Flat Roofing Alliance (www.fra.org.uk) publishes a code of practice for remedial works.

Flat roofs with continuously supported coverings – Code of practice, BS 6229:2003, BSI.

BLP Construction Durability Database www.componentlife.com

This section is based on an article originally written by Trevor Rushton for the RICS *Building Surveying Journal* (July 2006 edition), copyright RICS. Material is reproduced here with permission from RICS.

Thin stone cladding

Since the advent of steel frames in buildings, the claddings used to conceal those frames have become progressively thinner and more lightweight. Whereas in the early 20th century, stone claddings were often 100mm or so in thickness, advances in saw cutting technology meant that from the second half of the century, it was possible to produce stone panels in thicknesses much less than this, with 30mm or so being the norm for many buildings constructed from the 1970s.

Thin stone panels could be fixed with dowels to concrete cladding panels or could be 'hand fixed' using restraint straps and gravity fixings fitted into the edges of the stone or slots cut in the back face of each panel.

Whilst many natural stones can perform satisfactorily if used in this way, certain types of marble, particularly calcitic marbles have been found to deteriorate, with very serious results. The Amoco building in Chicago is a notable example: here some 43,000 Carerra marble panels had to be stripped off the building within 18 years of its construction at a cost in the region of $80 million (15 years is a common period of time for problems to become manifest).

At microscopic level, marbles are composed of a series of grains. The shape of the grains and the pattern of the bond vary according to type – and this effectively governs how the marble will perform in service.

Marble is usually made up of the minerals calcite and dolomite, with some having a higher proportion of either. Both exhibit an anisotropic tendency, that is they expand at different rates according to axis. Imagine rolling out a sheet of pastry – as pressure is applied, the size of the piece increases, but the thickness reduces. This form of movement affects calcitic marbles. On the other hand, dolomitic marbles expand in three directions, but at different rates. Such patterns of movement are initiated by changes in temperature. Whilst a metal component will expand and contract uniformly, marbles tend not to do this, and so a gradual and progressive movement occurs.

Thermal expansion of stone materials is inevitable, and temperatures of around 40–50 degrees are sufficient to initiate movement. Temperatures of this magnitude are often found on the facades of buildings in Europe. The change in temperature creates stresses within the body of the stone, allowing tiny micro-cracks to form around the body of each grain. In much the same way as soil bulks up when it is excavated (the volume of excavated material being much greater than the volume of the hole) the marble expands but is prevented from returning to its original volume.

In turn, micro-cracking increases the porosity of the stone making it more vulnerable to atmospheric pollution with decohesion of the fabric of the stone – termed sugaring – being the result. Flexural strength also decreases and the panels warp in either a convex or concave pattern. Such movements can be enough to dislodge fixings or break the panel away from the fixings with obvious results.

Once anisotropic expansion has occurred, there is probably no going back, bowing and cracking of the panels will be irreversible and progressive. For this reason, inspections of buildings clad in thin white marble panels should invite questions as to the nature of the stone and its propensity for movement.

Building defects

Common defects in commercial and residential properties

Period	Typical problem	Possible effects
Pre 1900	Failed or lack of damp-proof course	Rising dampness, penetrating damp, efflorescence on plaster, decay to skirtings and the like
	Poor ventilation of floor voids	Decay in wall plates, joists, etc.
	Poorly fitting sash windows, risk of decay within window reveals, water penetration beneath sub-sills	Draughty or dangerous operation, decay in concealed areas, lack of security
	Damp penetration through 225mm brick walls	Damage to plaster and finishes, decay to wall plates and bonding timbers
	Poor quality repairs to roofs and gutters	Risk of timber decay
	Roof covered with concrete interlocking tiles	Overloading of roof structure, bowing of rafters and purlins, roof spread
	Lack of restraint to flank walls	Bulging or instability, associated cracking on front and rear elevations
	Settlement of internal partitions	Plaster damage, distortion in floors and door openings
	Alterations to trussed (loadbearing) partitions	Removal of support gives rise to distortions in floors, reduction of loadbearing capacity and possible risk of collapse
	Failure of brick arches and timber lintels	Cracking and distortion of brickwork above window heads
	Defective rainwater goods	Risk of decay in built-in timbers
	Settlement of bay windows	Internal cosmetic damage, distortion in loadbearing elements
	Insect attack, particularly in poorly ventilated and damp areas such as floor and roof voids	Loss of strength if particularly badly affected
	Lead water mains	Hazardous to health – partly depends on plumbsolvency of the water
	Delamination of brick skins	Bulging of brickwork

Period	Typical problem	Possible effects
1900–1939	Wall tie failure in cavity brickwork	Bulging of brickwork, horizontal cracking or 'pagoda effect'
	Delamination of render finishes to walls	Cracking and bulging of render, detachment of same
	Corrosion of roofing nails	Slipping of tiles
	Lead water mains	Possibly hazardous to health
	Outdated electrical services	Possibly dangerous
	Corroded rainwater goods	Risk of decay in built in timbers, damp penetration
	Corroded galvanised steel or steel windows	Cracked glazing, high maintenance costs
	Timber joinery	Decay to cills and softwood frames
	Use of boot lintels	Rotation of lintel due to eccentic loading
1945–1970	Poor installation of lateral bracing to trussed rafters	Lack of restraint to gables, lateral buckling of trusses
	Poor cavity tray details	Water ingress
	Wall tie failure	Bulging of brickwork
	Poor quality joinery	Decay of external joinery
	Cold bridging, particularly to concrete structures	Condensation
All	Over notching of floor joists	Reduction in strength, sagging
	Removal of chimney breasts	Possible lack of support
	Provision of insulation, blocking ventilation paths	Condensation
	Blocking of airbricks	Lack of ventilation, risk of decay
	Removal of loadbearing walls or walls affording stability	Possible long term structural consequences
	Removal of, or planting of, trees or large shrubs	Possible desiccation or re-hydration of subsoil, damage to drains or foundations
	Replacement windows	Poor support to bay windows, distortion of brickwork

Problem areas with 1960s and 1970s buildings

The 1960s saw a frantic period of innovation and experimentation. The need for replacement housing following the Second World War gave rise to the development of numerous system types using innovative materials. Construction had started to drift toward an assembly process and away from traditional craft-based skills.

Some 1960s construction was appallingly bad, for example, some high rise social housing, but other schemes were of a very high standard using good quality and durable materials. Many buildings are now facing or have undergone major refurbishment or change of use (for example, office to housing or hostel accommodation), but many examples of good and bad construction remain.

Rather than look at typical problems associated with each style of building, this list overleaf is intended to give a very brief introduction to a number of common or typical materials or construction faults. The list is not exhaustive.

Brief résumé of some problems

Key to common building types – these are indicative only:

>   W = Warehouse or industrial
>   O = Office or commercial developments
>   H = Housing
>   A = All types.

Item, element or material	Effects
Aluminum sash windows (O) A common type of window was the vertical sliding sash. Instead of the vision glazing being held in a frame, the glass ran in aluminium tracks, with horizontal top and bottom frame members clipped onto the glass. Spring balances were used to hold the windows open.	By now, these windows will be very worn. Defects in the springs or breakage of the glass can lead to the ejection of an entire sash window – clearly a health and safety issue. Treat these windows with caution.
Asbestos (A) Very common in 1960s buildings. Chrysotile (white) for some insulation boards, roof sheets, water tanks, cill boards, etc. Artex, floor tiles, partition wall linings, fire doors, etc. may also have a content. Amosite (brown) used as insulating boards, fire protection or fire breaks, behind perimeter heaters, partitions, etc. Crocodilite (blue) often paste-applied friable material in boiler rooms, pipework, calorifiers, etc.	Major health risks depending on type, location, risk of disturbance. Deleterious material – detection, management and control are highly regulated. Ask for a copy of the asbestos register.
Asphalt roofs (O) These could be of quite good quality and may have performed well if laid on a concrete deck.	The lack of insulation would have helped to reduce temperature ranges and so restrict thermal movements.
Calcium chloride concrete additive (A) Often used by manufacturers of precast elements or for concreting in cold weather. Enables rapid set and removal of moulds. Can also be found in brickwork mortar. Use of unwashed sea dredged aggregates may have led to chloride contamination as may exposure to de-icing salt or a marine environment.	Considered a deleterious material. Creates conditions of high electrical conductivity in the concrete with consequent high risk of corrosion of steel reinforcement. Very difficult to repair effectively. Look out for spalling concrete and very black, stained steel. Can result in severe pitting corrosion without disruption of the surface of the concrete. Tests should always be recommended. Since about 1978, this material should not have been used. In brickwork, risk of corrosion of wall ties. Exposure to de-icing salts, salt spray, etc. can also be very damaging. Watch out for coastal locations, car parks, road bridges, etc. (See also the section on calcium chloride, page 272.)

Item, element or material	Effects
Calcium silicate bricks (A) A smooth, often creamy coloured brick made from lime, sand and flint. Small particles of flint can sometimes be seen in cut bricks or weathered surfaces. Can be mistaken for concrete bricks (see next page). Widespread use in 1960s and 1970s and still manufactured and gaining popularity again. Flank wall of calcium silicate bricks – shrinkage cracking.	Prone to shrinkage (unlike clay bricks which expand after laying). If movement control joints are missed or badly spaced (which they often were) diagonal cracking can occur. Thermal or moisture cracking often visible at changes in the size of panels, eg long runs below windows coinciding with short sections between windows. Look out for thin bed cracks and wider cracks to vertical joints. Do not confuse with subsidence cracking or corrosion of steel frame. Use as a backing to clay brickwork likely to cause problems as a result of expansion of clay brick and contraction of calcium silicate brick.
Cold bridging and condensation (A) Poor insulation standards led to problems with severe cold bridging particularly in housing where humidity levels are higher. Polystyrene insulation was sometimes used but this was usually no more than 25mm thick. In the mid to late 1970s thermal insulation standards were increased, particularly in industrial buildings.	Watch out for cold bridging around balcony structures and precast lintels. Provision of insulation within industrial buildings resulted in a spate of condensation problems within roofs. Cold night sky radiation gave rise to condensation on the underside of metal roofing, while poor application of vapour control layers meant that problems were exacerbated.
Cold flat roof construction (A) Little thought was given to vapour control or for that matter roof insulation. It was common to provide sealed flat roof construction with minimal insulation and sometimes a foil backed plasterboard ceiling lining. Ventilation to the roof void was often ignored. Built-up felt roofs were often asbestos based, but had a life of around 15 years and no more. For this reason most felt roofs would have been replaced by now.	Risk of condensation occurring, with subsequent risk of decay to roof decking or to structure.

Item, element or material	Effects
Concrete (A) Can be of mixed quality, sometimes poorly compacted and with lack of cover to steel reinforcement. Under codes, depth of cover for external work should have been circa 40mm.	Sometimes poor durability, corrosion due to the effects of carbonation or chloride content. Tests should be recommended. Poor curing methods could mean lack of durability. Calcium chloride added as an accelerator either in precast or in situ work. Waffle slab showing the effects of chloride attack.
Concrete boot lintels (A) Concrete lintels designed to have a projecting nib to support the outer leaf, and built only into the inner leaf, to provide a neat appearance externally.	Rotation of the lintel under eccentric load, creating diagonal cracking to the brickwork above the window. Other signs are opening of the bed joint immediately above lintels and splitting of the reveal brickwork immediately beneath. Once rotation has taken place, brickwork will tend to arch over the opening, thus relieving some of the load on the lintel. Cracks can then be repointed.
Concrete bricks (A) Similar in appearance to calcium silicate brick but often used in dark brown, dark red or dark grey variants. Harder and coarser texture than calcium silicate bricks.	Suffer from similar shrinkage related problems. Can be hard to differentiate between these and calcium silicate bricks, but may be harder and contain small particles of visible aggregate.
Corrugated 'big six' asbestos cement sheet (W) Often found on industrial buildings and warehouses well into the 1970s. Name given as a result of the 6-inch profile, but in fact 'big six' was one of several different profiles of sheet. Often based on an asbestos content of around 12-15% chrysotile, (white asbestos) with profiled eaves and ridge pieces and hook bolt fastenings. By the end of the	Obvious health risks from fibre release. Friable surface, and very fragile – never walk on such a covering without crawling boards. Corrosion of hook bolts will cause sheeting to split. Often coated with bitumen or rubber solutions as a remedial treatment. Be very cautious of the effectiveness of these treatments.

Item, element or material	Effects
1970s insulation was being added to the roof construction and this brought about condensation problems.	
	Rigid foam spacers were sometimes used below cement fibre sheeting in order to create a void into which insulation could be placed. The rigid foam compresses with time and occasional traffic loads, leading to 'chattering' of the roof sheets and possible water ingress.
External ceramic tiling (O) See 'mosaic tesserae'. Tiles were often prism shaped or ridged in some way.	Similar problems to mosaic tesserae in terms of delamination of background materials.
Flat concrete floor slabs (Plate floors) (O,W) Fairly thin slabs with mushroom head thickening around column heads.	Very high shear stress around column head has been found to be cause of structural failure. Beware of flat slab car park construction – recent major collapse of car park of flat slab construction at Pipers Row.
GRC (A) Lightweight cladding panels, balustrade panels, permanent shutters, planters.	Early forms of GRC contained fibres that deteriorated in alkaline conditions. Loss of strength, cracking and bowing can result. Later alkaline resistant types (Cem-fil) perform better.
High alumina cement concrete (O,W) Often used in precast and prestressed work rather than in situ work. Mainly (but not exclusively) for roof and floor beams. X and I profiles were common. Some variants for precast factory units (portals and purlins). Sometimes used to form an in situ stitch between two precast beam members or column to beam connections. Developed high early strength. Can have a brownish tinge.	Loses strength with age. Susceptible to chemical attack in damp conditions and contact with gypsum plaster. Strength and durability assessments to be recommended. Since 1974 the material should not have been used in buildings. Considered to be a deleterious material. Several roof failures in the 1970s, but no known cases of flooring collapse. (See also the section on HAC, page 271.)

Item, element or material	Effects

Hollow clay pot floors (O)

Quite common during the 1960s. Concrete poured between pots and in the form of a topping. Sometimes screed could be structural. In other case, non-structural screeds may have been removed to gain additional load or headroom.

Watch out for clay spacer tiles between the pots. These can conceal honeycombing of the concrete rib, lack of fire protection, durability or strength. Removal of tiles and Gunnite repairs may be necessary.

Concrete topping and rib

Risk of voiding

Lack of movement control joints (A)

Cement masonry walls are prone to thermal and moisture movements. Cement mortar is less flexible than older lime mortars, and the stresses induced by thermal movement are relieved by cracking. Centres of joints depend on nature of brick, size and shape of panel, etc. Lack of joints was common in 1960s buildings.

Oversailing of brickwork on dpc, particularly in warehouses. Also watch out for joints that have been filled with Flexcell impregnated board, as this is not very compressible and can reduce the benefit of a joint. Early sealants were also resinous and could lead to staining of adjoining surfaces. Hardening and embrittlement of joint sealants to be expected now.

Large panel buildings (H)

A number of different systems were constructed. Large panels formed the external enclosure and also supported precast floor planks or slabs. Connection details were made on site with wire hoops and in situ work.

The design of joints in panel systems was critical in the success or failure of the system. A variety of types were often employed, in some cases using baffles in the form of open drained joints or face sealed joints using mastic or neoprene gaskets. The success of the building from a structural point of view relies on the connection between the individual panels The ability to withstand local damage by means of alternative load paths is critical.

Risk of disproportionate collapse – see Ronan Point disaster. Following this, high-rise blocks were strengthened. Some low-rise blocks may not have been checked.

Poor quality control of structural connections led to weakness, poor fire stopping or corrosion risk. Possible lack of tying in of precast components. See 'Tying-in' later.

Large panel systems suffer from many of the defects described previously; the more important being rain penetration, corrosion of reinforcement, poor thermal insulation, distortion or physical damage to panels.

Calcium chloride was not used in most precast systems although in some types it was added on a batch by batch basis to aid manufacture perhaps where there were particular programming problems. Thus the inclusion of the material is unpredictable.

Item, element or material	Effects
	The most common faults with these types of systems relates to the gradual deterioration of either the baffle, particularly where butyl rubber was used, ageing of the sealants or ageing of gaskets in face sealed joints. Misplacement of baffles or insufficiently sized baffles in wide joints can lead to water penetration.
	It is quite common to find that quality control standards during manufacture were not up to scratch, with the result that reinforcement was commonly misplaced in the fabrication of the concrete panels. This later led to corrosion of the reinforcement and spalling of the concrete.
	In many cases dry packing used between infill concrete and the panel above is missing or poorly compacted, so that vertical loads are transferred only on the bolt fastenings, resulting in localised cracking around fixing positions.
	In the long term, panels can distort generally as a result of shrinkage in the concrete structure behind and as a result of normal thermal movements in the building as a whole. This can lead to damage at joints, displacement of seals and baffles and subsequent water penetration. Furthermore, smoke stopping between floors and compartments can be damaged with the result that in a fire, smoke can transfer rapidly between occupancies or zones.
Mineralite render (O) A thin (2-5mm) coating of fine grained minerals with a textured surface. Often applied to exposed concrete columns and beams or in larger areas such as spandrel panels. Variety of colours available.	Beware of adhesion failure – can be widespread. Difficult to match repairs.

Item, element or material	Effects
Mosaic tesserae (O) A common finish comprising small (25mm square) ceramic or glass tiles applied to a render background. Often supplied in paper backed sheets of around 300x300 to facilitate laying. 	Adhesion failure of tiles leads to individual tiles falling off and scattering over a wide area. Obvious health and safety risks. More often than not however, it is the render background that fails, losing adhesion to the concrete or brick substrate. This is potentially more serious as larger and heavier sections could collapse. A hammer survey is to be recommended to check for soundness and to identify hollow areas. Repairs are possible using vacuum injection techniques, but hacking off and repair of spalled areas can lead to peel back and cracking of adjoining surfaces and deterioration due to water ingress and freeze/thaw cycles.
Mosaic tesserae in overhead situations (O) Often used as a soffite finish to projecting balconies, shopping mall covered ways and the like. Tiles would be bedded on render or possibly applied over expanded metal lathing. 	Watch out for corrosion of the metal lathing or fixing screws as these may not have been protected against corrosion. Timber fixing battens behind the lathing can also be a problem. In severe cases, large sections of render and tile finish can collapse. If water penetration is suspected recommend further intrusive investigation.
No fines concrete (H) Used in the manufacture of large panels for housing and similar structures, intended to create slightly better insulation properties.	Very low level of resistance to carbonation, hence risk of carbonation and corrosion.
Panel joints (O,H) Panel joints in large panel systems often comprised a plastic or metal baffle sprung into grooves in the edge of each panel. To prevent leakage, it was common to provide a tape back seal to the rear face of the joint.	Baffles may be missing or dislodged. Back seals often missed with consequent risk of water penetration. Flat roof abutments often dressed under the bottom edge of panels, which makes them very difficult to repair. Often the need to modify the drained joint into a face sealed joint.

Item, element or material	Effects
Reconstituted stone (A) Often used as window cills or window surrounds, string courses or other projecting features in all types of buildings. Sometimes fixed with ferrous cramps rather than phosphor bronze. Contain light reinforcement.	Propensity to carbonate fairly rapidly with the result that reinforcement corrodes, causing the features to spall. Corrosion of cramps can lead to displacement of features such as projecting window surrounds.
Render backgrounds (A) Used in conjunction with tile finishes and mosaic tesserae. Often very strong Portland cement based mixes were used.	Possible adhesion failures on concrete due to presence of traces of mould oil on the surface. Sometimes used water-based bonding agents (giving a white milky appearance when render is removed) when there was a poor mechanical key. Later bonding agents were of SBR, which were more durable. Inflexible renders, high vapour resistance and risk of water entrapment.
Reinforced aerated autoclaved planks (W,O) Often used as roof decks – 'Sipporex' or 'Durox' or sometimes as vertical walling. Thin reinforcement, 300–750mm width. Made from a mixture of cement, blast furnace slag, pfa plus aluminium.	If designed before 1980 may deflect excessively, evidenced by transverse cracking on soffite. Some concerns over durability of reinforcement.
Sand faced fletton bricks (A) These were a popular and cheap brick type manufactured by the London Brick Company near Peterborough. Often found in 1960s housing or industrial applications. Often, but not always, a red/pink colour with a heavy textured wire cut type of surface. Rear face of brick is smooth with colour bands or 'kiss marks' arising from the burning process.	No problem in sheltered applications, but bricks in exposed situations such as parapets, chimney stacks and free-standing walls, where saturation is common, are at risk of sulphate attack. The bricks have a very high sulphate content. When wet, soluble sulphates react with Portland cement bedding mortars, causing the mortar to expand and so disrupting the brickwork. Once this occurs, the damage is terminal. Often rendered in mistaken belief that this will cure the problem, but this is a very short-lived solution and will only make matters worse.
Softwood joinery (A) External joinery was often of poorly seasoned sapwood with a low life expectancy.	Very poor durability, especially glazing beads, cills and horizontal rails. Further decay where timber has been pieced-in during repair.

Item, element or material	Effects
Steel windows and cladding (O,W) Typical single glazed windows were manufactured using a section known as W20 by Crittal Windows. Either casements or tilt and turn varieties. Larger curtain walled sections were manufactured by coupling window units together with galvanised steel tee bars.	By now, early windows may be paint bound or distorted. Ironmongery may be defective. Timber subframes were common and may be decayed.
Stramit roof decking (A) An insulation board often used as a roof decking. It comprises a rigid board about 50mm thickness of compressed straw sandwiched between two layers of building paper. The boards were about 1200x450 width and had a brown paper finish. Check in plant rooms, lift motor rooms, roof access housings and the like. Used in some domestic applications.	The material had a very low resistance to water and would decay easily. For that reason it is less usual to find it nowadays. The boards had a grain and needed to be laid correctly, with support perpendicular to the grain. Failure to do this could lead to distortion of the board and subsequent 'wave' effects in the roof line. This in turn could stress the covering and cause failure. Saturated Stramit board would turn into a brown silage-like mess. Beware of safety issues (risk of collapse) when walking on Stramit roofs. Failed Stramit roof deck
System built housing (H) In general terms these types of buildings were prefabricated, based on either steel or concrete construction. Examples would be the British Iron and Steel Federation properties or, if concrete, Woollaway, Unity, Airey, etc. The form of construction was generally based upon the erection of a frame with cladding fitted to it or alternatively a panel system.	Problems have occurred as a result of carbonation in the concrete and initial lack of cover, use of unsatisfactory materials such as thin steel tube used as reinforcement, problems of interstitial condensation, damage to sealants, etc. In some cases the decay of structural parts has reached severe proportions and it has been necessary to contrive methods of reinforcing the frame or alternatively providing a new cladding system, possibly based on conventional brick and block cavity walling systems. In summary, the major problem areas are as follows: • corrosion of reinforcement due to carbonation and/or chlorides,

Item, element or material	Effects
	resulting in expansion of the steel and disruption of the concrete;
	• corrosion of metal ties securing cladding panels and the resultant expansion disrupting the cladding and compromising weathertightness;
	• poor or uneven insulation, cold bridging giving rise to interstitial condensation;
	• insufficient fire protection;
	• poor wind bracing;
	• deterioration of timber components such as window frames, particularly where they form part of the primary structure.
Trussed roof construction (H,O) Trusses were introduced into the United Kingdom during the mid-1960s and were primarily intended for the housing market, although gradual improvements in stress grading and timber engineering have now taken them into commercial, educational and leisure buildings. Commonly designed to pitches of between 20°–35°, with a span of around 3–10m, trussed rafters are usually jointed with factory fixed galvanised steel fasteners, although plywood gussets are sometimes used. With the use of stress graded timber, sizes can be reduced to as little as 35mm in width, with trusses arranged at 450mm or more, usually 600mm centres. Spans of greater than 10m can be achieved, although buckling of compression members can become a problem – and transport to site may be uneconomic.	The correct positioning of the connector plates is essential so that sufficient teeth engage in the timber to prevent the joint, particularly at the apex, from pulling apart. If this happens the truss will settle, or fail. The signs of this may be hogging in the roof and damage to internal finishes. Shrinkage of timber after fabrication can affect the adequacy of the truss as a whole. If the timber members cannot meet, all the joint forces will be taken up by the metal connections, which could buckle or pull out. Diagonal bracing was not a requirement of the Building Regulations before 1976. Corrosion of gang nails used in the manufacture of trussed rafters due to interaction with certain timber preservatives. Compression members may be subject to sideways buckling under load. Bracing is also needed to prevent buckling. Trussed rafter roofs are often clad with large interlocking roof tiles which, together with the tiling battens, tend to produce a relatively stiff plate. They are nonetheless vulnerable to long term vibrations which can lead, in an inadequately braced roof, to lateral buckling where the trusses adopt a sideways lean – domino effect – either in one or two directions towards gable walls. The structure will also be expected to afford support to gable walls and this is usually achieved by the use of

Item, element or material	Effects

galvanised steel straps turned down into the cavity and fixed to at least two adjacent trusses. Lack of adequate restraint to gable walls or other unrestrained elements could allow an unacceptable degree of movement to take place.

Tying-in of precast concrete floor and roof slabs (O,H)

Prior to 1972 (CP110) tying-in was left to engineering judgement. There is a need to form a connection between wall structures and internal precast floor planks. This can be achieved with continuous metal straps or structural toppings to prevent planks from gradually moving apart.

Failure to tie-in properly can lead to the elevation gradually parting company from the floors. Evidenced by a series of parallel cracks in the floors, gradually increasing in severity higher up the building. If neglected, collapse could occur under accidental loads.

Vitrilite panels (O)

Used in conjunction with steel windows as above, these single glazed spandrel panels were made from annealed glass with a powder coating fused into the rear surface during manufacture.

Risk of failure due to heat build up in spandrel panels, bird strikes or mechanical damage from cradles. Water penetration can cause staining and deterioration of rear surfaces. Replacement panels no longer available and may have been made from painted glass with less life expectancy.

Wall ties (A)

Often wire butterfly ties. Thin steel sections and poor galvanising standards. Cavity walls were rarely insulated and cavity tray detailing may be poor.

During the 1960s it was common to, in use galvanised wire ties and, in some cases, vertical twist ties with substandard protection coatings. The life expectancy of bitumen and zinc coatings on these ties is frequently well under the 60 years that was originally predicted. In fact, in 1981,

Factors which could have an influence on the life of the tie are the steel alloy used, the quality of the protective coating and the mortar type – particularly if this was contaminated with chlorides or if the building was in an exposed location.

Research work undertaken by the Building Research Establishment suggests that average zinc loss is about 2.1 microns a year. For pre-1981 ties, this results in a predicted coating life of 12–26 years for wire ties and 25–46 years for vertical twist ties. On the inner leaf, where the circumstances are less aggressive, the zinc coating can be expected to last much longer.

Item, element or material	Effects
BS 1243 tripled the minimum allowed zinc coating thickness on wire ties.	If wire ties have been used, these have the unpleasant tendency of corroding away without any substantial physical disruption to the brickwork. Damage becomes manifest by the sudden collapse of an outer leaf particularly in conditions of high wind. With the thicker, vertical twist ties the amount of metal is significantly more and if corrosion occurs it is likely that the thickness could increase by as much as four times. The cumulative effect of this corrosion will be the creation of horizontal cracks in the brickwork and eventually the lifting of the roof covering at eaves level to give the so-called pagoda effect.
Woodwool as permanent shuttering (W,O) Often used in basement car parks where additional insulation was required, or in some office buildings.	Risk of poor compaction of concrete during placing, or grout loss leading to honeycombing around re-bars. This could prejudice fire protection, durability or in extreme cases strength. Intrusive investigation required to determine if steel is covered properly.
Woodwool slab roof decks (A) Often with galvanised steel tongue and grooved edge strips and with a pre-screeded finish, or an applied finish reinforced with chicken wire. Size about 1200x 450 or 600mm. (See for use in permanent shuttering.) The material offered some thermal insulation qualities. Often used in plant room roofs, access housings and the like.	Reasonably durable and, contrary to popular belief, does not degrade rapidly when wet. However, failure of screed is probable during re-roofing operations, leading to need to renew the deck.

Item, element or material	Effects
Cladding systems (O, W) Early curtain walling systems relied upon the use of galvanised steel window components coupled together or fixed within framed openings. These systems were often single glazed and incorporated Vitrilite spandrel panels. In the early 1970s more aluminium curtain walling systems were developed. Early systems were single glazed and face-sealed but, latterly, drained systems were installed, incorporating double glazed units.	Inspect opening sashes for signs of distortion – usually due to paint build up. Window fittings are usually worn or inoperable. Pay particular attention to the security of fanlight fixings. Early double glazed systems were fully bedded. Volatalisation of sealants is common, leading to voiding, leakage and deterioration of edge seals. Be suspicious of early face-sealed systems in terms of future durability.
Concrete frame (W,O) Expressed concrete frames were common in the 1960s, often with brick infill panels. In the 1970s there was a move away from this form of construction to brick cladding, with the frame concealed either by brick slips or by a brick outer leaf supported on steel angles.	In both cases, there is a risk that the brick panels can become stressed as a result of the normal shrinkage (axial forshortening) of the concrete frame. A failure to provide movement joints means that loads can be transferred to the panels with the result that the brickwork is disrupted.

Steel frame corrosion (Regent Street disease)

Until the early part of the 20th century, substantial buildings tended to be constructed using load bearing masonry – at least for the external walls. Because of the massive nature of these forms of construction, the walls were able to accommodate movements due to temperature and moisture as well as small building movements without significant harm. With the advent of steel as a versatile construction material, the position changed dramatically. By 1910, steel framing was becoming very popular, and this meant that walls could be reduced in thickness with obvious benefits in terms of economy of material, weight and cost. The use of these construction methods in London's Regent Street has given rise to the common description of Regent Street disease, but it is a problem that is by no means confined to this location.

Typically of many new construction materials, the properties of steel were not fully understood, or at least if understood, ignored. From the early part of the century up to the Second World War, it became common practice to construct load bearing frames of steel, clad on the external faces with stone, brick or terracotta. The external cladding would be notched around the steel frame, with the void between the two filled with low-grade mortar.

As we now know, moisture, oxygen and steel do not make good bedfellows: corrosion cells are set up which can cause significant delamination and loss of strength. The main problem is that corroded steel has the propensity to expand to at least four times its original volume. Given that the voids around the steel were filled, the expansion of the steel would inevitably result in cracking of the stone, and in extreme cases the loosening or loss of support to horizontal stonework, which could then collapse.

Whilst some corrosion protection was common after about 1930, the methods used were unlikely to offer a long term benefit, and so it is now very common to find evidence of corrosion in many steel framed, brick or stone clad buildings. Evidence will take the form of vertical or horizontal cracks reflecting the location of the steel frame. Parallel cracks indicating a column position may be less serious than horizontal cracks, but nevertheless investigations are needed to determine the condition of the steel. Whilst early evidence of corrosion is reflected by hairline cracks, more significant problems (particularly in glazed brickwork) can indicate advanced corrosion or loss of section.

Dealing with corrosion using traditional methods is expensive and disruptive. The steel must be exposed, cleaned and protected – not an attractive proposition when dealing with a listed building or an important facade. It is usual to provide a corrosion barrier to the steel and then to create a void around it so that if further corrosion does occur, it will not result in cracking.

Because of the cost and disturbance of these forms of treatment, more attention is now being paid to the application of cathodic protection systems, which rely upon the concealment of discrete anodes into the stone joints, and electrical connection to the steel frame and the introduction of an electric current to reverse the corrosion current. These systems require very careful design and installation and it is imperative that the entire frame is protected in this way to prevent stray currents from having a harmful effect.

Further information

Gibbs, P., *Cathodic protection of early steel framed buildings*, Monograph No. 7, Corrosion Prevention Association

Corrosion in masonry clad early 20th century steel framed buildings, Technical Advice Note 20, Historic Scotland Technical Conservation Research and Education Division

Warland, E.G., *Modern Practical Masonry*, London, Sir Isaac Pitman & Sons Ltd, 1929

Defects in concrete

The failure of concrete is often revealed by cracking, spalling and corroded reinforcement. While the outward symptoms of a number of faults may appear similar, repair methods must be based on a sound analysis of the cause.

Cracking can be caused before hardening due to workmanship problems or after hardening due to physical, chemical, thermal or structural effects.

The alkaline nature of concrete protects steel reinforcement against corrosion, a feature termed 'passivity'. A reduction in the level of alkalinity gives a risk of corrosion in steelwork provided water and oxygen are present. A summary of common defects and consequences are identified in the following table.

Fault	Reasons	Results
Carbonation	Carbonation is generally of concern on exposed concrete surfaces and will take place very slowly with high quality dense concrete. Features such as poorly compacted concrete, cracks or other fissures in the surface and the type of aggregates used could all affect the rate of carbonation.	A reduction in passivity of concrete coupled with water and oxygen can lead to corrosion of steel reinforcement and subsequent spalling of concrete. Lack of sufficient cover to reinforcement may allow steel to fall within the carbonated layer and become at risk. It has been found that the depth of carbonation is roughly proportional to the square root of the time $d=k\sqrt{t}$ (d=depth, k=constant, t=time). The constant will vary with the properties of concrete. By examining the age of the concrete and the depth of carbonation it is possible to make a rough prediction of the depth of carbonation at a future date.
Rust stains	An indication of reinforcement corrosion but avoid confusion with staining ferrous sulphide inclusions in the aggregate or rusting of small diameter wires. Chloride attack is difficult to deal with effectively and needs careful diagnosis Chloride induced corrosion will often result in dark stains around corroded reinforcement.	Although unsightly, staining such as this is unlikely to indicate reinforcement corrosion unless cracking is visible.
Chloride attack		See separate section on chlorides on page 272.

Fault	Reasons	Results
Sulphate attack	Sulphates are present in varying levels in many substances including gypsum plaster, certain aggregates and subsoils.	Possible disturbance to foundations and walls due to expansion of floor slabs. Loss of strength, material becomes friable. Rate of carbonation increases, expansive reaction occurs in the concrete.
Alkali aggregate reactions, principally alkali silica reaction	As a result of chemical inter-action between alkaline fluids in concrete and reactive minerals in certain types of aggregates, a calcium alkali silicate gel is formed. This gel takes in water and expands.	Relatively rare fault in UK structures. In non-reinforced concrete this cracking often illustrates a random pattern of fine, almost invisible cracks bounded by some larger cracks. This cracking is easily confused with shrinkage cracking or even frost attack. Gel can sometimes be seen on the surface of the concrete, possibly coupled with spalling lenses.
Aggregate reactions	Alkali carbonate reaction and alkali silicate reactions have similar problems, but are much less common in the UK.	In reinforced concrete, cracks tend to run parallel with reinforcing bars or prestressing tendons. In particularly severe cases, gel may be visible. Microscopic examination of concrete is the only sure way of identifying attack. Although rare, ASR is often only found in structures exposed to water.

Fungi and timber infestation in the UK

Fungi and moulds

Mould growths and wood rotting fungi are possibly the most common defects that will be encountered in buildings, particularly when inspecting domestic accommodation. Both moulds and fungi are effectively base plant forms that feed off nutriments, the former from the air and the latter from within a host material.

Wood rotting fungi are familiarly categorised as wet or dry rot. Whilst there are numerous forms of wet rot there is a single true dry rot, Latin name *Serpula Lacrymans*.

Fungi require both a source of nutriment and appropriate levels of moisture. Dry rot characteristically requires a lower average moisture content within the host timber than do wet rots, though to some extent dry rot is able to manipulate its environment to create more favourable conditions. Dry rot is known to grow through plaster and masonry in a search of fresh sources of nutriment, but takes no nutriment from the plaster or masonry itself.

The Fungi identification table on the following pages provides an easy reference guide to the most commonly encountered wood rotting fungi in the UK. Hyphae (thin strands often mistaken for cobwebs) spread out from the germinated spores, however it is often the sporophores (fruiting bodies) that are the first recognised indication of an infestation.

There are numerous companies offering rot treatment works within the UK, many being members of the trade association, the British Damp Wood Preserving and Damp-proofing Association (BWPDA). However, beware of recommending so called 'specialist surveys' as the specialists will have a vested interest in any repair recommendations that they may make.

Traditionally treatment of dry rot included:

❖ stripping off of plaster to 1m beyond the last identified point of infection;

❖ removal of visible indications of the fungi;

❖ cutting back of affected timbers to 500mm beyond the last recognised point of infection;

❖ surface spraying of an approved fungicide; and

❖ irrigation of the surrounding walling.

Any new timber introduced to the area should be pre-treated in accordance with BS 5268:1989, remaining timbers being cleaned and then treated, to BS 5707:1997, with a solvent preservative, and possibly with application of a preservative paste.

In recent years irrigation has come to be considered of limited benefit, not least because of the amounts of liquid required and the potential for resultant damage. It is currently considered more important to reduce the moisture ingress in the area concerned and promote rapid drying in order to deprive the fungus of one of its essential life sources. Any remaining fungus within the masonry should then remain dormant, if it does not die off completely. Such forms of treatment are to be commended, particularly where historic buildings are concerned.

Wet rots are potentially less destructive and easier to treat than dry rots, though again stopping the source of the moisture should be a significant concern.

With regard to remedial works, developments in resin systems in recent years have allowed less intrusive repairs and a reduction in the need for significant timber replacement. This is particularly beneficial when dealing with historic buildings or significant structural timbers.

However the works are undertaken the assurance of an insurance backed guarantee should be sought, rather than reliance on the treatment company's own certificate.

On a cautionary note it must remembered that the treatment systems utilise powerful chemicals. Safety procedures must be followed and current safety legislation must be adhered to, in particular the *Control of Pesticides Regulations* 1986 (COPR), as amended in 1997, and the Control of *Substances Hazardous to Health Regulations* 2002 (COSHH).

Consideration must be given to any wildlife that may come into contact with the works. Under the *Wildlife and Countryside Act* 1981, the *Wildlife and Countryside (Service of Notices) Act* 1985, and the [European Community] *Conservation (Natural Habitats, &c.) Regulations* 1994, treatment may require approval by one of the conservation agencies forming the Joint Nature Conservation Committee (JNCC), or indeed other appointed agencies.

Moulds are an increasing problem within the carefully controlled atmospheres of modern buildings. The advent of double glazing systems, and other modern building techniques, has often restricted air flow within properties and resulted in ideal environments for these microscopic plant forms to grow.

Fungi identification table

Type	Usually found	Effect on timber	Mycelium	Fruiting body	Conditions for growth
Wood rotting fungi					
Dry rot					
Serpula Lacrymens	Inside buildings, mines, boats – never attacks timber outside	Large cuboidal cracking (brown rot)	Cotton wool-like if damp; greyish white with purple/yellow and lilac patches if dry	Reddish brown centre, white margins; flat plate or bracket shape; possibly red spore dust nearby	Timber MC 20–40% (slightly damp) Temperature 0–26°C
Wet rots					
Coniophora Puteana (cellar fungus)	Most common of wet rots in buildings; associated with serious leaks – failed plumbing, etc.; also decays exterior	Cuboidal cracking – small cubes (brown rot); may leave thin veneer of sound timber; affected wood becomes dark brown	Brown branching strands on wood and masonry or brickwork; usually not in daylight areas	Rarely found inside; flat plate-like; greenish brown centre, yellow margin; knobbly surface	Timber MC 45–60% (very damp) Temperature –30°C to +40°C
Fibriporia Vaillanti (mine or pore fungus)	Associated with water leaks; most common species of poria group	Cuboidal cracking – large cubes (brown rot); affected wood darkens	Strands flexible when dry; white	Plate shaped – white pores; rare	Timber MC 45–60% (very damp) Temperature up to 35°C
Phillinus Contiguous	Decay of external joinery (softwood)	Timber becomes soft (a white rot) Wood becomes fibrous	Light brown masses	Plate-like with pores; dull brown	Timber MC 22%+ Temperature 0–31°C
Phillinus Megaloporous	Attacks oak heartwood; presence often associated with death-watch beetle		Yellow	Large, plate-like, hard; various browns in colour	Timber MC 20–35% Timber MC 20–35%

Fungi identification table

Type	Usually found	Effect on timber	Mycelium	Fruiting body	Conditions for growth
Wet rots (continued)					
Coriolus Versicolor (Polystictus)	Most common white rot decay of external hardwood	No splitting or decay but much weight loss	Rarely seen	Up to 25mm across; hairy ringed zones to pores to underside	
Lentinus Lepideus (Stag's Horn fungus)	Rare, but sometimes in flat roofs	Cuboidal cracking Darkens woods; wood feels sticky	Soft whitish needle shaped crystals on surface	Some resemble stags horns, others are inverted mushrooms on stalk – brown	Timber MC 26–44% Temperature 25–37°C
Non-wood rotting fungi					
Peziza (Elf-Cup)	Occurs on saturated masonry or plaster, internally and externally; associated with leaks			Buff coloured and fleshy; distinctive	
Moulds					
Aspergillus Penicillium Pullularia	Almost any damp surface in humid conditions	Superficial – easily removed	Like coconut matting	Toadstool – white head – spores released in black ink type liquid Microscopic but spores show up as various colours: black, green, white, brown, yellow, pink	Very humid conditions
Stratchbotrys Chartorum (Toxic mould)	On high cellulose content materials	Superficial to timber – various possible health risks	Green/black spots/mats		Elevated humidity

Mould has been a significant concern in the USA for some time, with black mould, *Strachybotrys Chartarum*, being blamed for various symptoms, including aggravation of asthma, and rashes. Site operatives may display flu-like symptoms as a result of Organic Dust Toxic Syndrome, when working in areas where widespread fungal contamination exists.

More seriously there is some evidence to suggest that black mould may also lead to bleeding in the lungs of infants exposed over long periods, and in turn to pulmonary hemosiderosis.

As well as reduction in moisture levels, improved ventilation is important in the fight against mould growth. Various proprietary chemical mould treatments are available and will help in the short term, though without solving the root cause the problem will reoccur. As with rot treatment, appropriate precautions and legislation will need to be considered.

Insect infestation

Within the UK, wood boring beetles are the major group of timber attacking insects. Wood boring beetles are often erroneously referred to as 'woodworm', possibly because it is the larval stage of the insect's life cycle that eats into the wood before emerging as adults to start the breeding process over again.

The female beetles lay eggs within cracks or end grain of timber, and from there the eggs hatch and feed on the nutriments contained within the wood, leaving frass (digested waste) in the tunnels they form. The maturation can take up to 11 years (depending on the species of insect) before the adult beetle emerges from the timber. The common furniture beetle (Anobium Punctatum) has a life cycle of three years, and is (as its name suggests) the most commonly encountered of the beetles in the UK. The following Beetle identification table details the commonly found wood boring beetles within the UK.

It is often the adult beetle's flight holes that are the first indication of infestation, by which time the damage has been done. The extent of damage will however depend on the type of beetle and the number of life cycles that have occurred before the damage has been observed.

Treatment with low odour insecticidal fluids can take the form of spray or brush application or gel or injection treatments. Fumigation may also be considered in certain buildings, though it is less effective as it does not directly target the infestation.

As with rot and mould, treatments utilise strong chemicals and the correct safety procedures and legislation must be adhered to (see the previous section on Fungi and moulds).

Beetle identification table

Species	Identification	Flight hole	Emerges
Common furniture beetle	Very common, estimated that up to 80% of houses over 40 years old in rural areas are affected. Infestation often in damp areas of house, for example, beneath WC. Beetles are around 3mm long.	1.5–2.0mm diameter	Adult beetles emerge May to September
Death-watch beetle	Infestation uncommon, often found in ancient buildings and therefore more expensive to eradicate. Confined to south and central parts of England and Wales. Attacks elm, chestnut and oak. Presence may indicate fungal attack.	Up to 4mm wide	Adult beetles up to 8mm emerge in spring
Bark borers	Found in timber where bark not completely removed. Larvae confined to bark areas and hence damage caused is superficial.		
House longhorn beetle	Only found in Surrey, Berkshire and Hampshire. Beetles are up to 25mm long. Regulations now require new timber to be treated prior to use. This is a very large borer.	Oval flight holes up to 9mm x 6mm	
Wood boring weevils	Several species – only attack partially decayed timber, cause considerable damage. Beetles are 3.5mm long.	1mm	
Powder post beetle	Beetle 5mm long, few flight holes, convert timber to powder veneer of 'sound' timber.	1–2mm	

Troublesome plant growth – Japanese Knotweed

Japanese Knotweed was introduced into the UK in the 19th century. It grows vigorously and can cover large areas to the exclusion of most other plant species. It has been known to grow through bitumen macadam, house floors and sometimes through foundations.

Japanese Knotweed is a highly invasive plant and is not easy to control due to its extensive underground rhizome system, which enables the plant to survive when all above ground parts of the plant are removed. It grows to a height of about 3 metres and is formed from stiff purple speckled stems or canes resembling bamboo. The canes grow densely in the summer and die back in the autumn with white flowers appearing late in the season. The costs incurred in control of the plant are significant.

In the UK it is a criminal offence under section 14 of the *Wildlife and Countryside Act* 1981 to cause the growth in the wild of, among other things, Japanese Knotweed, (other plants include Giant Hogweed, Japanese Seaweed and Giant Kelp).

Anyone found guilty of an offence can face up to two years in prison and/or an unlimited fine. Any waste material arising from attempts to control this plant should be disposed of in accordance with the *Environmental Protection (Duty of Care) Regulations* 1991 as controlled waste. Landowners can also face civil actions for allowing the weed to spread to neighbouring land if it can be shown that the owner knew or ought to have known of the weed and the problems that it can cause.

Soil from a site contaminated with knotweed must be disposed of at a suitably licensed landfill site at a depth of at least 5m. On site treatment is an alternative, but this is not an easy option. Detailed guidance has been published by the Environment Agency. For more information go to www.environment-agency.gov.uk

Key issues:

❖ Typical habitats include brownfield sites (which may be contaminated as a result of tipping of contaminated soil or knotweed cuttings), railway land, riverbanks, verges and the like.

❖ In winter, the leaves of the plant die off to leave tall, antler-like hollow stems with regular nodes in dense strands.

❖ In summer, the plants have green elongated heart shaped leaves with clusters of small white flowers. Young plants are often red stemmed with flower shoots spreading from the tip (not dissimilar to the appearance of bamboo, but more red than green).

❖ The rhizomes are yellow/orange when cut and snap rather like a carrot.

❖ The plant can be killed with the correct herbicides, but this is not a one-off treatment and can take up to three years.

❖ Controlled burning may destroy the plant at ground level, but the rhizomes can extend to 3m and may not be killed.

❖ Burial and covering with geotextile matting at a depth of at least 5m is possible, but very great care must be taken to avoid the spread of small fragments by mechanical diggers.

❖ Similarly, removal of contaminated soil carries the risk of spreading the plant; disposal must be under controlled conditions and transport off site could cost between £30 and £80 per ton.

Troublesome plant growth – Giant Hogweed

In contrast to the equally vilified Japanese Knotweed, Giant Hogweed not only creates serious environmental problems but also possesses the ability to create very unpleasant skin conditions in humans.

Like Knotweed, it is not a native species, having been originally introduced as an ornamental plant in the 1890s. Needless to say, the plant 'escaped captivity' to become common within the UK. Once established, it can dominate other plants rapidly and damage the natural habitats of insects and other animals. It is often found growing along railway land, footpaths, roads, rivers and wasteland. Seeds can be transported along waterways to infect areas further downstream.

During the winter, the plant dies down, leaving bare patches which can result in soil erosion. Carrot fly can inhabit Giant Hogweed infestations making it a very undesirable plant to have around.

Identification

As its name suggests, Giant Hogweed is characterised by its size, often growing to 3–5m over four years or so. The plant has a purple to red stem and furry, spotted leaf stalks. Leaf and flower growth is also large, 1.5m width is not unknown for leaves, whilst the flower heads (which resemble Cow Parsley) can be around 250mm wide.

Aside from the environmental problems associated with Giant Hogweed, the health risks can be serious. Brushing against the leaves, or breaking the stem releases sap. The sap contains a substance that reduces the ability of the skin to resist ultraviolet light. Burns can result: these often develop into large watery blisters after 20 hours or so of contact and exposure to sunlight. The condition can lead to a more serious and difficult to treat form of dermatitis called Phytophotodermatitis, a reoccurring skin condition that can persist for many years.

Under the *Wildlife and Countryside Act* 1981 and the *Wildlife (Northern Ireland) Order* 1985 it is an offence to 'plant or otherwise cause Giant Hogweed to grow' in the wild. Thus, a landowner could commit an offence by moving contaminated soil from one location to another rather than treating it as controlled waste.

The control of Giant Hogweed is difficult. Unlike Knotweed, plant propagation is by seed, with a single flower head producing upwards of 1,500 seeds and a large plant producing up to 50,000 seeds. Treating the active plant growth with the herbicide Glyphosate is effective, but unless retreatment is undertaken regularly, and over a period of several years, it is unlikely to be effective as the seeds can remain dormant for up to seven years. If spraying is to be undertaken it is vital that this is done early in the growing season, before the flower heads have time to develop and produce new seeds.

The alternative treatment is to dig up the plants and dispose of them as controlled waste. This treatment will often be coupled with spraying, although because of the health effects outlined above, great care is needed to minimise the risk of exposure to sap. If this does occur, the affected area must be well washed and protected immediately after contact.

When removing specimens, some of the seeds will fall to the ground, usually within a four metre radius of the plant. Care is needed not to distribute these seeds, particularly where tracked or wheeled equipment is likely to be used.

Further information

Natural Environment Research Council: www.nerc-wallingford.ac.uk

NetRegs: www.netregs.gov.uk

Royal Horticultural Society: www.rhs.org.uk

Rising damp

Research by the BRE and others suggests that rising dampness is often misdiagnosed by surveyors and so-called damp specialists, with the result that costly and unnecessary remedial treatments are specified.

In many cases, diagnosis is undertaken by means of electrical resistance or capacitance meters, but these can give very misleading and unreliable results in materials other than timber. Surveyors should not diagnose rising damp without first having undertaken a proper study. When rising dampness is suspected, do not automatically recommend a specialist inspection – more often than not the specialist will use exactly the same resistance equipment to make his diagnosis. A more reliable method has been prepared by the BRE and may be found in BRE Digest 245, 1989.

Symptoms

Typically these may include:

- ❖ damp patches;
- ❖ peeling and blistering of wall finishes;
- ❖ a tide mark 1m or so above floor level;
- ❖ sulphate action;
- ❖ corrosion of metals, for example, edge beads;
- ❖ musty smells;
- ❖ condensation; and
- ❖ rotting of timber.

The above symptoms do not of themselves indicate the cause of dampness. Common causes could be lateral rain penetration, condensation or entrapped moisture. High external ground levels, bridging of damp-proof courses, defective rainwater goods and the like should all be self-evident and could give rise to similar symptoms.

Soluble salts are present in many building materials. The salts can be dissolved and moved to the surface of the element as evaporation takes place. Hygroscopic salts (typically, nitrates and chlorides from groundwater) can be present in some materials. These salts absorb moisture from the atmosphere, and can in certain circumstances cause extensive staining and disruption of finishes.

Other possible sources of salt contamination include chemical spillage, splashing from road salt, etc.

Equilibrium moisture content

Many building materials absorb moisture, and when exposed to damp air will attain an equilibrium moisture content. This hygroscopic moisture content (HMC) will vary according to relative humidity. Typical relationship curves can be plotted for different materials, and although these can only establish general indications it is possible to compare readings from different materials in the construction of a wall. For example, at 75% relative humidity (RH) the moisture content (MC) of yellow pine would be 13% while the MC of lime mortar would be 2% and 0.5% in brick.

Some materials possess an HMC of as much as 5% without the introduction of salts from external sources. This figure should be regarded as an appropriate threshold as to whether or not remedial action is likely to be required.

Measurement of moisture content

Resistance or capacitance meters can give misleading results.

The presence of soluble salts on the surface of a wall will cause an electrical resistance meter to indicate a high reading, even if the wall were otherwise dry. Deep wall probes may give a more accurate picture, but will still be affected by soluble salts, as these are generally highly conductive.

A Speedy Moisture Meter (or carbide meter) will give a much more accurate reading of MC in all materials. (Resistance meters are usually calibrated for use in timber and can give an approximation of MC in that material.)

The Speedy meter comprises an aluminium flask fitted with a pressure gauge and a removable lid. Using a 9mm drill on slow speed, a sample of dust is taken from the brick, mortar or plaster. The sample is weighed and placed into the flask. A small quantity of carbide is then added and the flask sealed. Moisture in the sample reacts with the carbide to form acetylene gas. The pressure of that gas is then read off the pressure gauge, which is calibrated to read %MC. With care, the meter can give a very accurate reading, comparable with laboratory kiln dried tests. For brick and masonry, readings above 2% should be investigated, although the threshold can vary according to the nature of the material being tested.

Rising damp

Rising dampness within a wall is in a sensitive equilibrium. There must be a supply of water at the base of a wall and the height to which that water will rise depends upon the pore structure, the brick, plaster or other finish. Water will also evaporate from the surface of the wall at a rate dependant upon temperature and humidity.

During wet weather, evaporation may decrease and groundwater tables may rise, giving rise to an increase in the severity of the dampness. The reverse may happen during dry spells, and evaporation will be increased by central heating.

Soluble salts derived from groundwater or building materials will complicate the situation. Salts will increase the surface tension of the water and so draw it further up a wall. Furthermore, as evaporation occurs, stronger salt solutions are drawn towards the surface and may eventually crystallise out. This process reduces the amount of evaporation and so may raise the height of the dampness. The soluble salts are often hygroscopic and absorb moisture from the atmosphere. If this occurs, the situation will appear worse during wet weather and better during dry.

As noted above, the presence of hygroscopic salts does not necessarily indicate rising dampness.

Diagnosis of rising damp

BRE Digest 245 sets out a method of diagnosis. The method involves drilling samples from the wall to measure both their moisture content (MC) and hygroscopicity (HMC). Samples are taken from mortar joints from 10mm to a depth of 80mm every two or three courses from floor level up to a level beyond that which damp is suspected. While the carbide meter can be used to measure MC it will be necessary to send samples to a laboratory to measure HMC – to see if the samples could have absorbed the quantity of moisture found from the atmosphere.

By subtracting HMC from total MC, it is possible to determine the value of 'excess' moisture, which could result from capillary action or water from other sources. The comparison of HMC and MC gives an indication as to which is controlling the dampness at any position. If MC is greater than

HMC, then moisture is coming from some other source. If the reverse applies, then moisture is coming from the air. Plotting the results graphically can then assist in gaining an accurate picture of what is happening.

Surface damage arising from hygroscopic salts can be significant. The HMC of contaminated wallpaper or plaster can be as much as 20%. It follows, therefore, that contaminated plaster will need to be removed. BS 6576 deals with this subject in more detail.

Subsidence

Much of the UK's housing built on what are known as shrinkable clays has quite shallow foundations, usually less than 1m deep. Such clays are generally strong and able to support a building of four storeys on a single strip or trench-fill foundation. These soils shrink when their moisture content decreases and then swell when it increases. Slight movement of houses on foundations is therefore inevitable as a result of seasonal changes in moisture content resulting in downward movement or subsidence occurring during the summer and upward movement or heave during the winter.

Greater movements may occur during long periods of dry weather and may lead to sticking of doors and windows. Severe movements are almost always associated with localised subsidence caused by trees whose roots extract moisture from the soil. Conversely, removing a tree tends to cause heave as moisture gradually returns to the soil. Large broad-leaved trees of high water demand are notorious for causing damage.

Before World War II, it was common practice to use shallow foundations no more than 0.45m deep. Houses built within the past 25 years should comply with guidelines issued by the National House Building Council (NHBC) and the British Standards Institution (BSI). The former requires foundation depths often well in excess of 1m, while the latter requires a minimum depth of 0.9m for any buildings founded on clay and deeper foundations where there are trees nearby.

Because of the link between clay shrinkage and the weather, insurance claims for subsidence damage increase in long dry periods. There is an upward trend in claims and presently the background level of subsidence and heave damage in the UK is about £350 million annually. Analysis of insurance claims indicates that of those cases involving foundation movements caused by the shrinkage or expansion of clay soils, 75–80% are exacerbated by moisture abstraction by trees.

Subsidence may also be a consequence of mining activity. The extent of subsidence due to mineral extraction depends on the method used for winning the minerals from the ground, whether by mining, pumping or dredging. The main problems in Great Britain arise from coal mine workings.

In many coal fields in Britain the presence of old workings remain as a constantly recurring problem in foundation design where new structures are to be built over them. If the depth of cover of soil and rock overburden is large, the additional load of the building structure is relatively insignificant and the risk of subsidence due to the new loading is negligible. If however the overburden is thick, and especially if it consists of weak crumbly material, there is a risk that the additional load imposed by the new structure will lead to local subsidence.

The risk of subsidence associated with coal workings may be obtained via a Coal Mining Report obtained from the Coal Authority.

It is important to differentiate between subsidence and settlement.

- ❖ Subsidence is vertical foundation movement caused by failure or shrinkage of the subsoil.
- ❖ Settlement is vertical foundation movement caused by an increase in applied load.

Condensation and toxic moulds

Without question, surveyors do visit properties where black or green, or indeed other coloured, moulds exist on the walls, ceilings, floors, furnishings and fittings of the premises. Fungal mould spores exist in the air around all of us and when they alight on parts of the building that provide the right substrate and conditions for the mould spores to propagate and grow, they will.

Everyone will be familiar with dry rot, the product of one family of mould spores. There are many thousands of different moulds and they all occur naturally in our environment.

Condensation mould describes not a 'mould' but a set of conditions whereby various moulds can propagate. Moisture is a key requirement for propagation and if you have surfaces on which moisture is condensing then you are providing the conditions for moulds to grow.

There has been concern in the construction world in recent years over 'toxic mould'. This term is used for the discovery of either Strachybotrys chartarum or Aspergillus fumigatus in buildings, both of which can affect the health of people living or working in individual properties. Particular concerns surfaced in the United States and indeed the City of New York has an excellent website which gives useful guidance and advice, see www.nyc.gov/html/doh/html/epi/moldrpt1.shtml. Do please ensure that you refer to the enlarged 2007 edition of the document.

Such moulds also appear in the United Kingdom. Strachybotrys is a black or greenish-black mould that grows on material with a high cellulose content, including building materials such as the paper facings of plasterboard, chip and particle boards when these materials become water damaged. This mould requires very wet or high humidity conditions for days or weeks in order to grow. Excessive indoor humidity from water vapour condensing on walls, plumbing failures, splashes from bathing or taking showers or water ingress from outside may lead to the growth of many varieties of mould including Strachybotrys or Aspergillus.

If you do observe mould that you believe might be one of these two, then there are UK laboratories that can identify whether they are present by means of testing from swabs taken from the moulds. Searching the web with keywords such as 'toxic mould analysis' will lead to appropriate organisations.

The best option for buildings and their occupants is to ensure that conditions do not exist whereby moulds of any variants can propagate. This is best achieved by keeping the buildings warm, dry and free from external water ingress into the fabric of the building.

If you do find you have problems arising from mould of any variety then the following documentation and guidance will help you understand why you have it and how to get rid of the underlying causes.

The BRE's *Walls and ceilings: remedying recurrent mould growth*, Defect Action Sheet (DAS) 16 (1983) states the following:

'Mould growth requires sustained high relative humidity but is unlikely to start unless surface water is present. Persistent surface condensation is the commonest, though not the only, cause of such conditions … This occurrence of surface condensation depends on the relationship between, on the one hand, heating, ventilation, insulation, etc. and, on the other, the pattern of occupants' activities. The predominant cause can therefore either be in the design provisions or in the occupants' usage. There is no point in treating the symptoms unless the predominant causes have been identified and cured, since mould growth will otherwise recur.'

The BRE's *Controlling mould growth by using fungicidal paints*, Information Paper (1995) states the following:

'Removing the source of moisture

There is no doubt that the best way to achieve long-term control of moulds is to eliminate, or at least reduce, the incidence of dampness on the surfaces of buildings. Repair work to the structure will be necessary if the dampness is caused by rain penetration, plumbing leaks or rising damp. If it is due to condensation, the dampness can be reduced by improving the quality of insulation of the affected building surface, by increasing the level of heating and by improving ventilation (for example, by fitting humidistat-controlled extract fans in the kitchen and bathroom and trickle ventilators in the bedrooms). The occupants themselves can reduce condensation by a variety of measures, such as:

❖ Not drying washing indoors, or restricting it to rooms with open windows and closed internal doors.

❖ Ventilating rooms to the outside during and immediately after cooking, washing and bathing, or whenever the windows show signs of misting.

❖ Avoiding the use of flueless gas and oil heaters.'

The BRE's *Treating condensation in houses*, Good Repair Guide 7 (1997) states the following:

'What causes condensation?

Every day the average UK household puts about 12 litres of moisture into the air in their home, through normal activities such as cooking, washing clothes and bathing; breathing alone contributes about 1 litre per person every 24 hours. In homes where clothes are dried indoors, or which use paraffin or bottled gas heaters, the total can be over 20 litres a day.'

'The mechanics of condensation

There is always moisture in the air in the form of water vapour, although usually it cannot be seen. However, there is a limit to how much vapour the air can hold at any particular temperature: the higher the temperature, the more vapour the air can hold.

Therefore, when warm moist air comes into contact with a cold surface and is cooled, it can no longer hold so much vapour and the excess condenses as liquid water on the surface. A typical example is moist air from a warm kitchen which drifts to unheated rooms, such as bedrooms. The moist air cools when it reaches the walls and other cold surfaces, and the excess water is deposited as condensation. Another common experience is condensation on the surface of a solid floor when the weather turns warm and humid after a cold spell.'

'What's the cure?

There are two main factors involved in condensation in the home – the amount of moisture in the air, and the air temperature. To reduce the risk of condensation occurring, either the moisture content of the air must be reduced or the home must be made warmer. In practice it is usually necessary to do both.'

'Reducing moisture generation

The amount of moisture generated in a home depends on the size and lifestyle of the household. Most of the steps needed to reduce it can be carried out by the occupants themselves, including keeping lids on saucepans, drying clothes outdoors, and not using paraffin or flueless gas heaters.'

'Providing ventilation

High moisture production in homes need not be a problem if there is enough ventilation. The single most important step is to ensure good ventilation in kitchens, bathrooms and shower rooms, where most household moisture is generated, often in large amounts during a short period. This moisture must be vented to the outside to prevent it drifting to other parts of the house which are often colder and more likely to suffer from condensation.'

'Providing adequate heating

Condensation is almost bound to occur in rooms which are cold. The best remedy is to provide low background heating all day in cold weather, even when there is no one at home. It is far better to do this than to rely on a high level of heating for short periods, and the overall costs are often quite similar.

Background heating is particularly important in bedrooms, especially in bungalows and flats, where they are not above heated living rooms. If possible install a small, thermostatically controlled heater in each bedroom and in hallways. A minimum air temperature of 10°C is recommended, day and night.'

BRE material is reproduced with permission from Building Research Establishment Ltd. BRE publications are available from www.ihsbrepress.com.

BRE documents DG85 and DG297 (both 1985), DG370 (1992) and IP12/95 (1995) are all worthy of consultation.

A most useful paper, *Toxic Moulds and Indoor Air Quality* by Jagjit Singh of Environmental Building Solutions Ltd, describing the relationship between toxic mould and indoor air quality may be found at www.aspergillus.org.uk/secure/articles/pdfs/singh.pdf (Indoor Built Environment Review Paper, 2005, 14;3–4:229–234, accepted 21 February 2005).

The document *Research into mould and the implications for chartered surveyors* November 2004 (see www.rics.org/Practiceareas/Built environment/Buildingpathology/Research into mould.htm) has most useful and thought provoking lines of enquiry and research data into such moulds.

Testing

Materials and defects

Chemical and physical testing requirements

The following are some of the more common requirements for specific tests, although it is better to discuss the quantity or type of sample required with the testing laboratory before sampling to ensure that a suitable and representative sample is provided.

Testing laboratories should be provided with an outline of the location of the sample and the nature of the element inspected. This is often critical in evaluating results and the possible level of risk involved.

Primary rules

- ❖ Avoid contamination of sample.
- ❖ Label clearly.
- ❖ Inform laboratory of purpose of test.
- ❖ Consider health and safety aspects when dealing with hazardous substances; seek expert advice first.
- ❖ For comparison, 10 grammes = a sugar cube.

Chloride ion content

About 30–50 grammes (enough to fill a 35mm film canister) of sample material is required. Drilled dust is preferred obtained using a 10mm percussion drill bit. Discard first 5mm depth of material to avoid contamination from paint, plaster or other surface effects. Take samples from two adjacent holes drilled to the depth of reinforcement. As chloride levels will vary, many samples should be taken for analysis. For chloride profiling to identify ingressed chlorides then take incremental samples at depths typically 5–25, 25–45 and 45–65mm.

Carbonation

Best carried out in situ. Drill two 10mm diameter holes and break out concrete in between. Treat freshly exposed concrete with phenolphthalein. Concrete will turn pink if uncarbonated. This is not a precise test and carbonation should be recorded to the nearest 5mm.

If you find the depth of carbonation by testing and you know the age of the building, then the rate of carbonation increase in the future can be predicted according to the following formula: $d = k\sqrt{t}$ where d = depth of carbonation, k is a constant and t = age of concrete (years).

Refer to BRE Digest 405 (1995), *Carbonation of concrete and its effects on durability*.

High Alumina Cement (HAC)

Dust samples taken, as for calcium chloride ion, to determine aluminium content and assess 'proof negative' the presence of HAC. Differential Thermal Analysis (DTA) required on lump samples for 'proof positive' confirmation. Phenolphthalein test for carbonation is not applicable to HAC. It is necessary, therefore, to remove a lump sample of sufficient size to enable a thin slide to be made for petrographic laboratory analysis. This test is very expensive.

Refer to *HAC concrete in the UK: assessment, durability management, maintenance and refurbishment*, BRE Special Digest SD3, by A. Dunster, BRE, 2002 (also BRE Digest 392, *Assessment of Existing High Alumina Cement Construction in the UK*, which has now been withdrawn).

Sulphates in concrete

As for calcium chloride ion (30g sample should be sufficient for chloride sulphate and HAC).

Plaster/mortar

To determine mix proportions including, for mortar, cement content. Take dust or preferably solid sample as for chloride ion content.

Asbestos

Air monitoring and bulk sampling by specialists only. Samples must be taken with due regard to health and safety. Seal loose material after sampling. Sample of loose insulation may be taken with corer. About a thumbnail size sample is sufficient for analysis. Laboratory to be United Kingdom Accreditation Service (UKAS) accredited. Seal remaining material after sampling. Laboratory to report on asbestos type, % content and density.

Groundwater

Approximately 1,000ml of water should be sufficient to determine chemical signature of ingressed water. A similar quantity of mains tap water should also be taken simultaneously so that the results may be compared. Results of laboratory analysis sometimes are not conclusive.

Leaks may also be identified by 'sounding' by placing listening rods on pipe valves, covers, etc. This work is done by specialists often when quiet at night.

Decayed timber

Provide sample large enough to indicate pattern of cracking and/or mycelium growth. Powder material is not sufficient except in cases of insect attack, where frass may give indication of type of beetle.

Non-destructive tests

See BS 1881: Part 201, *Guide to the use of non-destructive methods of test for hardened concrete,* and information supplied below.

Non-destructive testing

There are a range of non-destructive testing (NDT) techniques which may avoid the requirement for large scale costly and disruptive opening-up. Often the findings of non-destructive testing survey may allow opening-up to be targeted in specific locations. Non-destructive testing techniques are particularly useful to establish construction details and the condition of the structure and fabric of a building, in particular relating to building defect analysis.

A summary of the more common NDT techniques are as follows:

Impulse radar

Radar is a widely accepted non-destructive technique for establishing details of the construction and condition. Radar is effective through most building materials including concrete, asphalt, brick, stone and also through soil. Defects may be mapped without damage or disruption to surface finishes.

Radar is an echo sounding technique where pulses of radio energy are transmitted into the structure by an antennae moved over the surface. Where material boundaries are encountered the different electrical properties reflect part of the energy back to the surface where it is detected by a receiver. Sampling is rapid and collected data effectively forms a continuous cross section enabling rapid assessment of thickness, arrangement and condition over large areas.

Thermography

Infrared thermography is a non-destructive testing method involving precise measurements of surface radiation to reveal changes in thermal performance caused by hidden changes in the construction or in a physical condition. Recent improvements in imaging and processing technology has enabled improved and compact handheld thermographic cameras to undertake surveys of large areas relatively quickly.

Modern thermo-imaging cameras are able to detect variations in surface temperature as small as 0.1°C. A major limitation of this method is that sufficient heat differential is required between the inside and outside of the building fabric. Environmental conditions favourable for thermographic surveys are therefore restricted to, for example, cold still winter nights when heat flows from the inside to the outside of walls. A major benefit of this technique however is that a great deal of work can be conducted some distance from the subject.

Ultrasonic pulse velocity

Ultrasonic pulse velocity is a non-destructive technique used in testing a wide range of building materials to determine properties including compressive strength and to investigate defects, such as the presence of delamination and the depth of cracking. The method can be applied to materials such as concrete, ceramics, stone and timber. The main advantage of this method is identifying general changes in condition such as areas of weak concrete in a generally sound structure. The technique involves the measurement of the compression wave velocity from a transmitter to a receiver.

NDT investigations

Often one or more of the above techniques may be required. Information may be provided relating to:

❖ debonding and delamination;

❖ compaction and voidage;

❖ spalling or micro-cracking;

❖ general details of construction, material types and layers;

❖ moisture content;

❖ reinforcement or other embedded ferrous metal; and

❖ brickwork details and conditions.

It is rare that NDT techniques will themselves tell the whole story. It is essential that NDT is considered as an investigation tool as part of a wider engineering assessment.

Cladding

Mechanisms of water entry

Ways rainwater can penetrate

- ❖ Kinetic energy;
- ❖ surface tension;
- ❖ gravity;
- ❖ capillarity;
- ❖ pressure differentials;
- ❖ any combination of these.

Kinetic energy

This is the direct action of the wind carrying a droplet of rainwater with sufficient momentum to force it through a sealed joint. Prevention or drainage overcomes this. Prevention can be by baffles, by a durable seal or by a labyrinthine shape within the joint. Drainage collects the penetrating water and diverts it back to the outside.

Surface tension

This can cause water to adhere to and move across surfaces. It is guarded against by drip edges or throatings along leading edges, and horizontal surfaces should slope down and out. Connecting components can also have appropriate grooves or ridges.

Gravity

This can take water through open joints that lead inwards and downwards. Reversing the slope overcomes this.

Capillarity

This occurs in fine joints between wettable surfaces. It is only severe when other mechanisms persist – for example, wind-assisted capillarity. In metal components it is resolved by capillary breaks within the joint surfaces.

Pressure differential

This frequently is the main mechanism. Since air at high pressure will migrate to areas of low pressure, it follows that high pressure, moisture-laden air can transport moisture into an area of lower pressure. It is overcome by maximising the outer deterrent and minimising the pressure differentials. This is achieved by self-contained (compartmentalised) air spaces behind the outer skin, which are well ventilated to the outside.

Composite panels

There has been some speculation of late that the use of metal faced sandwich panels is unsatisfactory, and that while buildings constructed from these materials can satisfy Building Regulations, there is an increasing reluctance on the part of building insurers to effect cover at reasonable commercial rates.

Given parallel concerns over fire safety and risks to occupiers and fire fighters it is clear that there is considerable potential for bad or misleading advice and unjustified criticism of composite panels in general.

In 1993, two firemen lost their lives tackling a serious blaze at the Sun Valley Poultry fire in Hereford. The fatalities were due to the early collapse of plastic foam cored sandwich panels, which contributed to the fire and generated significant quantities of thick black smoke and noxious fumes.

Sandwich panels are of a composite construction comprising two outer layers of steel or aluminium sheet with an inner core of an adhesive bonded lightweight core material. The resulting product is lightweight yet strong and able to span greater distances than would be possible with the individual component parts in isolation. Flexural strength is attained by maintaining the bond between the layers. One side will be in tension, the other in compression. Remove the bond to one face and integrity is destroyed and the panel will fail.

There are broadly four types of core:

❖ foamglass (fairly rare);
❖ polyurethane (PIR or PUR);
❖ polystyrene (EPS); and
❖ mineral wool (machine made mineral fibre).

If subjected to fire, polyurethane cores (which are thermosetting) will undergo localised charring, although flaming can take place if flammable vapours are released. The charred material will shrink and can lead to delamination of panels.

Polystyrene materials may burn fiercely, give off thick black smoke and allow burning droplets to fall.

Some of the adhesives used in mineral wool products can be combustible.

Foamed glass is generally non-combustible.

The two main issues are:

❖ instability of the panel facings in the event of a fire; and
❖ combustibility of the panel core material – method statements for fighting fires in composite panel buildings talk about 'fires of the building', rather than fires within the building.

Issue 1 was a contributory factor in the fire at Sun Valley, and could affect composite panels that are not properly supported or restrained. In the case of roof and wall cladding, there are usually additional supports in the form of purlins and sheeting rails and primary fasteners, which serve to tie the two leaves together and prevent them from becoming detached. However, in internal situations such as food processing plants, cold storage facilities, etc. the quantity of insulation required will often lead to panels of 200mm thickness or more. Such panels require less support and so present a greater risk of delamination. It is these panels which cause the greatest levels of concern – particularly as the core materials are often no more than EPS.

There will be a conflict between the requirements of the Building Regulations and the requirements of insurers. Building Regulations are aimed essentially at ensuring the health of users and neighbours of the building (and of course visitors as emergency services). Insurers may want higher standards of protection, fire suppression and/or more reliance upon non-combustible materials.

The relevant standards for composite panels were originally set by the Loss Prevention Council but are now administered by BRE Global under LPS 1181. Generally, materials with a PUR or EPS core will almost certainly not satisfy the requirements of LPS 1181, whereas PIR or stonewool products can be engineered to comply.

The Association of British Insurers has produced a report on the issue and it is hoped that insurers will now take a more relaxed view if buildings have been constructed using materials certified under LPS 1181 Part 1 (for external systems) or Part 2 (for internal applications). However, many buildings have been constructed (and still are constructed) using materials that do not satisfy these standards and, in these circumstances, it is important to consider the overall level of risk rather than the mere existence of the panels.

Whether or not sandwich panels constitute a risk is a matter of judgement and scientific fire risk assessment. A reasoned approach may involve the consideration of the following:

❖ Is there a sprinkler installation in the building?
❖ Are there any specific fire risks – use, storage of inflammable materials, arson, etc?
❖ Are the panels in the vicinity of battery charging areas?
❖ Are the panels perforated such that the cores are exposed?
❖ How are the panels fixed – are they properly restrained?
❖ What is the nature of the insulant?
❖ What is the extent of the material and to what extent could it contribute to fire load?

Many manufacturers keep records of consignments and can often, given the nature of the contractor, identify the nature of the material supplied to a specific site. More modern trends have included a small identifier that can be marked on the panels and revealed by exposure to a small UV light source.

Curtain walling systems

Curtain walling is a weatherproof and self-supporting enclosure of windows and spandrel panels in a light metal framework which is suspended right across the face of a building, being held back to the structure at widely spaced joints.

Types of curtain walling system

Stick system

Stick construction is the traditional form of curtain walling, comprising a grid of mullions and transoms into which various types of glass and/or insulated panels can be fitted. Most of the grid assembly work is done on site. The advantages include relatively low cost and the ability to provide some dimensional adjustment. The disadvantages are that performance is workmanship sensitive. It is not unusual to find systems failing initial waterproofing tests during erection.

Unitised system

Unitised systems comprise narrow width storey height units of aluminium framework containing glazed and/or opaque panels. The entire system is pre-assembled under factory controlled conditions. Mechanical handling is required to position, align and fix units on site onto pre-positioned brackets attached to the floor slab or the structural frame. Modern installation techniques increase the speed of erection and often minimise the requirement for scaffolding. Unitised systems have higher direct costs and are less common than stick system. Nowadays the curtain walling to most prestige buildings is of this type.

Panellised systems

Panellised curtain walling comprises large prefabricated panels of bay width and storey height which are connected back to the primary structural columns or to the floor slabs. Panels may be of precast concrete or comprise a structural steel framework which can be used to support a variety of stone, metal and masonry cladding materials. The advantages of these systems are improved workmanship as a consequence of factory prefabrication, allowing improved control of quality and rapid installation with the minimum number of site sealed joints. Panellised systems are less common and more expensive than unitised construction. Panel systems often appear similar to unitised systems.

Variations

Structural sealant glazing is a form of glazing that can be applied to stick or unitised curtain walling systems. With structural sealant glazing, the double glazed units are attached to the grid framework with factory applied structural silicone sealant rather than by pressure plates and gaskets in a more traditional system. The attraction of this form of glazing is that it provides relatively smooth facades which are visually attractive.

Structural glazing typically comprises large thick single panes of toughened glass assembled with special bolts and brackets that are supported by a secondary steel structure. This form of glazing is often referred to as 'planar' glazing and is commonly used to form the enclosure to atriums and entrances.

Weather tightness

There are various methods of preventing rainwater ingress and these are discussed as follows.

Face sealed systems

Early curtain walling systems tended to be face sealed relying on a weatherproof outer seal to prevent water penetration. The seal must remain completely free of defects to prevent leakage paths occurring. Where there is no provision for drainage, any water that bypasses the outer seal could result in internal water ingress. With drained systems any water within the glazing rebate can then drain away within the framing system. There are also a small number of proprietary systems incorporating front zipper gaskets containing a large rubber gasket with a central press-in segment or zip which, when pressed into place, forces the gasket out onto the surface of the glass. This system does not normally have provision for water drainage.

Fully bedded systems

The systems are now largely obsolete and were utilised on the early forms of curtain walling. Fully bedded glazing is a face sealed system relying on the glazing rebate being completely filled with glazing compound to prevent the passage of water. They are therefore 'undrained'. Any voids within the bedding are a potential weak link for water ingress and early failure of the double glazed units.

Drained and ventilated systems

Most cladding designers now accept that it is difficult to exclude water and therefore provision for a small amount of leakage can be made within a drained system. Typically these dry glazed systems comprise an outer decorative cover plate, and an aluminium pressure plate with two narrow rubber oyster gaskets either side clamped against the glass or insulated infill panel. The pressure plates are screw fixed through a thermal break into the mullion or transom member. A further inner gasket between the glass and the mullion or transom provides a further seal.

In drained and ventilated systems the front gaskets provide an initial barrier. The rebates and cavities are drained and ventilated to the exterior to prevent the accumulation of any water that bypasses the outer seals. Drainage is usually via small holes or slots in the underside of transoms that drain water down through the mullions.

Some systems also incorporate a foil faced butyl adhesive tape applied over the transom and mullion nosings directly beneath the pressure plate to serve as a secondary line of defence.

While these systems will accommodate a small quantity of water within the glazing rebates, it is important that the pressure plate is fixed to the correct torque so that the outer gasket seal forms a good seal against the glass.

Pressure equalised systems

Pressure equalised systems are an improved variation of drain and ventilated systems. Here the ventilation openings in the pressure plates are of an increased size to permit rapid equalisation of pressure in the glazing rebates with the external pressure thereby preventing water penetration of the outer face. Consider the following diagram:

The rectangular box may be considered as the area around the glazing in a cladding system. If the pressure inside the box is less than the pressure outside, the water will be drawn in. If we can equalise the pressure in the box then the probability is that water will stay on the outside. In curtain walling systems we must provide a perfect seal around the inside of the window and must also provide the number of slots around the perimeter of the glass to enable pressure within the glazing rebate to equal that of the external air pressures almost instantaneously. Fundamentally therefore, with pressure equalised systems the outer face is sealed as tight as possible against rainwater while the inner face is sealed as tight as possible against air inflow. Nearly all modern curtain walling systems are designed utilising the principles of pressure equalisation.

It is very difficult to identify the differences between a drained and ventilated system and a pressure equalised system. However for pressure equalisation to work properly, the various zones of pressure must not be too large. Thus it is common to consider the area around one glass pane as one zone and therefore drainage must be made from the transom members and not from the mullions. In practice it is very difficult to provide full pressure equalisation and there is some doubt in the industry as to whether it is fully effective.

Double glazed units

Double glazed units are often referred to as 'insulating glass units' comprising two or more panes of glass spaced apart and hermetically factory sealed with dry air in the unit cavity. The air may then be flushed out and replaced with a range of other gases to improve thermal or acoustic performance.

The perimeter edge sealant prevents moisture from entering the unit cavity and holds the unit together. Two forms of edge seal configuration are single seal systems and dual seal systems. Single seal systems rely on the edge sealant to act both as the vapour barrier and as an adhesive bond to hold the panes of glass together. Dual seal glazing units rely on two seals, an inner seal to control water vapour transmission and an outer secondary seal to hold the glass tightly against the spacer bar. The combined properties of primary and secondary sealant provide high quality glass units. Nearly all units are now of this type.

The appropriate British Standard for Dual Seal Systems was BS 5713: 1979 and although this remains current it is now obsolescent.

There is a wide variety of glass types that may be used.

Annealed glass is untreated glass manufactured from soda lime silicates. It is the least expensive and most readily available type of glass. Annealed glass breaks into sharp edged shards and is therefore considered to be unsafe in all fire and breakage situations.

Low e coatings reduce the omission of long wave thermal radiation from the glazing and increase the reflection of this radiation. In the winter, solar radiation can be trapped within a room and reduce the need for heating. In the summer however heating can also occur and so low e glass needs to be used in conjunction with adequate provision for ventilation. Most Low e glass can be toughened and laminated.

Thermally toughened glass is formed by heating and then rapidly cooling or quenching annealed glass. Differential cooling and hardening across the thickness of the glass generates a compressive stress in the surface layer of the glass. Toughened glass is always a safety glass and compared with annealed glass is four to five times stronger in compression and bending. In failure, toughened glass shatters into small, relatively safe fragments. All annealed glass contains nickel sulphate impurities and as the glass is heated during the toughening process these impurities change state. Spontaneous breakage of the glass may follow. The failure of toughened glass in service can be reduced by heat soaking to encourage reversion of the impurities to the low temperature state before installation. Poor design and careless handling of glazing are much more common reasons for spontaneous breakage of toughened glass than nickel sulphite inclusions. As a minimum requirement, toughened or heat strengthened glass located at height or overhead should be heat soak tested.

Heat strengthened glass is formed by heating annealed glass and then cooling it under controlled conditions. Heat strengthened glass offers some of the strength of toughened glass but a reduced risk of failure due to nickel sulphite inclusions because of the reduced tensile stress in the glass. This glass is often also referred to as 'partially toughened'.

Laminated glass is formed by bonding together two or more panes of glass using a plastic interlayer. Any of the above forms of glass may be used in any combination. Upon failure, laminated annealed glass breaks into shards which are held together by the interlayer. Laminated glass may include one or more panes of toughened glass. If all panes are of toughened glass then the broken glazing will lose all structural integrity and may pull free from the pane unless properly secured. Laminated glass is recommended for the inner pane of overhead glazing and is considered to be safety glazing.

Surface finishes

The metal components of a curtain walling system will nearly always require finishes to provide protection against corrosion or for appearance.

To preserve the decorative and protective properties of any metal finishing, it is essential that atmospheric deposits are removed at frequent intervals, particularly those surfaces which are not exposed to the washing effects of the rain.

Quality of workmanship is particularly important and it is therefore essential to choose a reputable applicator preferably covered by a quality insurance scheme. Independent acceptance inspection testing can be undertaken to ensure compliance with the specification.

Organic coatings (carbon based coatings)

Organic coatings are normally applied to either steel or aluminium and include polyester powder, PVDF, PVC, Plastisol, and polyester. The most common organic finish for windows and curtain walling is polyester powder coating, however a range of wet applied finishes is widely used for opaque cladding panels. Polyester powder coatings may be applied to either galvanised steel or aluminium and are available in a wide range of colours. Polyester powder coatings are tough and abrasion resistant. Manufacturers often provide a guarantee for 15 to 20 years.

Anodising

Anodising is an electrolytic process that produces a dense, hard and durable oxide layer on the surface of aluminium. The oxide layer is porous and must be sealed to prevent staining but can be coloured by introducing dyes or chemical treatment before sealing. Anodised finishes are generally harder and more abrasion-resistant than organic coatings with an expected life of 50 years or more. However, anodised surfaces are susceptible to alkaline corrosion from contact with fresh concrete or mortar and rainwater run off from concrete surfaces.

Testing

Many standard and bespoke curtain walling systems are tested in laboratory conditions to determine the resistance to wind load, air tightness and water tightness. These tests are undertaken on a very small number of test panels assembled in factory conditions. By necessity they are a test of the design rather than on-site workmanship.

It is therefore critical that all installed curtain walling systems are subject to on-site testing to establish that the fabrication and installation has been undertaken to a satisfactory standard.

Water tightness on site is typically assessed using sprayed water from a hose in accordance with the AAMA (American Architectural Manufacturers Association) Standard 501-94 or CWCT (Centre for Window and Cladding Technology) test methods. Ideally, the first areas to be tested should be among the first areas of each type of curtain wall to be constructed on site. Typically, the test areas are at least one structural bay wide and one storey in height, providing that all horizontal and structural joints or other conditions where leakage could occur are included.

Water is applied via a brass nozzle on the end of a hose that produces a solid cone of water droplets with a spread of 88°. The nozzle is provided with a control valve and a pressure gauge between the valve and nozzle. The water flow to the nozzle is adjusted to produce 22 +/− 2 litres per minute, producing a water pressure at the nozzle of 220 +/− 200 Kpa (Kpa = 1000 pascals). Water is directed at the joint perpendicular to the face of the wall and moved slowly back and forth over the joint at a distance of 0.3m from it for a period of five minutes for each 1.5m of joint. There should be an observer of the inside of the wall, using a torch if necessary, to check for any leakage.

Glazing – windows and doors satisfying the Building Regulations

Amendments to Part L of the Building Regulations have brought about important changes in the specification of windows and doors. Essentially, compliance with the regulations will involve improving the insulation value of the frame (perhaps by reducing its size and increasing the extent of the better insulated glass panel) or by using more advanced glazing specifications such as low e coatings.

Specifically, measures could include the following:

❖   increase the width of the thermal break;

❖   utilise an alternative type of thermal break;

❖   provide alternative gasket design;

❖   increase the air gap in the double glazed unit;

❖   provide a gas filling to the glass;

❖   provide an alternative spacer (warm edge technology);

❖   utilise low e glass (either hard or soft coatings);

❖   triple glazing; and

❖   dual double glazing.

Increase the width of the thermal break

The width of the thermal break will have a significant impact on the thermal performance of the frame. Pre-April 2002 designs were often in the order of 12mm or less, but widths of 36mm are now realistic. Even with low e glass and an argon gas filling, a standard 4mm thermal break in a metal window will not meet the requirements.

Utilise an alternative type of thermal break

There are broadly two types of thermal break: those comprising a strip or 'web' of nylon 66 (polyamide) or glass fibre reinforced polypropelyne inserted into locating channels in the aluminium sections.

There are also those of resin which is poured into a single extrusion. When the resin has set the aluminium is then cut out.

By replacing a polyamide break with one made of polyurethane, one can reduce the u-value from say 3.95W/m²K down to 3.72W/m²K. However, polyurethane is not capable of accommodating the wider break designs.

Provide alternative gasket design

The thickness and positioning of gaskets, particularly those types which also compartmentalise the glazing rebate, can influence thermal performance to a comparable degree.

Increase the air gap in the double glazed unit.

Many domestic double glazed units (DGUs) are of 12mm width, with some timber window frames being only able to accommodate a 6mm air gap with two panes of 4mm glass. By increasing the width of the gap to 16mm, thermal performance is improved. Beyond 16mm there is little thermal benefit to be gained.

Provide a gas filling to the glass

Conventional DGUs are air filled, although the substitution of air with argon or krypton gas will lead to a marked improvement:

- ❖ Air filled low e double glazed unit U=1.9 W/m²K.
- ❖ Argon filled low e double glazed unit U=1.6 W/m²K.
- ❖ Krypton filled low e double glazed unit U=1.35 W/m²K.

(W/m²K = watts per square metre per degree Kelvin – the U value – the amount of heat in watts which is transferred through one square metre of a material per degree Kelvin difference between internal and external temperature.)

If the gas filled unit is well made it is possible that the gas will remain contained for many years. Estimates suggest that after manufacture, about 90% of the volume will be the specified gas with the remaining being air. A good unit should not lose more than a further 5% of gas over the next 25 years. However, there are no established test methods for establishing how much gas has been lost in service. The quality and effective life of gas filled units is therefore unknown at the present time.

Provide an alternative spacer (warm edge technology)

A high performance DGU such as those described above would not function as effectively as it could because standard aluminium spacer bars have a high thermal conductivity. By replacing the spacer bars with systems of low conductivity, it is thought that improvements of as much as 10% can be achieved. However, there are some concerns over the long term durability of these units. Additional types of warm edge spacers such as silicone foam cannot be tested under the methods described in prEN 1279-2 and this could restrict their use in the future.

Utilise low e glass (either hard or soft coatings)

Low e or low emissivity glass is made by coating one surface of a pane with a special metal coating. The treated pane is then encapsulated into a DGU, with the treated pane on the inner or room side. The coating reduces the amount of light that can pass through in the infrared spectrum, thus more heat is trapped on the inside of a room.

There are two types of low e glass:

❖ pyrolitic hard coat; and
❖ post applied soft coat.

Pyrolitic hard coat (for example, Pilkington k and SGG EKO Plus) is applied while the glass is being made. Thus the coating is very resilient, meaning that the glass can be toughened, cut and assembled without the need to remove the coating at the spacer bar contact point.

Soft coat (for example, SGG Planitherm) is applied post manufacture. Very high thermal properties will be dependent upon the type of coating used, but most soft coats cannot be toughened and are easily damaged. DGU's must be assembled within a short time of being cut. For these reasons, soft coatings tend to be more expensive, but some manufacturers will claim that they can provide improved thermal performance over hard coatings.

Triple glazing

A triple glazed window using float glass is not as effective as a DGU with low e glass, and is much thicker, resulting in heavier frame sections. However, a triple glazed unit with two low e panes can achieve 1.0 W/m²K, while if the voids are filled with krypton, 0.7 W/m²K can be achieved.

Dual double glazing

As its name implies, this involves setting two DGUs within a frame. However, the system would be very heavy with associated handling and cost implications. Thermal bridging at openings might be reduced because of the increased width of these systems.

Spontaneous glass fracturing

Nickel sulphide is one of several chemical contaminants that can occur during the manufacture of glass. There is some debate as to its origin, but it is thought that it is due to the mix of nickel and sulphate impurities within the glass batch materials, the fuels or even the furnace equipment, and this creates polycrystalline spheres which vary from microscopic to 2mm in diameter.

All glass has some of these inclusions present; they are impossible to eliminate entirely and therefore they are not considered a product defect.

In untreated (annealed) glass they are not a problem. But when glass is heat treated (toughened or tempered), the inclusions are modified into a metastable state. The particles initially decrease in volume, but over a period of time (sometimes years) gradually revert to their original volume; this expansive force acts on the glass around the particle.

In a majority of cases this has little effect but dependent on size and proximity to the centre of the pane where the forces are greatest, this can eventually cause the glass to break.

There is a theory that for an initial period of approximately one year after manufacture there are relatively few breakages. After this, the number increases for up to several years, thereafter decreasing in frequency. There have been reported incidences where fractures have occurred more than 20 years after the installation of glass.

Prior to pr EN 14179, a breakage rate of 1 per 5 tonnes of glass was thought an average level. However, this corresponds to only 200m² of 10mm glass. This, on a glazed roof of say 6000m², could be expected to have a failure rate of 30 breakages.

Panes in external situations are at greater risk. However, there have been a small number of cases where spontaneous breakage has occurred in internal glazing, remote from external influences, for example, panels to a staircase balustrade or an internal partition.

Although the safety risks are very small, because of the risk of falling debris, some companies will not recommend or supply and glaze toughened glass for sloped overhead applications where it will be used either as a single pane or as the inner leaf of a sealed unit.

In 'heat strengthened' glass, nickel sulphide inclusion is not generally regarded as a source of fracture. The difference between this and toughened glass is the rate of cooling. In the former this is less rapid, reducing surface compressive strength and making it much less susceptible to the transformation of nickel sulphide inclusions. Offering 5.5 times the strength of annealed glass, in many circumstances it is a useful replacement for tempered glass. However, it is not a suitable substitute where safety glass is required.

'Heat soaking' is a quality controlled process which gives increased reassurance against the presence of critical nickel sulphide inclusions by subjecting the glass panels to accelerated elevated temperatures to stimulate the transformation of the crystals and thus initiate immediate failure. It is thought that this process identifies 90% or more glass, which might have subsequently failed after installation. The heat soaking process could be used either as a sampling method or as an additional treatment, which in the case of clear toughened glass could add up to 20% to the cost.

Heat soaking does not change any of the physical properties of toughened glass and therefore there is no means of distinguishing whether or not this process has been carried out. Current best practice dictates that specifiers should ensure that they specify 'heat soaked toughened glass to pr EN 14179. This standard reduces the anticipated failure rate to 1 per 400 tonnes of glass used.

Identification

When toughened glass is broken, the tensile stress is spread out from the source causing the pane to crack into small fragments (dicing). These fragments tend to be slightly wedge-shaped, emanating from the source of the fracture and are often held into position wedged against the frame due to their increased volume.

If the fracture is as a result of expansion of the nickel sulphide inclusion, those fragments immediately adjacent are more hexagonal and at the epicentre of the breakage the two larger particles form a distinctive butterfly shape linked by a central straight line crack. If large enough, the inclusion may be seen in the form of a black spec, or its presence may be confirmed by optical microscopy.

When carrying out an investigation, all possible causes of failure should be considered, including poor glazing tolerances and insufficient allowance for subsequent movement of the frame and any supporting structures. Possible causes may include deflection or rusting of steel frame, shrinkage of concrete frame, thermal movement, normal air pressures and even sonic booms. If the fracture is a result of impact or of local point loading, there should be evidence of local crushing.

The chances of installing a toughened glass pane, which may later fail due to the expansion of nickel sulphide inclusions, are very small.

Where it is essential, for reasons of accessibility or safety, that the pane should not fail, alternative forms of glass should be considered. One particular example would be in overhead situations – say in a shopping mall.

Testing

Samples should be sent intact with the epicentre protected with clear film to a suitable testing laboratory. Microscopic analysis will be sufficient for an initial diagnosis, but a scanning electron microscope will yield more information.

Glazing – ten things to look out for

Modern curtain walling systems are complex, and glass failures can be misdiagnosed easily. This section describes ten questions to consider when making an assessment of a commercial building.

What is the glass specification?

Reference to operating and maintenance manuals may help in identifying glass type, the configuration of double glazed units and whether they are coated, gas filled, toughened, laminated tempered or annealed glass. Identify the age of manufacture if possible, either by reference to drawings, or sometimes, if you are lucky, by reference to a date stamped on the inside of an aluminium spacer in the double glazed unit (DGU). Such stamps commonly have the month and year of manufacture and can be a good guide as to the possible future life expectancy of the unit. Estimating the life of an edge seal is very difficult because of the wide range of service conditions that could apply.

What is the glazing method?

Is the glass gasket glazed or 'wet' glazed with glazing compound? Is there a mechanism for allowing water to drain out of the glazing rebate? If not (and this is particularly the case with fully bedded systems) there is an acute risk that the edge seal to the DGU will deteriorate and become vapour permeable. When this happens, the pane will mist up with condensation. Typically, in fully bedded systems, a life expectancy of 10–15 years is common for DGUs – sometimes even shorter if the edge seals are in permanent contact with moisture.

Even if the glazing system is drained and ventilated (most modern buildings will be) it is best to check to make sure that the drainage system is not obstructed, that drainage slots line up or are present and that sealing tape (where present) has been cut in appropriate locations to allow drainage blocks to function – unfortunately, this is more than a straightforward visual check as the cover plates and pressure plates need to be removed.

Check gaskets for fit, particularly at corners and by pressing the back gaskets determine whether there is sufficient clamping pressure – they should not be able to be pushed inwards easily. Defects in either could allow water penetration into the system.

How is the glass supported?

The way in which glass is fitted and supported in a frame can be critical to its future performance. Aside from the visual indications of failure (cracking or shelling), poorly located or incorrect setting blocks may not be immediately apparent unless glazing beads or pressure plates are removed. Block dimensions should be equal to the sum of the glass thickness and the back face clearance to maintain proper support. Look out for blocks that are positioned incorrectly – if the glass panel is obviously out of square with the frame it could mean that the setting blocks are defective – too soft perhaps, or poorly positioned.

Is the glass coated?

There are a variety of different coatings that can be applied to glass – most adding some degree of reflectivity or solar control. Some low emissitivity glasses are coated with soft coatings – these are effective but vulnerable to damage during manufacture. Is there evidence of deterioration? Will it be possible to source replacement tints of the same colour or will they need to be specially made at high cost?

Is there a history of breakage?

If toughened glass has been used, has there been a history of failure due to nickel sulphide inclusions? Although research in Australia has identified a photographic method of identifying installed glass at risk of breakage, the system is not available commercially in the UK and there are no practical tests that can be undertaken to assess the risk.

If the glass is toughened, is it likely to be restrained if failure occurs?

Vertical glazing, whether this be obscured or vision glass, can be contained as it cracks and expands and will not necessarily fall out so long as it is contained within a rigid frame. However, if the frame is inclined to the vertical, or if the glass exists in an overhead situation, the glass will fall out. Whilst toughened glass breaks into small individual dice, it can clump together, particularly if the glass has a fritted finish. Larger clumps of glass could cause serious injury to occupants or passers by. Similarly, if the glass is not contained – say, for example, a glass balustrade, sudden failure will inevitably lead to collapse – the effects of this happening should be considered.

Is the glass damaged?

Glass is a strong material, but surface defects can weaken it significantly. The stress at which a material fractures depends on the size of the largest flaws present, the larger the flaw, the lower the fracture stress. Invisibly small cracks can cause stress concentrations, which allow cracks to propagate. Poor handling causing edge damage can be material, and deep pointed shells on the edge of a pane can be critical to its performance. Look for evidence of handling damage – this may not be apparent unless cover caps and pressure plates are removed. Examine the glass for evidence of scratching – this can happen with cleaners using abrasives or wearing diamond rings.

Can the glass cope with service temperatures?

Thermal stress can result in failure – particularly where the centre of the pane is heated to a higher temperature than the edges. Solar controlled glass and DGUs containing 'warm edge' spacers are also susceptible to thermal stress. In this type of failure, cracks will usually propagate from one or more small defects in the edge of the glass. Coloured glass spandrel panels can be susceptible to high temperature ranges, and unless the glass is able to cope with this, failures can occur. Toughened or tempered glass is usually better able to cope with temperature than ordinary annealed glass, but the manufacturing methods can give rise to optical distortions known as roller wave.

Is the glass located in an area that is 'at risk' within the meaning of regulation 14 of the Workplace (Health, Safety and Welfare) Regulations 1992?

The provision of suitable safety barriers, safety film or replacement glass may be required if it is. Glass testing kits are available to help determine whether toughened, laminated or annealed glass has been used. Remember that wired glass is not necessarily safety glass and that, depending upon the size of the panel and its thickness, ordinary annealed glass may be sufficient to satisfy the Regulations.

Is the building located in an area that could attract terrorist activity?

Consider the risk of blast damage. the primary aim of the facade should be to transfer the pressures generated in a blast back to the structure, so that the overall inertia of the building can absorb lateral forces.

Ordinary annealed glass is not a safety glass, and if it breaks, dangerous shards of glass can and often will cause the most severe injuries. Laminated glass offers the most advantageous properties, as the glass is held together by the action of the polyvinyl butyl (pvb) interlayer. However, for the system to work properly, laminated glass must be securely bonded to the frame with silicone. The installation of anti-shatter film (ASF) can be a useful strategy, particularly if combined with special net curtains. However, if used in unsuitable situations it can actually make matters worse. For example, its use in conjunction with single point fixed glass will mean that the relative stiffness of the filmed panel will permit failure at fixing positions. Applying ASF to a window that already contains laminated glass is not to be commended since it alters the flexural properties of the original glass which may then show a greater propensity to rupture around its edge and fall out.

The above questions are not exhaustive by any means: if in doubt it is best to consult an experienced facade consultant for detailed help and advice.

Further information

See BS 6262 and BS 8000 Part 7 for recommendations on glazing practice. The Glass and Glazing Federation (www.ggf.co.uk) publish recommendations for glazing and inspecting glass, whilst hugely valuable material can be found at the Centre for Window and Cladding Technology (www.cwct.co.uk) and glassfiles.com (www.glassfiles.com).

This section is based on an article originally written by Trevor Rushton for the RICS *Building Surveying Journal* (May 2006 edition), copyright RICS. Material is reproduced here with permission from RICS.

Sustainability

Sustainable development

What is sustainability?

The following summarises the meaning of sustainability, (source: the 1987 Brundtland report on sustainable development):

> 'Meet[ing] the needs of the present without compromising the ability of future generations to meet their own need'.

Sustainability is essentially concerned with living within environmental limits, ensuring a strong, healthy and equal society and maintaining a sustainable economy.

Why do we need to be more sustainable?

The world, in particular the developed world, has discovered and exploited a wealth of mineral and natural resources such as oil, water, coal, gas, and other natural resources. The increasing world population, mass consumerism and mass consumption has contributed to climate change and the rapid depletion of the natural resources relied upon to sustain our way of life.

It has been estimated by the World Wildlife Fund for Nature that the average person in the UK has an ecological footprint of 5.4 global hectares. A global hectare is the equivalent amount of land needed to produce the food, clothing, energy, water and other materials each person consumes throughout their life!

We must therefore give serious consideration to how we may conduct our personal lives and business in their operations, to ensure we are not unduly consuming the earth's limited resources in an unsustainable way that could compromise the health, well-being and survival of current and future generations.

Current generations must take immediate steps to be more sustainable now to protect future generations.

Climate change has been identified as the biggest threat to our existence on the earth, therefore the buildings we design and construct today need to be of low carbon intensity or ideally 'carbon neutral' and must be adaptable for our future climate.

'Sustainability' has become something of a buzz-word in recent years, a term which has been over-used, misused, or plain misunderstood, and often means different things to different people.

Sustainability is commonly referred to in terms of the 'triple bottom line': optimising the three key elements of **economic**, **social** and **environmental** sustainability and is often talked about in the same way as Corporate Social Responsibility (CSR).

Businesses are recognising the increasing importance of green credentials as a key part of corporate responsibility reporting and maintaining reputation. By engaging in sustainable practices, business organisations have peace of mind in the knowledge that stakeholder interests are managed and, additionally, new business opportunities can be realised.

Sustainable development

Sustainable development is primarily concerned with environmental sustainability, however the economic and social elements must also be considered in unison to measure the entire impact of development. The breadth of what sustainable development entails is vast. It covers waste reduction, recyclable materials and water, energy efficiency and local sourcing of energy, renewable energy and water efficient delivery, to name a few key areas.

The guidance document *Constructing for Sustainability*, produced by the Construction Industry Council, points out that sustainable development:

> 'Aims for synergy, rather than compromise, between economic, social and environmental factors. It secures a profitable project that functions well financially and for all stakeholders, whilst maintaining economic, social and environmental costs'.

The above text is reproduced from *Constructing for Sustainability – a basic guide for clients and their professional advisors*, with permission from the Construction Industry Council.

The solutions to achieving sustainable objectives will demand an holistic and often innovative approach. It must be recognised that many construction activities and buildings will not always achieve total sustainability, as it will not always be practicably or feasibly possible. However, by demonstrating a positive commitment to environmental 'damage limitation', surveying professionals can collectively contribute to providing a more sustainable built environment.

When a development is being proposed, fundamental questions that should initially be considered are:

- ❖ Is development necessary? This is a key question to establish what factors are driving the need and what is the benefit of development, other than financial.
- ❖ What economic, social and environmental benefits would development create?

Property professionals should consider:

- ❖ if there is a 'green' alterative to the materials specified, i.e. have **all options been considered**;
- ❖ **a review of contractor's experience and commitment**; and
- ❖ **a review of on-site procedures for waste management and storage, and recycling**.

There are a number of assessment tools available, the most common being BREEAM, which can rate the sustainability impact of a development, particularly with regard to the environmental impact of development.

The environmental impact of construction activities and the built environment

Everyday modern activities within business or domestic life have an impact on the environment and therefore it is up to every individual or business to take responsibility and accountability for taking action to minimise the impact we humans have.

A difference is made by individuals asking, 'What can I do?' and acting in a seemingly small everyday way.

The increase on landfill taxes, costs of hazardous waste disposal, the climate change levy and Building Regulations, for example, are designed to encourage more resource efficiency. This by implication will have an effect on the sustainability bottom line, and stimulate improvement in efficiencies.

The construction industry and the built environment have an important contribution to make in supporting long term sustainability objectives associated with the effective management of:

- ❖ materials and natural resources;
- ❖ energy;
- ❖ water;
- ❖ emissions, effluents and waste;

- ❖ transport;
- ❖ ecology; and
- ❖ land use, urban form and design.

Developments must be designed and procured (from client inception) to embrace all of the environmental, social and economic issues associated with immediate and long term sustainability objectives.

Creating a sustainable built environment

The following guiding principles should be followed to design for sustainable developments:

- ❖ Make existing buildings more energy efficient.
- ❖ Use less energy.
- ❖ Use energy saving materials.
- ❖ Recycle more in order to save the energy used to manufacture, transport and dispose of materials – even the steel in car tyres can be reused.
- ❖ Consider use of renewable energy sources and alternative technologies.
- ❖ Physically orientate buildings to maximise their capacity to exploit solar energy.
- ❖ Consider how existing materials could be reclaimed, recycled and reused in construction.
- ❖ Minimise the energy consumption in the transport of materials.
- ❖ Utilise prefabricated components.
- ❖ Incorporate natural building materials where practical into construction.
- ❖ Specify low maintenance materials in order to reduce further energy and resources use during the future life of the building.
- ❖ Dispose of ozone depleting substances responsibly.
- ❖ Use materials that do not emit harmful gases, radiation or dust.
- ❖ Recycle rainwater and grey water and specify water efficient devices.
- ❖ Reduce transport needs by procuring local materials, manufacturing and labour when practical.
- ❖ Use more sustainable resources where possible, such as timber.
- ❖ Design buildings to be sympathetic with their local environment and encourage ecology and habitat restoration.
- ❖ Design to minimise waste generation and consider the long term impacts of design decisions.
- ❖ Adopt 'just-in-time' ordering where possible to prevent the wastage of unused materials.
- ❖ Educate all personnel, especially on site, to enhance their understanding and their capacity to reduce waste and increase recycling.
- ❖ Specify energy efficient mechanical and electrical installations.
- ❖ Encourage occupiers to purchase only energy efficient electrical equipment and appliances.

These guiding principles are by no means comprehensive. They simply provide a flavour of the scope that environmental sustainability might encompass. It is, however, important to consider the hidden environmental costs of recycling and reusing – travel to recycling facilities should also be factored in when considering overall carbon footprints.

Sustainability and risk

A sustainable approach to development has also become an exercise in risk management and risk avoidance. For example, the exposure to the high costs of green taxes can be mitigated by taking the time to include sustainable design solutions at inception. Another example, in respect of planning applications, is a development which focuses on sustainable objectives, thereby increasing its chances of gaining planning permission, thus minimising opportunities for stakeholder objections.

The current UK Government has become reliant upon policies, regulations and legislation that penalises unsustainable practices and will reward those who actively promote sustainability. Therefore, compliance with these policies, regulations and legislation is imperative to mitigate and manage business risk, particularly with respect to prosecution for breach of regulations, public relations, business survival and cost exposure.

The cost of being sustainable

Consideration beyond capital costs alone must be made and more emphasis put on the analysis of life cycle costs together with the tangible and intangible investment for the life an asset. Payback periods and life cycle can be a compelling argument when proposing sustainable design.

Many individuals or businesses would not typically undertake a payback analysis for the purchase of a car or flat screen TV, yet these same individuals or businesses may baulk over capital cost of solar water heating, for example. Therefore, more objective and alternative value assessments need to be considered to demonstrate the entire benefits and not just the capital costs in isolation otherwise, looking just at pay back periods, photovoltaic cells are many years from being economically viable within their life cycle.

Sustainable development may inevitably cost more to implement, however, it can provide longer term investment benefits to building owners and occupiers, particularly when the life cycle and payback costs are factored into any calculation. A long term view must be taken with buildings as assets because in the future, buildings that are more sustainable and energy efficient will become more sought after and may command higher market and rental values.

Establishing the appropriate sustainability objectives

There are numerous opportunities for adopting sustainable practices. However, these opportunities cannot always, without qualification, be implemented in all circumstances for reasons of practicality, feasibility or cost. The key here is to target sustainable objectives that will have the most beneficial impact on a development. The decision, therefore, must be based upon a structured evaluation process. The most obvious method of analysing and adopting sustainability objectives is to set SMART targets, that is:

> **S**pecific
>
> **M**easurable
>
> **A**ffordable
>
> **R**ealistic
>
> **T**ime-related

A structured approach provides a focused application for construction teams to deliver sustainable performance. Without such an approach there is the risk of attempting to do everything and not actually achieving anything.

As surveying professionals we can make a significant contribution to making the built environment more sustainable but we do need to be focused and to consider the whole picture and all aspects of sustainability and recycling, rather than just ticking boxes for their own sake.

Further information

Construction Industry Council, *Constructing for Sustainability – a basic guide for clients and their professional advisors.*

Our Common Future, Report by Brundtland in 1987.

The British Land Company PLC, *Sustainability Brief*, November 2004 (developed with the assistance of Arup).

Contaminated land

Environmental due diligence is now commonplace in property transactions. The presence of contaminated land can adversely affect site value and rental income and can hinder transactions if not properly managed. With an increasing move away from greenfield development, it is no longer possible for the majority of investors or tenants to avoid owning or occupying some land affected by contamination, whether as a city centre property that has had a variety of past uses, or a new out of town development constructed on an old industrial site.

Statutory definition of contaminated under Part IIA of the Environmental Protection Act 1990

Under Part IIA legislation 'contaminated land' is:

> 'land which appears to the Local Authority in whose area it is situated to be in such a condition, by reason of substances in, on or under the land, that:
>
> (a) significant harm is being caused or there is the significant possibility of such harm being caused;
>
> or
>
> (b) pollution of controlled waters is being, or is likely to be, caused'.

© *Crown copyright material is reproduced with the permission of the Controller of HMSO and Queen's Printer for Scotland.*

Many sites that are contaminated will not fall within the definition and will not be classified as 'contaminated land' under Part IIA. However, such contamination could still have implications for owners and occupiers (for example, in terms of liability affecting the saleability and marketability of a site) and may still require a Phase II investigation.

Land is only defined as 'contaminated land' if there is a 'significant pollutant linkage' present. There must be evidence of a 'source – pathway – target' relationship. This means there should be a source present, a receptor that could be harmed by the source (e.g. humans), and a pathway linking the two.

Documentation

Documentation is the key to ensuring a smooth property transaction. Documentation should be in place to demonstrate the site condition has been adequately assessed. This can be undertaken by commissioning an

Environmental Audit and/or an intrusive ground/groundwater investigation. These assessments, which are discussed in further detail below, should ascertain the following:

- ❖ the site condition has been adequately assessed by an environmental assessment or review (commonly known as either an Environmental Audit or Phase I) and/or an intrusive site investigation (Phase II) and there are no significant information gaps;
- ❖ whether contamination is present (or is likely to be present), and the types of contaminants;
- ❖ where contamination has been identified, it does not represent a risk to the existing or proposed use of the site;
- ❖ contamination is not migrating off-site within groundwater;
- ❖ contamination does not represent a significant risk to groundwater and surface water resources or other sensitive receptors (e.g. sites of special scientific interest);
- ❖ contamination does not represent a risk of regulatory authority action (e.g. under Part IIA of the *Environmental Protection Act* 1990);
- ❖ contamination does not represent a risk of third party action (e.g. from adjoining land owners); and
- ❖ whether any potential liabilities may exist from any forthcoming business transaction.

Environmental Audit

Whilst an Environmental Audit desktop study does not include a site visit, an Environmental Audit (also known as a Phase I or an Environmental Assessment) is based on background research and should include a site inspection or walkover. A walkover would normally be advised to ensure all present day site issues are appropriately assessed. The research will normally include a review of:

- ❖ current site uses;
- ❖ historical site activities;
- ❖ environmental sensitivity;
- ❖ regulatory authority records; and
- ❖ a risk assessment and environmental risk rating.

Intrusive ground/groundwater investigation

An intrusive ground/groundwater investigation (also known as a Phase II) is based on a physical assessment of the underlying site conditions, and usually comprises chemical analysis and/or monitoring of soil, groundwater and ground gas.

If an Environmental Audit or existing knowledge identifies a potentially significant contamination issue, then it may be necessary to conduct a Phase II investigation to gain an understanding of whether contamination is actually present and whether it is likely to represent a significant risk or liability.

A Phase II investigation will normally include:

- ❖ a summary of the Environmental Audit findings;
- ❖ a description of the Phase II investigation methods;
- ❖ data and observations recorded during the site work, including field evidence of contamination;
- ❖ data from chemical analysis of ground/groundwater/ground gas samples;
- ❖ interpretation of the results and an assessment of risk; and
- ❖ recommendations for remediation (if required) of the underlying ground and/or groundwater.

The Phase II investigation should be designed to address the specific issues raised by the Environmental Audit, such as the range of contaminants highlighted as possibly being present (for example, hydrocarbons at a petrol station, ground gas from a landfill site, etc.).

Typical sampling methodologies are detailed below:

❖ **Soil sampling:** Soil samples are required for chemical analysis to determine the presence of any contamination. Methods of soil sampling differ depending on the contaminants being tested. Usually disturbed samples are adequate for testing most chemicals. These can be obtained from the excavator bucket when trial pits are being used, from the cuttings from boreholes or from the window within a window sampler.

Samples are analysed in the laboratory for a wide range of 'base line' contaminant chemicals, often supplemented by further specialist testing depending upon the type of contamination present.

❖ **Water sampling:** Water samples can be obtained by inserting a standpipe into a completed borehole. Water samples will be taken after insertion for further chemical analysis. The well may also be used for the monitoring of gas. Installation can be permanent/semi-permanent to facilitate further sampling at a later date. Laboratory analysis is similar to soil samples.

❖ **Gas sampling:** The presence of methane and carbon dioxide may be established on sites which are landfills or close to neighbouring landfills. Monitoring wells constructed for water sampling may also be used to sample the presence of land gas. In-situ measurements of gas concentrations and flow are taken at ground level on the head of the monitoring well using an infrared gas analyser. Wells may be constructed to measure gas concentrations and flow at different depths.

The majority of sites undergoing development will require a Phase II investigation, particularly where the previous use was industrial. Phase II investigations can often be combined with geotechnical investigations for foundation design. Sites that are not being developed may also require Phase II investigations (e.g. during transactions). This may depend on whether a significant pollutant linkage has been identified or if the local authority may investigate the site as part of their Part IIA inspection strategy in the near future.

Remediation

Remediation of sites can be achieved by removing sources of contamination, reducing levels of contamination or modifying the 'pathways' between the source and the identified sensitive receptors. The main approaches include:

❖ excavating and removing contaminated material off site to landfill (dig and dump);
❖ encapsulating or separating contaminated material on site, by severing contaminant pathways with barriers (e.g. underground bentonite walls); and
❖ treating the contaminated material, either in situ or after removal (e.g. bioremediation or soil washing).

Remediation can often be combined with the redevelopment of the site. Remediation strategies should be approved in advance by the local authority and the Environment Agency. Post-remediation validating sampling (e.g. of soil/groundwater) should be undertaken to document that the remediation has been effective.

Environmental insurance

Environmental insurance is increasingly being used in property transactions to cover risks associated with contaminated land. Environmental insurance can be obtained directly from specialist underwriters, or through an insurance broker. A broker will normally obtain quotations from a number of different underwriters, in order to negotiate the best insurance cover and premium for a client.

The most common type of environmental insurance covers regulatory and third party claims due to land contamination. Other types of insurance can provide protection against unpredictable costs should site remediation expenses prove difficult to quantify at the planning stage.

When taking out environmental insurance, one of the most important aspects is to understand what circumstances the policy would cover. Furthermore, as with many insurance policies, environmental insurance policies are often written in a language that is sometimes unclear.

Common exclusions from policies are:

- ❖ known contamination;
- ❖ business disruption costs;
- ❖ remediation costs on change of land use; and
- ❖ loss in value.

Key contaminated land legislation

The government believes that the planning process provides the best means of remediating sites. In most cases the planning system is capable of handling such issues, for example by requiring Phase II investigations or by requiring remediation to be approved by the local authority prior to development. A new contaminated land regime was introduced in 2000 in the UK (as Part IIA of the *Environmental Protection Act* 1990). This is intended to deal with problem contaminated sites that are not being developed and which would therefore not be dealt with under the planning system.

Enforcing authorities

The local authority is duty bound to provide a public register containing information about land that has formally been identified as potentially contaminated, and the action which has been taken to remediate it. Any land that has satisfactorily been remediated prior to a remediation notice being served will not appear on the public register. Furthermore, if land is to be redeveloped in the near future it is unlikely that a notice will be served.

The cost of any clean up will normally lie with the person (or 'appropriate persons') who knowingly caused the contamination. The local authority will ensure the clean up is carried out either through the planning process, via voluntary remediation, or if necessary by serving a remediation notice requiring them to clean up the site. In the case of an emergency the council will remediate the site and recover the costs afterwards.

Local authorities have primary responsibility for the identification of contaminated land, although the Environment Agency will respond to requests from a local authority for information on land that it is considering to prioritise for inspection. Where a site has been determined as contaminated land, they must take into account any information held by the Environment Agency on issues of water pollution.

Special sites

Land may also be categorised by the local authority as a 'special site'. This definition includes sites which may be affecting underlying water supplies or major aquifers such as military land, oil refineries and nuclear plants.

Once the local authority has made this designation then the Environment

Agency takes over the enforcing role. The Environment Agency would then maintain full responsibility for the site including both the cost of enforcement and also any testing and monitoring required. Should the site become an 'orphan site' (when no knowing polluter is found) then they will also be responsible for the cost of remediation. The disadvantage from the local authorities' perspective is that they do lose control of what can be politically sensitive sites. If there is a dispute as to whether or not the site is a special site the matter can be referred to the Secretary of State for determination.

Remediation notice

The local authority cannot serve a remediation notice until three months have elapsed since the person or persons were notified of the designation of their land as contaminated. If the local authority finds, in the course of the consultation period, additional appropriate persons, it must notify them of the designation of the land as contaminated, and then wait a further three months before serving any remediation notice on them.

Although the local authority is under a duty to serve a remediation notice, it may wait for more than three months before doing so. This may well be the case where discussions about voluntary remediation are ongoing. It is vital that time limits be set for the actions that are going to be required otherwise it will not be possible for the local authority to initiate enforcement proceedings on the basis that the action has not been carried out. Any remediation notice must effectively be justified with reference to the statutory *Contaminated Land (England) Regulations* 2006 (SI 2006/1380) guidance by including the following:

 ❖ the remediation scheme proposed;
 ❖ any exclusion from liability; and
 ❖ any apportionment of costs.

The remediation notice may, therefore, have to be a fairly lengthy document. It should be carefully drafted, so as to attempt to avoid an appeal being made against it. It should be remembered that there might be several remediation notices for each site. Copies should be provided to all the parties that were consulted about remediation, and to the Environment Agency. Where there are several appropriate persons for a given action, a single remediation notice may be served on all of them. Details of the notice must be included in the register.

Appeals

There is a right of appeal against a remediation notice. Where the local authority serves a remediation notice the appeal is heard in the local Magistrates' Court. An appeal is made by way of a summary application to the Court. If the Environment Agency serves the remediation notice because it has taken over regulation of a site and it is now the appropriate authority an appeal will be heard by an inspector appointed by the Secretary of State.

The time limit for bringing an appeal is 21 days beginning with the first day of service. A remediation notice, on appeal, can be modified, confirmed or quashed. The remediation notice may be quashed if there is 'a material defect' in the notice. The grounds for appeal are set out in the *Contaminated Land (England) Regulations* 2006. There are a large number of grounds of appeal including:

 ❖ the appellant is not the appropriate person;
 ❖ the authority failed to exclude the appellant;
 ❖ there has been an improper apportionment of costs;
 ❖ there is some error with the notice;
 ❖ the requirements of the notice are unreasonable having regard to the costs and benefits; and
 ❖ the period of time for compliance is insufficient.

Who is liable under Part IIA?

❖ Remediation notices are served in the first instance on 'Class A' persons, i.e. polluters or knowing permitters of contamination. If these responsible parties cannot be found, the current owner or occupier may be responsible (although for a more limited range of liabilities) – 'Class B' persons, Several parties may be implicated.

❖ Sellers can avoid liability where there are payments for remediation, with an explicit statement in the sale contract that a purchaser is being paid to clean up land or that the purchase price is being reduced to reflect the contaminated state of the land.

❖ Sellers/landlords can also avoid liability by selling with information – giving the purchaser (or tenant under a long lease) the necessary information to identify contamination before buying. Where transactions have occurred since 1990 between large commercial organisations, the granting of permission by the seller for the buyer to carry out its own investigations as to the condition of the land, is normally sufficient to indicate that the buyer had the necessary information.

Progress with Part II implementation

The latest available Environment Agency figures indicate that of the estimated 100,000 contaminated sites UK wide, local authorities have formally designated only 406 sites as 'contaminated' under the Part IIA definition, of which 22 have been designated as 'special sites'.

Furthermore, the number of remediation notices served by local authorities remains very low. In most cases remediation is undertaken by site owners via the planning system with infrequent use of remediation statements. Local authorities have so far served only four remediation notices.

Ground gas including radon

Methane and carbon dioxide

The occurrence and associated dangers of methane and carbon dioxide within the construction industry are well understood. Both gases occur naturally, although prominence of issues arises around areas of made ground, i.e. landfills.

Methane (chemical formula CH_4) is a basic hydrocarbon and is explosive in air at concentrations of between 5–15%. Methane is generated by the anaerobic (absence of oxygen) degradation of organic material.

Carbon dioxide (chemical formula – CO_2) is a product of aerobic (presence of oxygen) organic degradation. Carbon dioxide is classed as highly toxic. Where 3%v/v carbon dioxide is present, this can result in headaches and shortness of breath, with increasing severity up to 5%v/v or 6%v/v. (Source: *Guidance on evaluation of Development proposals on site where Methane and Carbon Dioxide are present*, NHBC, March 2007.)

Both methane and carbon dioxide are asphyxiants (methane by its capability to displace oxygen). Numerous studies have identified the risk presented by the entry of these gases into building voids and other confined spaces. Perhaps the best known UK incident concerning landfill gas is at Loscoe, Derbyshire in March 1986 when a bungalow adjacent to a landfill site was destroyed by an explosion of accumulated methane. A subsequent investigation attributed a rapid drop in atmospheric pressure (27 millibars over seven hours) resulting in gas being drawn in towards the property through the permeable underlying geology.

Another well documented incident at Abbeystead in March 1984 resulted in 16 fatalities. Natural dissolved methane in water passing through a valve house at the Lune/Wyre water transfer scheme was released and allowed to accumulate during a period of inactivity. An unknown source (thought to be either an electrical fault or cigarette lighter) triggered the subsequent explosion, occurring at a time of an organised tour and demonstration of the valve house.

Sources

Natural sources of ground gas include:

- ❖ peat bogs and mosslands;
- ❖ limestone and chalk;
- ❖ coal measures;
- ❖ river and lake sediments;
- ❖ made ground;
- ❖ farmland; and
- ❖ sewers.

Detection and control

The assessment of risk from ground gas within new developments is a material consideration in local authority building control, planning and environmental health legislation.

- ❖ The *Town and County Planning Act* 1990 requires that the potential for contamination and risk from landfill and ground gases must be considered during development. If the development is within an area of potential risk, a planning condition will likely be attached to any permitted application, requiring satisfactory assessment and mitigation. The duty of the developer to maintain any gas protection systems may be conditioned within the planning consent.

- ❖ Ground gas is also dealt with under Part IIA of the *Environmental Protection Act* 1990. Where a significant potential of significant harm exists to a development (either existing or being developed), the local authority can enforce appropriate remediation or mitigation.

- ❖ Approved guidance to the *Building Regulations* 2000 (Approved Document C, 2004 edition) states that where there is a potential risk, further investigation is required to determine whether gas measures are required and what level of protection is necessary.

A number of measures can be undertaken to reduce the risk of ground gas.

A desk study may be undertaken to determine the probability of ground gas affecting the site. This includes a desk-based study of the history and geology of the area and any additional information such as mining or landfill activities. If a source of gas is identified, gas monitoring installations and monitoring may be recommended.

British Standards BS 1017:2001 *Investigation of potentially contaminated sites – Code of Practice* and BS 5930:1999 *Code of Practice for site investigations* recommend a minimum of 12 months' monitoring.

The most common method of detection is a standard landfill gas analyser and flow meter, which measure methane, carbon dioxide and oxygen concentrations. Photo ionisation detectors (PID) and flame ionisation detectors (FID) can be used where other gases such as organic volatiles are suspected.

Protection measures

The type of mitigation measures required depend on the type of development, gas type, volume, source and emission rate.

In ground barriers

These are physical barriers to block gas migration and usually comprise compacted clay, bentonite or polyethylene. This method is often used for large areas, for example, closed landfill sites. However, it is a relatively expensive protection measure.

Ventilation

Ventilation (either active or passive) is the most commonly used gas protection measure. A secondary level of protection is often required, as ventilation is influenced by factors such as wind speed and direction, and atmospheric pressure.

Ventilation can comprise underfloor venting or trench venting. Underfloor venting uses an open void space with connection to the atmosphere such as air bricks, pipe riser and gravel filled trenches. Trench venting involves excavating a trench or series of columns and backfilling with a permeable infill such as gravel. Gas permeates freely to the open atmosphere rather than migrating laterally. This method is commonly used at the boundaries of landfill sites.

Gas resistant membranes

Membranes are often used in conjunction with other measures. A number of different types of membrane are available depending on the volatility and density of the gas. The effectiveness of a membrane is dependent on techniques of sealing the membrane to the building fabric, ensuring that gas cannot leak through to occupied areas or accumulate in voids.

Alarm systems

Alarm systems are designed to trigger when gas concentrations reach a certain level. Gas probes are situated around the building and feed data into a central system. These are mainly used as additional protection for high risk sites or existing buildings where it is not possible to use other protection measures. They are, however, costly and require regular maintenance.

Radon

Radon is a colourless, odourless gas that is radioactive. It is formed where uranium and radium are present and can move through cracks and fissures in the subsoil, and so into the atmosphere or into spaces under and in dwellings. Where it occurs in high concentrations it can pose a risk to health. (Source: *Radon: guidance on protective measures for new dwellings*, Building Research Establishment, 1999.)

Radon is everywhere but usually in insignificant, variable concentrations. Problems occur when it enters enclosed spaces, such as basements, where concentrations can accumulate. Some areas in the UK are more exposed to radon due to localised geology.

The Health Protection Agency (HPA) publishes maps of radon affected areas across England and Wales and areas of Northern Ireland. The HPA has set threshold levels for both commercial and residential properties. Where potential health risk may exist, detectors should be installed and remedial work be undertaken to reduce exposure.

The HPA offer a search service and report, specifying whether a property is in a radon affected area. The British Geological Survey (www.bgs.ac.uk) also states whether radon is likely within a particular area as part of its Address-Linked Geological Inventory.

Identification of radon

Radon levels can vary substantially with time, so prolonged measurements are required for reliable results. Short measurements can be misleading, low or alarmingly high. The government recommends that people in affected areas test their property for a period of three months using passive monitors in order to provide a reliable estimate of the average radon level. Passive monitors are easy to use, inexpensive and available from Defra.

Remedial action for high radon levels can be quite straightforward. The best approach is to prevent radon entering the building from the ground by altering the balance of pressure between the inside and outside.

This can be achieved by carrying out the following:

❖ Install a small sump pump below the floor and connect to a low power fan in order to extract the air and reduce the pressure under the floor. Multiple sumps can be used in large buildings.

❖ Improved ventilation under suspended timber and concrete floors. New airbricks are installed, sometimes together with a fan.

❖ Increase the pressure in the building by blowing air (called positive pressurisation) from the roof space with a small fan. Best results are in buildings with low natural ventilation. Secondary benefits may include a reduction of other indoor pollutants such as carbon dioxide, reduced condensation and a 'fresher' indoor environment.

❖ Alternatively, one may seal ducts, joints and cracks in the floors, although this is rarely effective by itself and always laborious. It is helpful to close large openings when a sump is used.

❖ Install a membrane barrier. This is very difficult to successfully achieve in an existing building.

Radon and the Building Regulations

With the new understanding of radon risk, the government legislated that houses built since 1988 in parts of Devon and Cornwall and 1992 in parts of Somerset, Derbyshire and Northamptonshire had to have radon protection measures built in. Additionally, the precise areas where radon protective measures should be taken are periodically reviewed by Defra as new data is provided by the Health Protection Agency. Two zones of risk were allowed for. First the primary zone (the area with the highest risk). Requirement C2 of Schedule 1 of the Building Regulations requires that each house has a radon proof area, together with other precautionary measures that can be upgraded if a risk shows high radon levels. In the secondary zone (where the risk is lower) only precautionary measures must be built in. If a house has precautionary measures, upgrading them (for example, adding a fan to a sump and pipe system) could solve the radon problem quickly and simply. The BRE has published guidance on protective measures for new dwellings in support of the Building Regulations entitled BRE Report *Radon: Guidance on Protective Measures for New Dwellings*. Equivalent advice has been prepared by the HSE within a document entitled *Radon in the workplace*. The document recommends many similar measures are applicable for non-domestic buildings.

Energy conservation

Some of the ways in which energy efficiency can be enhanced are outlined below.

❖ **Greater thermal insulation:** This is one of the most cost-effective ways of increasing a building's energy efficiency. With new buildings, obviously the starting point is to meet the standards of thermal insulation set out in the current Building Regulations. However, there is a strong argument for further increasing thermal insulation and the level chosen will depend upon a variety of factors including the pay-back period required, the user's pattern of occupation and whether environmental concern outweighs strictly financial considerations. Our existing buildings offer great scope to increase insulation and this can be carried out during refurbishment or maintenance periods when better use can be made of access equipment and other site overheads.

❖ **Efficient lighting:** In commercial buildings, lighting costs usually run between 40% and 50% of total energy costs. Highly efficient lighting that can significantly reduce running costs is now available for both new and existing installations.

❖ **Efficient services:** These require preventative maintenance to ensure that all plant is operating at maximum efficiency. When plant requires renewal, consideration should be given to alternatives, such as condensing boilers or combined heat and power plant, or even whether the plant is required at all; many are re-evaluating the need for air conditioning.

❖ **Building management systems:** These monitor and control all service installations. Due to recent technological advances, these systems are becoming less expensive and can therefore be installed on smaller properties. Even where a full BMS is inappropriate, simple systems are available which control single services such as lighting management systems.

❖ **Using locally sourced materials:** This minimises energy consumption when transporting materials to site.

❖ **Building materials:** Those with a long life expectancy imply energy efficiency because they make good use of resources. The manufacture of building materials entails energy consumption and this varies widely depending on the product. Unfortunately, there is insufficient research into the energy consumed during the manufacture of building materials to allow choices to be made with a great deal of confidence. In the meantime, a useful rule-of-thumb is that the greater the degree of processing or manufacture, the greater the energy consumed.

❖ **Making use of solar gain:** Even with their humblest dwellings, our ancestors frequently designed their buildings to make use of solar gain. Generally this entails the use of large areas of glazing on southern elevations and minimal openings to the north. Increasing numbers of building designers are re-interpreting these techniques.

❖ **The use of soft landscaping:** Trees and other planting can conserve energy in buildings by minimising heat gains and losses. A screen of deciduous planting at the south of a building will filter strong summer sun but will allow for natural heat gain from weaker winter sun. Soft landscaping also has an important part to play in influencing the micro-climate around buildings by reducing wind speeds.

❖ **Out-of-town schemes:** Many of these schemes are built with high levels of thermal insulation and efficient building services. Nevertheless, because of the fuel used in transporting building users from their homes, the whole scheme may be very inefficient in energy terms.

Increased energy efficiency is available at little extra cost – it is just a matter of adopting an environmental train of thought. Increased awareness of these issues by players in the property market and pressure of legislation should be seen as an opportunity to create more energy efficient buildings.

Ozone depleting substances

Ozone depletion

Ozone (O_3) is a triatomic gas consisting of three oxygen atoms. Ozone has a similar molecular structure to atmospheric diatomic oxygen (O_2) but is much less stable.

Ozone can be both an air pollutant or an important atmospheric gas depending upon its location within the atmosphere. At ground level ozone is a hazardous pollutant, which can potentially cause respiratory problems in humans and animals. Ozone located in the upper atmosphere in a zone known as the stratosphere is essential for filtering and thus reducing the amount of ultraviolet (UV) radiation from the sun reaching the earth's surface. It is commonly understood that a group of man-made chemicals containing chlorine and bromine (known as halocarbons) have potential to cause significant damage to this ozone layer.

The best-known group of halocarbons are chlorofluorocarbons (CFCs). The emission of CFCs to the atmosphere has largely been due to their use as refrigerants within air-cooling equipment, refrigerators and as aerosol propellants. This low reactivity of CFCs affords the gases enough time to disperse to the upper levels of the atmosphere where UV radiation from the sun breaks down the CFCs releasing chlorine atoms. The chlorine atoms act as highly reactive free radicals, which catalyse a number of reactions resulting in the breakdown of ozone into oxygen. As these reactions generally regenerate the chlorine atom, a single atom has the potential to destroy many thousands of ozone molecules.

The aforementioned reactions are widely believed to be the cause of the 'holes' in the ozone layer above the earth's polar regions. The first observation of an ozone hole was recorded in 1985 above Antarctica. Data published by NASA and the Royal Netherlands Meteorological Institute has suggested that in recent years the ozone hole has covered an area equivalent to the size of North America.

Protection of the ozone layer is considered vital to minimise the harmful effects of UV radiation on human health and other flora and fauna. Health problems such as increased rates of skin cancer, eye cataracts and reduction in human immunity to disease are all effects considered attributable to increased UV radiation.

In reaction to the issue of ozone depletion, an international agreement between world leaders was sanctioned in Montreal in 1987. The Montreal Protocol comprised an international treaty designed to protect the ozone layer by phasing out and banning certain substances known to deplete stratospheric ozone. Since its inception the Protocol has undergone five revisions, most recently in Beijing in 1999. The Protocol concentrates on several groups of ozone depleting chemicals and provides a timetable for their phasing out and eventual elimination. Overall, this has been regarded as one of the most successful pieces of international legislation to date, resulting in a recorded 95% reduction in ozone depleting substance consumption by developed countries and a 50–75% reduction by developing countries (Defra, 2004). The extent of the recovery of stratospheric ozone remains uncertain. However, providing the provisions of the Montreal Protocol are adhered to, some predictions state the ozone layer could be replenished by 2100.

Existing plant

Where CFCs or HCFCs (hydrochlorofluorocarbons) are identified as being contained within existing air conditioning or refrigeration plant, the contract administrator is to be informed immediately and instructions obtained.

Where the plant is scheduled, or instructed subsequently, for removal then under no circumstances is the gas to be dumped by venting into the atmosphere. The gas is to be collected for recovery/destruction by a specialist firm.

The contract administrator is to be informed in writing of the specialist undertaking the works, the date for removal and be provided with a copy of the recovery/destruction certificate.

New plant

The contractor shall receive and transmit to the contract administrator documentary evidence from suppliers, subcontractors and designers of all new installations that no new or reused plant contains refrigerants with an ozone depletion potential of more than 0.06 (or with any ozone depleting potential). Furthermore, compounds with the lowest possible ozone depleting potential are to be selected where there is a choice.

As an alternative, consideration can be given to the use of absorption chillers or ammonia chillers.

Halon fire fighting systems

The general requirements for decommissioning the systems shall be the same as for CFCs and HCFCs in plant.

If the system is to be tested, then compressed air or some other non-ozone depleting gas shall be used.

If the system is to be recharged, a leak detection system should be installed. However, the preference is for some other form of fire extinguishing system wherever possible. Depending on the circumstances options include inert gases (Inergen, Argonite, etc.), carbon dioxide and water fog/mist systems.

Hand-held fire extinguishers

All fire extinguishers on site supplied by the contractor, or specified to be supplied in the Schedule of Works section shall be either powder, foam, carbon dioxide, water spray or some other type without the use of halon.

Additional measures

CFCs and HCFCs are used in the manufacture of a variety of other products including insulating materials, carpets, furnishings and aerosol sprays. They must not be used unless specifically instructed by the contract administrator.

Building Research Establishment Environmental Assessment Method

The Building Research Establishment Environmental Assessment Method (BREEAM) is the world's most widely used system for assessing, reviewing and improving a range of environmental impacts associated with buildings.

Since its launch in 1990 BREEAM has been increasingly accepted in the UK construction and property sectors as offering best practice in environmental design and management. Buildings are assessed against performance criteria set by the BRE and awarded 'credits' based on their level of performance. The building's performance is then rated as pass, good, very good or excellent.

BREEAM covers a range of building types: offices, homes (known as EcoHomes), industrial units, retail and since January 2005, schools.

BREEAM 2002 was launched on 31 August 2002 by the Building Research Establishment and all new assessments are carried out under this scheme.

BREEAM for Offices is updated every year to ensure best practice and relevance to changing standards and regulations. The challenge to achieve the highest rating has increased as targets are being continually raised.

Developers and designers can utilise BREEAM for a range of reasons, including creation of better environments for people to work in, increased building efficiency, improved marketability, increased value and rentals and also as a checklist for comparing buildings. Clients and developers can use BREEAM as a tool to define and specify the environmental and sustainability performance requirements of their buildings at the briefing stage. Agents can use the rating to promote the environmental credentials and benefits of a building to potential owners and tenants. Designers can use BREEAM as a method to improve the performance, environmental and sustainability aspects of buildings.

A BREEAM Office assessment of the building fabric and services is undertaken plus, as appropriate, the quality of the design and procurement and also management and operating procedures. The scheme requires a commitment to a number of areas, listed below, that are reviewed by independent assessors who are trained and licensed by the BRE.

- ❖ Management: overall policy, site management via the Construction Confederation Considerate Constructors Scheme and procedural issues.
- ❖ Health and well being: both internal and external issues affecting occupants' health.
- ❖ Energy efficiency including operational energy and carbon dioxide issues.
- ❖ Transport: carbon dioxide and location related factors.
- ❖ Water consumption and efficiency.
- ❖ Materials: environmental implications and life cycle impact.
- ❖ Land use regarding greenfield and brownfield sites.
- ❖ Ecology including enhancement of the site as well as ecological value conservation.
- ❖ Pollution of air and water.

To achieve an excellent rating the most cost effective way is to address the main issues at the earliest point of the design process with input from the full project team. A design and procurement prediction checklist is available to assist with this process.

A BREEAM assessor can be used to coordinate and collate input from the team and to track the development of ideas. The assessor can also give advice about BREEAM to the entire project team at the start of the project. As the scheme progresses, the assessor can provide specialist advice on the specification of products to achieve particular BREEAM credits, undertake preliminary BREEAM assessments to assess the predicted rating and provide a sustainability report inclusion with submission for planning approval.

At completion a certificate is awarded and this can be used for promotional purposes.

The European Directive on the Energy Performance of Buildings

The European Directive on the *Energy Performance of Buildings* (EPBD) took effect from 4 January 2006. The Directive will play a vital role in delivering the government's energy objectives.

Buildings account for more than 40% of carbon emissions in the UK. The purpose of the Directive is to promote the improvement of energy performance in buildings by encouraging owners and tenants to choose energy efficient buildings when seeking new premises and to improve the energy efficiency of existing buildings that they occupy.

In the UK, the Directive is being enforced through major changes to the Building Regulations (Articles 5 and 6) and the introduction of energy certification and will affect both domestic and non-domestic properties.

A number of changes are being implemented through the Building Regulations resulting in the need to upgrade existing building stock when undertaking certain repairs and refurbishment works to a property. This applies to both the building fabric and the services installations. For example, upgrading of the roof insulation is likely to be required when stripping and re-covering a roof. Further information in this regard can be found within Part L of the Building Regulations and the accompanying Approved Documents.

The Directive's key provisions are:

❖ minimum requirements for the energy performance of all new buildings (enforced through Building Regulations);

❖ minimum requirements for the energy performance of existing buildings more than 1000m^2 that are subject to major renovation (also enforced through Building Regulations – improvements must be undertaken but only where they are technically and economically feasible and with a 15 year payback. Historic buildings are not exempt. Improvements will also be required on buildings less than 1000m^2 through Building Regulations where, for example, parts of the building envelope are renewed, such as windows and doors);

❖ energy certification of all buildings (which on public buildings needs to be prominently displayed). Certification will be required to be in place prior to sale or lease of buildings and will need to be renewed every ten years; and

❖ regular mandatory inspection of air-conditioning systems in buildings (a practical inspection and assessment method is available from CIBSE publications, TM44 refers).

Energy Performance Regulations

The *Energy Performance of Buildings (Certificates and Inspections) (England and Wales) Regulations* 2007 (the 'Energy Performance Regulations') come into force over the next few years up to 2011. These Regulations implement Articles 7, 9 and 10 of the EPBD in England and Wales.

❖ Article 7 requires **Energy Performance Certificates** (EPCs) to be produced when buildings are constructed, sold or rented out. EPCs are also required (under Building Regulations) for existing buildings which undergo major alterations. The EPC provides the property with an asset rating.

❖ **Display Energy Certificates** (DECs) are required in large buildings occupied by public authorities and certain public institutions. DECs are intended to show the public how well a building is performing and are required where the useful floor area is over 1,000m^2. DECs are based on actual energy usage from energy meters and are valid for 12 months. DECs apply to public authorities (such as central government departments) and institutions that provide public services (such as public museums and swimming pools). This requirement could be extended to retail and hospitality. Certificates must be displayed prominently so that they are visible by the public.

❖ EPCs will show the energy demand of a building on scale between A–G.

❖ The Regulations require that EPCs must be accompanied by recommendations on improving the energy performance of the building.

❖ There are a number of exemptions under the duty to provide an EPC, including places of worship, temporary buildings with a planned time of use of two years or less, certain buildings with low energy demand (as identified in Approved Document L2A 2006), stand alone buildings less than 50m² and certain limited buildings which are to be demolished.

❖ EPCs are valid for ten years (both residential and commercial).

❖ Article 9 requires regular inspection and reporting on the energy performance of air-conditioning systems. This applies where the collective cooling capacity is larger than 12kW. Inspection intervals are not to exceed five years. The report must contain advice on improving the efficiency of the system and also must be undertaken by a member of an approved accreditation scheme. There is no requirement to act on any advice given though.

❖ Article 10 requires the use of qualified and/or accredited energy assessors to carry out the certification process in an independent manner. Also, those that undertake the preparation of EPCs or DECs must be members of an accreditation scheme approved by the Secretary of State.

❖ In respect of commercial property, penalties for breaches of the Regulations apply depending on the rateable value of the property, subject to a maximum penalty of £5,000. The penalty for failing to display a DEC is £500 and failure to obtain an advisory report is £1,000. Failure to have an air-conditioning system inspected is fixed at £300. DECs will be enforced by Trading Standards Officers.

The Regulations require that sellers and prospective landlords make available an EPC of the property to prospective buyers and tenants at the earliest opportunity.

Timetable (England and Wales)

(Please note that the dates detailed below may be subject to change.)

Date	Requirement
14 December 2007	EPCs required on the sale of all residential property.
6 April 2008	EPCs required on the construction of all new dwellings.
6 April 2008	EPCs required for the construction, sale or rent of buildings over 10,000m², other than dwellings.
1 July 2008	EPCs required for the construction, sale or rent of buildings over 2,500m², other than dwellings.
1 October 2008	EPCs required on the construction, sale or rent of all remaining buildings other than dwellings.
1 October 2008	Display Energy Certificates (DECs) required for all public buildings >1,000m².
4 January 2009	First inspection of all existing air-conditioning systems over 250kW must have occurred by this date.*
4 January 2011	First inspection of all remaining air-conditioning systems over 12kW must have occurred by this date.*

* Note: A system first put into service on or after 1 January 2008 must have its first inspection within five years of it being first put into service.

Details on the DEC training and accreditation scheme are still to be agreed at the time of writing.

Qualified and/or accredited independent experts will be required to carry out inspections and issue certificates. Details are due to be provided from the department for Communities and Local Government (CLG) in due course.

To help the government implement the Directive, a high level working group has been established called Directive Implementation Advisory Group (DIAG). This has been formed by representatives of more than 22 key professional bodies and trade associations.

For more information visit www.diag.org.uk or www.communities.gov.uk

Scotland energy certification

Responsibility for implementing the EU energy Directive on behalf of Scottish Ministers has been given to the Scottish Building Standards Agency (SBSA). This has been implemented through a new building standards system in Scotland, introduced on 1 May 2005. Energy certificates are required when buildings are constructed, sold or rented out. This applies to residential and commercial property, both public and private sector. These are being phased in as follows:

- ❖ construction from 1 May 2007; and
- ❖ selling or leasing of a commercial building over 1,000m², 4 January 2009.

The Scottish Building Standards Agency (SBSA) entered into an agreement with the Chartered Institute of Building Services Engineers, Scotland (CIBSE Scotland) on 17 May 2007 which will accredit members to deliver services in relation to Energy Performance Certificates (EPCs) for existing buildings.

Agreements were also made with RICS, EI and ABE in November 2007 to accredit members to provide services.

Two EPC model certificates have been approved for use in Scotland, one for dwellings, the second for all other building types. These forms can be downloaded in pdf format at www.sbsa.gov.uk/european issues/epcformat.htm

Northern Ireland energy certification

The EPBD is being implemented jointly by the Department of Finance and Personnel and the Department for Social Development. HIPs (Home Information Packs) are not required although EPCs are to be produced as stand alone reports.

Articles 3–6 of the EPBD were implemented in November 2006 through an update to Building Regulations. Articles 7–10 are still to be implemented. The timetable for both dwellings and non-dwellings will be:

- ❖ new build – early 2008;
- ❖ sales – mid-2008; and
- ❖ rentals – January 2009.

There will be no public consultation in NI as only the minimum requirements of the EPBD are to be implemented. From November 2007, a wide public awareness campaign will be undertaken instead, including television and radio advertisements and road shows.

Renewable energy

Renewable energy relates to naturally available sources that are constantly being replenished and capable of being harnessed for human benefit, such as energy from the sun, the wind and tides, and energy from replaceable matter such as wood.

Low or zero carbon energy (LZC), synonymous with renewables, is the term normally applied to renewable sources and to technologies which are more efficient than traditional solutions or emit less carbon. LZC technologies being applied to buildings include:

- ❖ solar thermal systems;
- ❖ photovoltaics;
- ❖ district heating and cooling;
- ❖ combined heat and power;
- ❖ ground source cooling;
- ❖ ground source heat pumps;
- ❖ wind power;
- ❖ biofuels; and
- ❖ fuel cells.

Solar thermal systems

Solar air or water collectors absorb solar radiation, which is transferred directly into the interior space or to a storage system to be distributed to the building later.

Photovoltaics

Photovoltaic (PV) systems use solar cells to convert sunlight into electricity. PV is usually installed in parallel with the grid, although stand-alone generation is not uncommon, particularly in isolated areas.

District heating and cooling

District heating, also known as community heating, provides heat from a central source to more than one building or dwelling via a network of distribution mains. Heat may be generated from LZC sources such as CHP or biomass boilers, or heat that would otherwise be dumped to atmosphere can be used.

Combined heat and power

Combined heat and power (CHP), or cogeneration, refers to the simultaneous generation of electricity and heat in the form of hot water or steam. Electricity is generated using an engine or turbine, and useful heat is recovered from the exhaust gases and cooling systems. Tri-generation is a term applied to a CHP system that produces electricity, heating and cooling. The cooling output is generated from the waste heat feeding an absorption chiller.

Ground source cooling

Fluctuations in ground temperature reduce with depth and stabilise to around 9°C to 12°C at about 12m below the surface in the UK. This stored 'coolth' is suitable for directly cooling buildings. The two most common methods use either an 'open' or 'closed' loop circuit embedded within the ground. In an open loop system water is abstracted from the ground and then passed through a heat exchanger, before being discharged back into the ground or to a river. In a closed loop system a continuous loop of pipework is buried in the ground, with water circulated through the pipework network, which acts as a heat exchanger being in direct contact with the earth.

Ground source heat pumps

Ground source heat pumps (GSHPs) make use of refrigeration equipment to extract heat from the stabilised ground temperature and raise it to a more useful output temperature to heat the building. The heat is abstracted from the ground by either an 'open' or 'closed' loop circuit, as described under ground source cooling. The depletion of the heat source is matched by the rate of heat flow back from the surrounding earth and under these circumstances the technology is a renewable source of energy. Because the ground is at a constant temperature the refrigeration process can be very energy efficient. GSHPs can also be used as a means of generating cooling in a building by utilising reverse cycle heat pumps, with the recovered waste heat dissipated to the ground, similar in principle to ground source cooling.

Wind power

Wind power is used to turn a turbine and generate electricity, which is distributed in much the same way as for photovoltaic systems. In order to generate worthwhile quantities of electricity average wind speeds of more than 5–6m/s are typically required. There are essentially two basic kinds of wind turbine in use, defined as horizontal axis and vertical axis. Horizontal axis turbines are the more common comprising a central hub with evenly spaced blades, supported on a tower. Vertical axis systems can be installed without the need for a tower and may be easier to integrate with a building's structure.

Biofuels

Energy from biomass is produced by burning organic matter such as trees, crops or animal dung. The biomass is carbon-based so when used as a fuel it also generates carbon emissions. However, the carbon that is released during combustion is equivalent to the amount that was absorbed during growth, and so the technology is carbon-neutral. The bio-energy created may be in the form of electricity, heat, steam, and solid fuels.

Fuel cells

Hydrogen fuel cell technology, although still at an early stage of development, is starting to be used as a means of storage as opposed to a source of energy. The hydrogen fuel cells can produce heat, power and pure water without releasing any greenhouse gases.

Environmental Liability Directive

The *Environmental Liability Directive* (ELD) came into force in all European Union (EU) member states in April 2004. In the UK, although existing legislation already applies to many of the areas covered, the ELD will enforce some important changes, particularly in the area of remediation.

The ELD aims to establish a framework that would prevent 'significant environmental damage' or rectify damage after it has occurred, by forcing industrial polluters (or 'operators') to pay prevention and remediation costs. In this respect it is no different to the *Environmental Protection Act* 1990 and its accompanying Part IIA legislation dealing specifically with contaminated land, which was introduced in 2000.

For this reason, it is thought unlikely that the ELD will lead to an increase in the number of contaminated sites for which UK operators find themselves liable. However, at a more detailed level it does introduce a number of key changes. There will be new, specific criteria for determining environmental damage, as well as the two new categories of complementary and compensatory remediation, which will have implications for UK businesses.

Determining damage

As described in the ELD, 'significant environmental damage' will be defined by reference to:

❖ biodiversity, whether protected at EU or national levels;

❖ waters covered by the Water Framework Directive; and

❖ human health (including land contamination when it is a threat to human health).

The ELD provides specific criteria to assess when damage is 'significant'. Member states will be under a duty to ensure that the necessary preventive or restorative measures are actually taken but will have the flexibility to decide when measures should be taken by:

❖ the relevant operator;

❖ the competent authorities; or

❖ a third party.

What are the implications?

Operators carrying out 'hazardous' activities will be held strictly liable (i.e. no need to show fault or negligence) for preventing or restoring any damage caused by those activities to land, water and protected habitats and species. In addition, operators carrying out other less harmful activities will be held liable when damage to protected habitats and species has been caused by their fault or negligence.

For UK businesses, the most significant changes that will be introduced by the ELD are the two new categories of 'complementary' and 'compensatory' remediation. Under existing UK legislation, operators are only held liable for what the ELD calls 'primary remediation'. This means remedying the particular damage caused in order to return the damaged natural resources and/or impaired services to or towards 'baseline' condition (or that which would have existed had the damage not occurred). However, in the future liability will be extended to include:

❖ complementary remediation – any remedial measure taken to compensate for the fact that primary remediation does not result in fully restoring the damaged resources and/or services; and

❖ compensatory remediation – any action taken to compensate for interim losses of natural resources and/or services that occur from the date of damage occurring until primary remediation has achieved its full effect.

Operators will automatically be exempt from having to compensate for damage caused:

❖ by emissions within the terms of permits;

❖ despite the use of best practice;

❖ by war or an act of God; or

❖ by a third party, despite having taken all safety measures.

Damage from nuclear and maritime accidents falls outside the regime's scope and remains subject to existing treaties.

Opportunities

The ELD is expected to provide opportunities for environmental and property consultants to advise their clients on:

❖ whether or not significant damage has occurred to the environment as a result of their business activities;

❖ whether or not they can be held liable;

❖ what type of remediation will be required and at what cost; and

❖ when successful remediation of the site has been achieved.

Progress

The deadline for the transposition of the ELD into national law within member states was set for 30 April 2007. This deadline was not met by the UK government. To date, only Italy, Latvia and Lithuania have reported full or partial transposition of the ELD to the European Commission, out of the 27 member states.

A consultation document relating to the options for implementing the ELD within England, Wales and Northern Ireland was published by Defra in November 2006. The consultation ended in February 2007 and the government has been attempting to finalise its policy since this date. Defra have stated the delay has been a result of the need for extensive consideration as to how the ELD overlaps with existing domestic regimes. A further consultation period on the draft regulations is expected to take place during early 2008.

A parliamentary committee report entitled *Implementation of the Environmental Liability Directive*, dated 4 July 2007, has criticised the government's 'minimum implementation' approach to the ELD to date and has highlighted areas of concern, which it recommends to be addressed within the draft regulations. The key issues are to clarify how the government would be the first point of recourse for remediation when the operator is not deemed to be liable, to make clear that the ELD will only apply to incidents occurring after the date of implementation and for the ELD to extend to include nationally-protected biodiversity.

Water Framework Directive

Water quality in England and Wales has improved dramatically in recent years. Building on progress to date, the *Water Framework Directive* sets out to enforce sustainable water use and promote a range of ecological objectives.

The *Water Framework Directive* (WFD) is the most substantial piece of EC water legislation to date. The Directive came into force on 22 December 2000 and was transposed into law in England and Wales in 2003, with implementation from December 2006. The WFD requires all inland and coastal waters to reach 'good status' by 2015. This new standard is far more rigorous than existing water quality measures, with an estimated 95% of water courses at risk of failing to meet the criteria set out by the Directive. The Environment Agency has statutory duties in England and Wales to implement the Directive and ensure the environmental objectives are met by the 2015 deadline.

The key environmental aims of the WFD are to:

❖ prevent deterioration of aquatic ecosystems;

❖ protect, enhance and restore polluted waters and groundwater to 'good status', which is based on ecological and chemical factors for surface water and water quantity and chemical status for groundwater;

❖ comply with water-related standards and objectives for environmentally protected areas established under other EU legislation;

❖ progressively reduce pollution from priority substances (pollutants that represent a significant risk to the aquatic environment) and cease or phase out discharges from priority hazardous substances (those that are the most polluting); and

❖ prevent or limit input of pollutants into groundwater and reverse any significant or sustained upward trends in the concentration of groundwater pollution.

These demanding new environmental objectives will be set within an integrated river basin district structure. Each river basin will have its own management plan (RBMP) for surface and groundwater; all with common objectives and principles. The first RBMPs are to be published by December 2009, with the aim of avoiding the difficulties that can arise from a piecemeal approach. Issues such as the availability of water supply, maintaining water quality in rivers and managing flood risk will, in future, be considered as a whole, not addressed in isolation. The RBMBs will be enacted between 2009 and 2012.

For planners and developers the WFD has far-reaching implications. However, according to the Royal Town Planning Institute (RTPI) many planners remain unaware of the impact it will have on the planning process. As a result, a report has been produced jointly by the RTPI, the Environment Agency, the Local Government Association and the Welsh Local Government Association, to provide advice for planners in advance of the final details of the WFD. The report, *The Water Framework Directive and Planning: Initial advice to planning authorities in England and Wales*, outlines the key elements of the Directive and focuses strongly on its future ramifications.

Spatial planners are increasingly aware of the fundamental need to manage development pressure against a background of challenging water-related issues and constraints. The report recognises the additional requirement on planners, who now need to balance the need to provide water and to treat waste water with a requirement to maintain/improve the water environment.

In some parts of England, major growth is proposed in places where water resources and the ability to handle increased volumes of sewage are already stretched. Implementation of the WFD means that future development will have to be carefully planned so that it does not result in further pressure on the water environment.

However, new development can provide an opportunity to tackle existing pressures on water, through imaginative, high-quality project design and planning as well as the use of planning conditions and obligations attached to planning permissions. The RTPI makes the point that these positive impacts can be linked to the remediation of contaminated land and hence improvements to ground and surface water quality, river habitat restoration, water-use efficiency and protection of natural ecosystems. Where waste or a legacy of contaminated land or mine water is causing pollution, intervention by a range of authorities and agencies will be needed to clean up or at least mitigate these problems. All this will add a new element to both the planning and development processes and therefore it is important that client organisations are aware of the implications for their future projects.

And it is not only at planning stage that property and construction will be affected by the Directive, there may be more technical issues to deal with. For example, the Building Research Establishment (BRE) is in the process of undertaking research into the use of recycled and secondary aggregates (RSA) in structural concrete in the context of the WFD. There is a perception in the construction industry that use of RSA may lead to hazardous materials leaching into the soil from foundations and resulting in drinking or groundwater pollution. BRE is keen to determine whether or not this is the case and is working with the Waste & Resources Action Programme (WRAP) to research the issue. It seems inevitable that other building materials and techniques will also be called into question in future.

The implementation of the Directive will take place in a number of planning cycles with reviews every six years. This will allow a better understanding of basin characteristics and long term trends, such as climate change, to be taken into account. The first cycle is due to be completed in 2015.

At present, a great deal of the detail of the WFD is still to be finalised. However, as it becomes clearer what the full impact of the Directive will be, developers and the construction industry will gain a fuller understanding of its implications.

Recycled materials

In 2006, the government's Sustainable Procurement Task Force identified construction as the top priority spending area for action. It stated that 'the public sector should reduce the footprint of its procurement in three key environmental areas: carbon, water and waste, in areas of big spend as part of a move towards a carbon neutral, low water use, zero waste public sector'.

The Waste & Resources Action Programme (WRAP) is a major UK programme established by the government in 2000 as part of its waste strategy. Its particular focus is on creating stable and efficient markets for recycled materials and products and removing the barriers to waste minimisation, reuse and recycling.

WRAP has identified a series of what it calls 'quick wins' – options with a higher recycled content that are cost-effective (or at worst cost-neutral), which offer comparable performance and quality, and are readily available in the marketplace. Both WRAP and BRE consider that using good practice it should be perfectly possible to increase the value of recycled products well above the 10% minimum. Ideally a quick win should also inject useful environmental advantages into a building – a particular product could, for example, be composed of a high proportion of recycled material and yet require a considerable quantity of energy to produce, or be available only in specific locations which could then make transport (and the effects of transport) a relevant issue.

The recommendations for recycled content are based upon a percentage of the value of materials in a building excluding labour costs, with the expectation that the 10% minimum be achieved at no extra overall cost. The recommendations are such that the target could be achieved by using a large amount of low-grade material, such as hardcore or recycled aggregate, or in the alternative a much smaller amount of a higher value material.

Definition of recycled materials

Recycled materials can be defined as any materials that have been redirected from landfill. Primary materials are those with no recycled content – see *Environmental labels and declarations – Self-declared environmental claims* (Type II environmental labelling) (AMD 13493 – renumbered from BS ISO 14021:1999).

Definition of reused components

WRAP defines a reused component as being:

❖ supplied from another location (either within the same organisation or from a third party);

❖ reconditioned or relocated (e.g. for demolition waste) within the same location; or

❖ any foundations or other infrastructure that is retained in new construction.

The value of reused materials is taken to be the purchase price of the material (if bought) or the cost of equivalent materials, if inset materials are reused.

Concerns over performance

Whilst one might be tempted to believe that the case for recycled materials is the product of recent concerns for the environment, the reality is that for many years recycled materials, particularly aggregates, have been commonplace. For example, pulverised fuel ash and ground granular blast furnace slag have been covered by British Standards for at least 15 years. Furthermore, very many construction products use a proportion of recycled materials in any event. Specifying a higher recycled content may mean the use of one manufacturer over another, but no loss in performance. In most cases, the standards and tests that apply to one material are exactly the same that apply to another material that uses a higher recycled content.

Why recycle?

Construction and demolition produce around 90 million tonnes of waste each year. Of this, around half is recycled, mainly into construction applications, but the expectation is that a much higher percentage could be recovered. For example, WRAP expects that with better practice and management at all levels:

- ❖ a further 20 million tonnes of suitable recycled aggregates could be used;
- ❖ the proportion of recycled glass could rise well above the 1.1 million tonnes currently used to a figure much closer to the 5.5 million tonnes of waste glass that is produced annually;
- ❖ the proportion of recycled plastic in construction could rise well above the 0.14 million tonnes currently used to a figure much closer to the 1.4 million tonnes actually available;
- ❖ the proportion of recycled timber or wood products could rise well above the 0.3 million tonnes currently used to a figure much closer to the 3–5 million tonnes of waste timber available.

Furthermore, by redirecting organic materials from landfill to make compost it is possible to reduce the volume of greenhouse gas emissions, notably methane.

By designing buildings to minimise waste (designing to modular sizes, for example), designers can play a significant role. This can be further extended by specifying materials with a higher recycled content (these are already mainstream products).

Some of the benefits of a recycling policy are listed below:

- ❖ demonstrate performance against corporate environmental policy;
- ❖ satisfy planning requirements and government initiatives;
- ❖ set a unique selling point or differentiator in a competitive market;
- ❖ responding to public or employee demand for sustainable policies;
- ❖ reducing waste management and landfill costs; and
- ❖ creating local markets for reprocessed materials and so reducing costs.

The ultimate aim of policy makers ought to be to achieve a zero net waste concept whereby the wastage of non-renewable materials is compensated by a sufficient quantity of recycled and/or renewable materials.

Policy requirements

Many developers have, or are developing, sustainability policies. Some, for example, have offered an incentive/penalty basis for reducing the numbers of skips used on a site. A policy ought to have some guidance as to recycled content of buildings, with a minimum expectation that at least 10% of the total value of materials used should derive from recycled and reused content in the products and materials selected. In addition, attempts should be made to identify opportunities to increase the value of recycled content wherever it is technically and commercial viable to do so. A policy may also aim to raise the 10% threshold year-on-year over its life.

Ten per cent is a modest target. Given the high proportion of recycled materials currently in production, it should be easy to achieve this. By adopting good practice methods, a target of 15–20% ought to be achievable – on the basis that such a regime does not add to the overall cost of the development. A desire not to increase cost is important – it not only acts as a good driver for the whole process, it also serves to create a demand for products that extends up the supply chain to the demolition contractor and ultimately stimulates new reclamation/waste processing businesses.

Drivers

The *Secure and Sustainable Buildings Act* 2004 has, amongst other things, extended the scope of the Building Regulations to cover the use of recycled and reused materials, and specifically includes a duty on the Secretary of State to report on the recycled content of buildings in England and Wales every two years – a measure intended to prevent the provisions from 'gathering dust on the shelf'.

The government collects a levy called Landfill Tax on every tonne of waste dumped in British landfill sites. The Landfill Tax Credit Scheme allows landfill operators to use 20% of the tax collected to promote more environmentally sustainable methods of waste management and environmental improvements. In any given project, 90% of the funding can come from the Landfill Tax Credit Scheme but the last 10% must come from another source.

A further measure to encourage sustainable practices is the Aggregates Levy. This levy reduces demand for primary aggregates by increasing their cost and makes the use of recycled and secondary materials more viable.

The Aggregates Levy Sustainability Fund uses some of the revenue from the Aggregates Levy to further address the environmental impacts associated with quarrying operations (noise, dust, visual intrusion, loss of amenity and damage to biodiversity).

Under EU law (Article 1 of the EC Framework Directive on waste – 75/442/EEC – as amended by 91/156/EEC), waste is defined as any substance or object which the holder discards or intends or is required to discard. Regulation 1 of the *Waste Management Licensing Regulations* 1994 is the UK enactment of the Directive; this essentially requires that, other than where an exemption is prescribed, a waste management licence is required by anyone who deposits, recovers or disposes of household, commercial or industrial waste (the term 'controlled waste' is used to describe these types of waste). Part II of the *Environmental Protection Act* 1990 also deals with this subject.

Under the *Control of Pollution (Amendment) Act* 1989 and the *Controlled Waste (Registration of Carriers and Seizure of Vehicles) Regulations* 1991, anyone who, in the course of a business, or in any other way for profit, transports controlled waste within Great Britain is required to register as a waste carrier. Similarly, someone who arranges for the disposal or recovery of waste but is not the holder of the waste (i.e. a broker) is required to register.

The above provisions could be seen as a barrier to the use of waste products for construction, although this should not necessarily be the case.

The Regulations do not apply to materials that do not fall under the definition of waste, although ascertaining whether or not waste is 'waste' can require some thought at an early stage. In particular, the following questions need to be addressed:

❖ Does the substance or object fall into one of the categories set out in Part II of Schedule 4 to the *Waste Management Licensing Regulations* 1994?

❖ If so, has it been discarded by its holder, do they have any intention of discarding it, or are they required to discard it?

Further information on the definition of waste may be found in DoE Circular 11/94 (Annex 2) and the Appendix to the *Waste Management Duty of Care Code of Practice* (available on the Defra website – www.defra.gov.uk/environment/waste/legislation/duty.htm#code).

Planning Policy Statement 1 (PPS1) sets out the government's planning policies on the delivery of sustainable development through the planning system – this replaced Planning Policy Guidance Note 1: *General Policies and Principles* (PPG1). One of the key policies is to ensure that sustainable development is pursued in an integrated manner, in line with the principles for sustainable development set out in the UK strategy. Regional planning bodies and local planning authorities should ensure that development plans promote outcomes in which environmental, economic and social objectives are achieved together over time. Development plans should consider the management of waste in ways that protect the environment and human health, including producing less waste and using it as a resource wherever possible.

Calculating recycled content

The target figures given earlier are based upon the value of recycled materials in a building and not the total cost of installation. The recycled content is a function of the quantity and cost used and the percentage of the component by mass that is derived from recycled content.

So, if a material cost £50 per square metre and has a 10% recycled content, the value of recycled content of 100m² would be £50 x 100 x 10% = £500.

To work out the recycled content of the entire building involves calculating the sum of the individual component parts. For example, if the sum of all the materials in a building is calculated at £200,000, of which the sum of the individual recycled content amounts to £22,500, the recycled content of the building would be £22,500/£200,000 x 100 = 11.25% – a total that exceeds the 10% target, but one which, with some thought, could probably be increased.

However, this simple illustration ignores the fact that it would be impracticable to consider the recycled content of every single component. Whilst in theory it would be possible to do this, the calculation would be unreasonably long winded, and in all probability a good deal of the minutiae would make very little difference to the overall calculation. One method is to consider the overall value of the construction and then to consider the impact of up to ten elements that are likely to play a key role – this could include, say, the walls, roof and internal finishes as in the following example:

❖ Overall construction cost = £500,000.

❖ Value of materials and labour examined in detail = £400,000, split, say 50/50, between materials and labour.

❖ Value of unallocated elements = £100,000, split 50/50 between materials and labour.

❖ Therefore, total value of material = £200,000 plus £50,000 = £250,000.

❖ Of which the recycled content has been assessed at £22,500.

❖ Therefore total recycled content = £22,500/£250,000 x 100 = 9%.

Setting targets

WRAP publish a considerable volume of information appertaining to recycling materials. It has identified three performance levels:

❖ standard practice is defined as what is most commonly available, i.e. the most likely material to be used if no request is made for recycled content;

❖ good practice is defined as a level of recycled content which is better than standard and readily available, but not necessarily as high as current technology or market conditions would allow; and

❖ best available is defined as the highest recycled content currently available on the UK market.

Faithful and Gould, Cyril Sweett and Solstice Associates have designed an online toolkit to assist designers in the construction of new build projects. The toolkit can be accessed at http://rctoolkit.wrap.org.uk/. It is based on reference values for recycled content and materials costs from around 500 standard specifications and includes data from BRE, AMA Research and Davis Langdon.

The RC Toolkit is designed to be easy to use and allows the user to:

❖ estimate the baseline and good practice levels of recycled content;

❖ identify the top ten 'quick win' opportunities to improve environmental performance by substituting cost-competitive products with a higher-than-standard recycled content;

❖ refine the analysis to reflect actual product choices and design details; and

❖ quantify the projected recycled content and report how it will be achieved.

When applied during the planning and design stages, it can be used to check that a construction project will meet its targeted outcome for recycled content.

Reclamation

The *Reclaimed and recycled construction materials handbook* (CIRIA and DTR), in part 2, invites designers to consider the following questions:

❖ Which of the materials already on site (e.g. from buildings to be demolished) can be reclaimed or recycled for use in the new works?

❖ Can reclaimed or recycled materials from off site be used?

❖ How can the percentage of materials used in this project that will be reclaimed or recycled at the end of its life be maximised?

These questions will prompt a debate as to whether or not aiming for recycling or reclaiming is a sensible thing to do because, it may be perceived, the specification introduces additional risks into the construction process. Similarly, in order to design for recycling, component parts must be capable of being dismantled – and this in itself creates challenges. For example, conventional building orthodoxy dictates the use of Portland cement mortar in masonry construction. This effectively means that once laid, masonry units, whether they are bricks or blocks cannot be reclaimed. Portland cement prevents the clean dismantling of a wall and results in damage to the masonry during demolition. Conversely, if the masonry units are bedded in lime mortar (as they were 100 years ago) taking down and reclamation is perfectly feasible. Yet using lime mortar is something of a 'black art' to many engineers, specifiers and bricklayers – they are simply not trained to use it.

CIRIA advocate that a strategy towards using recycled or reclaimed materials should be the default position and not the alternative – such a move would be in line with the UK Government's stance towards sustainability and waste management. But this will not happen if the key decision makers are not in tune with the concept, or if they lack the will to drive it through.

Are there any risks to health?

This is a difficult question to answer, but it could also apply equally to virgin products; there is no reason why recycled products need to be considered any differently – indeed in some circumstances, recycled products can actually perform better. Recycled carpets, for example, (made from Polyethylene Therephthalate (PET)) will release far less in the way of volatile organic compounds or formaldehyde than their virgin counterparts. Each case needs to be examined on its merits and a risk assessment based approach adopted. Where materials are being utilised for site works, sources of potential hazards are recognised and quantified, pathways identified along which the hazards may migrate through the environment, and receptors or targets on which any potentially hazardous substance(s) may impact are assessed.

Human and animal health may be considered to be the ultimate receptors but consider also the quality of water, including fresh water/marine life, surface water or groundwater, and the accumulation of toxic material in plants or soil may also be legitimate receptors.

Is there a sufficient local supply?

Sources such as WRAP and the National Green Specification have links to suppliers. On-site processing of waste concrete can yield a good supply of recycled aggregates, although authorisation will be needed from the local authority and the environmental impact of crushing operations will need to be considered. Care will be needed to ensure that the operations do not fall within the definition of controlled waste given earlier.

Can the client be persuaded to accept the use of recycled or reclaimed material?

Can recycled materials be expected to perform as well as primary or virgin materials? Provided they are selected and specified properly and used in the way that the manufacturer intends, there should be no reason why they will fail to perform. As noted earlier, many materials are mainstream products, although quality in reclaimed material can be hard to control.

Is the selection of reclaimed/recycled material the best thing from an environmental point of view?

Some products contain high embodied energy as a result of remanufacturing processes or transport. Similarly, for example, the environmental consequences of crushing concrete in a congested city centre site might make the process unacceptable.

Can delivery/construction programmes be maintained?

For very many recycled materials, delivery schedules can be planned in advance – many products are mainstream (blocks, plasterboard, carpets etc.) are purchased in much the same way as virgin products. Difficulties can arise, however, in the supply of aggregates and products selected locally, particularly if the level of supply is likely to fluctuate.

Conclusion

By specifying materials that are either reclaimed or recycled, the overall value of recycled content in a building can be increased significantly and without there necessarily being any addition to cost. Reclamation of materials assists local economies and stimulates demand. But recycled materials are not new; they have been around for many years. All that needs to happen is a shift in awareness of what is available and the compelling arguments for taking greater care in specification and purchasing to ensure that the opportunities are met.

Further information

WRAP (the Waste & Resources Action Programme): advice on specifying recycled materials in house-building, construction, highways, estates management and other sectors www.wrap.org.uk.

Aggregain (WRAP): www.aggregain.org.uk – source of practical information on the use of recycled and secondary aggregates.

BRE: www.bre.co.uk – BREEAM related assessment schemes and the Green Guide to Specification.

Salvo: www.salvo.co.uk – Market place for reclaimed construction materials/products.

National Green Specification: www.greenspec.co.uk – Technical specifications, design and product information for sustainable construction.

Ecoconstruction: www.ecoconstruction.org – Details of 'green' products for house building.

The *Reclaimed and recycled construction materials handbook* – DETR and CIRIA.

http://londonremade.com/product/product_directory.asp – provides a directory of recycled products.

Electromagnetic fields

Electromagnetic fields (EMFs) are a combination of electric fields and magnetic fields.

Electric fields are produced as a result of voltage within wiring. The higher the voltage, the stronger the field. Electric fields exist even when an electrical appliance is not in use as voltage is always present. Electric fields can be blocked by objects such as buildings and trees. Electric fields are measured in volts per metre (Vm^{-1}) or kilovolts per metre (kVm^{-1}).

Magnetic fields are created when electric currents flow and therefore are not present unless an appliance is turned on. Magnetic fields are measured in nanotesla (nT), microtesla (μT), millitesla (mT) or tesla (T). Magnetic fields are not usually blocked by objects, although certain types of metal can shield against magnetic fields.

Awareness of the health effects of electromagnetic fields (also known as electromagnetic radiation) has been steadily increasing since the 1970s as exposure to human induced EMFs has increased both in the home and in the workplace according to the World Health Organisation (WHO) 2007.

The Radiation Protection Division of the Health Protection Agency have responsibility for providing advice on limiting exposure of the general public to EMFs.

What are the common sources of electromagnetic radiation?

EMFs are present everywhere in the environment existing through the generation and transmission of electricity, the use of electrical appliances and telecommunications (WHO, 2007). Of particular concern have been the effects of overhead and underground power lines, electricity substations, microwave ovens, computer and television screens, security devices, radars and, within the last ten years, the use of mobile phones.

Transmission power lines in the UK operate at 275 and 400 kilovolts (kV) and distribution lines at 440V, 11kV, 33kV, 66 kV and 132kV. The strength of EMFs decreases rapidly with increased distance from the source. Human epidemiology studies of magnetic fields have tended to use a field of 0.4 microtesla (μT) or above to identify potential risks. For high voltage power lines at 132kV and above, average field levels of 0.4μT or above may exist at ground level at distances greater than 100 metres. For lower voltage lines, a field of 0.4μT or above may occur up to a few tens of metres away.

EMFs can also occur naturally within the environment through the build up of electrical charges associated with thunderstorms within the atmosphere.

What are the health effects associated with exposure to electromagnetic radiation?

A wide variety of symptoms and illnesses have been associated with exposure to EMF although these are not scientifically proven. These include:

- ❖ headaches;
- ❖ anxiety;
- ❖ suicide and depression;
- ❖ nausea;
- ❖ fatigue;
- ❖ premature pregnancies and low birth weight;
- ❖ cataracts;
- ❖ cardiovascular disorders;
- ❖ neurobehavioral effects and neurodegenerative disease;
- ❖ cancer, including childhood leukaemia;
- ❖ sleeping disorders; and
- ❖ convulsions and epilepsy.

Research and current knowledge

A large number of epidemiological studies have been undertaken across the world on the effects of exposure to EMF on human health. One of the most highly publicised issues is whether there is an increased risk of cancer within populations living near power lines or other sources of EMF. A great deal of research has been focused upon the risk of childhood cancer, in particular leukaemia.

Analysis of several studies has indicated 'the possibility exists of a doubling of the risk of leukaemia in children in homes at high levels of exposure to extremely low frequency (ELF) magnetic fields' (Health Protection Agency – Pooled Analysis, 2000). A task group set up by the WHO in October 2005 to assess risks to human health as a result of exposure to ELF EMFs concluded that additional studies since 2000 do not alter this view on the risk of childhood leukaemia.

The WHO task group in 2005 also assessed whether there was an association with ELF EMF exposure and the aforementioned associated health effects. It was concluded that 'scientific evidence supporting an association between ELF magnetic field exposure and all of these health effects is much weaker than for childhood leukaemia' (WHO, 2007).

The advisory group to the Health Protection Agency on non-ionising radiation has stated in relation to adults 'there is no reason to believe that residential exposure to EMFs is involved in the development of cancer'. However, it should be noted that there have been far fewer studies on the health effects on adults than on children.

What guidelines exist within the UK relating to EMFs?

A report published in 2004 by the former National Radiological Protection Board recommended the adoption in the UK of the guidelines produced by the International Commission on Non-Ionizing Radiation Protection (ICNIRP) for limiting exposures to EMFs having a frequency less than 300 GHz. The ICNIRP exposure guidelines relate to occupational and public exposure to EMFs.

Research into the effects of EMFs is under constant review by the Health Protection Agency to ensure guidelines are in line with the most up to date information. Guidelines are therefore susceptible to change. For the most up to date guidelines and information, the Health Protection Agency and ICNIRP websites should be consulted.

References

World Health Organisation, June 2007, *Electromagnetic fields and public health – Exposure to extremely low frequency fields*, Fact Sheet No. 322 from www.who.int/mediacentre/factsheets/fs322/en/print.html

National Radiological Protection Board, 2004, *Advice on Limiting Exposure to Electromagnetic Fields (0–300 GHz)*, Documents of the NRPB, Volume 15 No. 2

Health Protection Agency website: www.hpa.org.uk

Green legislation

Introduction

The sustainable, environmental and 'green' landscape legislation has changed enormously over the last few years. There is still a great deal of uncertainty as to how the government will shape future legislation, but one of the main drivers is the Eco-Homes Very Good Standard pushed forward by the Housing Association in conjunction with the *Code for Sustainable Homes* and the desire to reach carbon neutrality or zero carbon for housing by 2016. This, coupled with the 2012 Olympics and the regeneration of the Lea Valley and East London, is a prime opportunity for local and central government to attempt to control legislation on the environment.

Legislation which is already active or on the statute book

A Code for Sustainable Homes

This is the main documentation with legal status for setting the standards with regard to environmental performance for **new** homes. The basis for this document comes from the BRE's Eco Homes Rating, which this now replaces.

The whole purpose of the Code is to establish minimum standards for energy and water use, surface water management, site waste management, household waste management and the use of construction materials on site. All the levels, which have been introduced through this legislation, are higher than the corresponding levels of the previous or underlying Building Regulations. An example of this is that Level 1 requires a 10% betterment of energy performance than the 2006 Part L Building Regulations. At Level 5 it is set at 100% above Part L, which arguably allows for some aspirational and future targeting. At this level there should be no emissions from heating, hot water and ventilation, and lighting. Level 6 advocates a zero carbon contribution in individual homes and housing schemes.

Furthermore, the standards for the future Building Regulations revisions will be based upon this Code. Initially the scheme is voluntarily, with the exception of registered social landlords and developers developing properties for registered social landlords who will have to build to at least Level 3 – at present they have to build to the slightly less onerous Eco Homes 'Very Good' rating. Ultimately the Code could become compulsory for all new homes regardless of the end user. It is important to note here that the vast amount of housing, and indeed commercial building stock within the United Kingdom, is over 100 years old. It will take over 100 years to adequately refurbish and upgrade existing stock at normal rates. Arguably it would have more impact if existing buildings and refurbishments were included in this sort of legislation, although this is difficult to police.

For more detail see the section on the *Code for Sustainable Homes* on page 32.

Building Regulations Part L

The Part L of the Building Regulations, entitled *Conservation of Fuel and Power* has been operational since April 2006. The purpose of this addition is to establish energy standards for all types of buildings. It is under this section that new buildings particularly are required to be air pressure tested, although again there is an anomaly here in that extensions to existing buildings and existing refurbishments are not captured by the current Part L.

There are four elements to Part L:

- ❖ L1A – new dwellings;
- ❖ L2A – new non-dwellings;
- ❖ L1B – existing dwellings; and
- ❖ L2B – existing non-dwellings.

The most significant change from the 2002 version is that whole building carbon emission methodology must be used to calculate compliance, whereas previously compliance could be achieved by ensuring that building elements met minimum performance standards.

Part L advocates that compliance is calculated using the proven software SAP 2005 for dwellings and SBEM for non-dwellings. A building that meets the new Part L requirements should be responsible for 25% less carbon emissions than a building that conforms with Part L before 2002. Naturally these targets are according to building type, but pressure testing above is mandatory for all the buildings.

For more detail see the section on Part L on page 149.

PPS 22 Renewable Energy

This initiative enables local authorities to ensure that a significant percentage of buildings and energy requirements are generated from on-site renewables as a condition of planning. It links in with the future requirements of Part L as projected. Different councils vary their requirements. Typically 10% is requested but some authorities are demanding 20%. The running has been made primarily by the local authorities in the south east, in particularly Merton and Croydon, which is why this is often called the 'Merton Rule'. There have been recent indications that the government may try to drop this, which has triggered threats of litigation from green bodies and a debate from local government that there are better ways to cut carbon emissions. At the time of going to press, the government are considering changes to the Merton rule, but no details are available as yet.

Energy certification of buildings

The *Energy Performance of Buildings Directive* (EPBD), spurred on by a wider European initiative, governs and controls energy certification of buildings and is currently in force for some housing (see Home Information

Packs on page 28). EU Directive 2002/92/EC *Energy Performance of Buildings* came into force on 4 January 2003, with legislation required in member states by 4 January 2006 (the UK has an extension). The EU as a whole has pledged to reduce CO_2 by 330 million tonnes between 1990 and 2010 in line with the Kyoto Agreement. The concept requires that energy performance of a building fabric is assessed each time the building is sold or rented and given an energy rating on an A to G scale – so that future occupiers are able to take into account a building's likely energy performance when deciding to either purchase or rent the property.

This could have a significant effect on commercial property in the medium to long term, although current thinking is that in the shorter term there are likely to be wider issues and implications (such as balancing a tenant's requirement for additional thermal values against an increase in rent to cover this, and the balance of what a tenant is prepared to pay extra for prior to legislative changes). The *Energy Performance of Buildings Directive* allows for a ten-year life of the certificate if the building is not sold or rented to other parties during this term. Certification for non-residential or dwelling properties will be phased in progressively through 2008.

For more detail see the EPBD section, page 352.

Timescales

1 August 2007	Energy Performance Certificate for sale of existing dwellings (with HIP).
1 October 2007	Certificate on construction of all dwellings and on sale of dwellings built to 2006 standards.
6 April 2008	Certificate for sale or rent of non-dwelling buildings of 10,000m². Certificates on all non-dwellings and display of energy certificates on all public buildings over 1,000m².
1 July 2008	Certificate for sale or rent of non-dwelling buildings of 2,500m².
1 October 2008	Certificate for sale or rent of all remaining buildings.

Building a Green Future: A Step Closer Towards Zero Carbon

This is a consultation paper that was published by the department for Communities and Local Government (CLG) on 13 December 2006. It proposes that all new homes should be zero carbon by 2016, and this is to be achieved in three consecutive stages:

❖ 2012 – new homes to perform to 25% better than current Part L of the Building Regulations;

❖ 2013 – this should increase to 44%; and

❖ 2016 – this should be zero carbon.

These targets are equivalent to Levels 3, 4 and 6 in the *Code for Sustainable Homes*, which has been driving this initiative.

It is also thought that central and local government and control of development within the Unitary Development Plans will be used as a tool in moving towards zero carbon housing in terms of location, design and energy used from the site. The draft planning policy statement, known as Planning and Climate Change (PPS1), published at the same time as this document; and Building Regulations and the *Code for Sustainable Homes* will be used in an attempt to achieve zero carbon housing.

Water Efficiency in New Buildings

This was published as a consultation paper on 13 December 2006 and aims to try to reduce domestic water usage by setting minimum standards. Again this covers new homes, as well as domestic use of water in non-dwellings and it also covers flushing toilets in offices and water use in canteens. Controls for non-dwellings include setting a maximum limit of water use per day or setting required standards for fittings. A 'whole building' performance standard is being considered for homes, which could be set between 120 to 135 litres of water per person per day. The standard is likely to tighten on a year to year basis. However, it will be important to ensure that there is no conflict between different regulations and guidelines. Level 1 in the *Code for Sustainable Homes* is set at 120 litres of water per person per day. Again, this will be implemented through Building Regulations, probably through Part G, which covers hygiene. Water efficiency could also be increased by greater control of the water supply networks – water boards have been guilty in the past of allowing pipes and networks to leak and of poor maintenance. This is an example of how more groups and ideas need to be integrated.

Site based management plans for waste

These are currently voluntary and the Department of Trade and Industry (DTI) wishes to make these compulsory by 2008 for sites with a value greater than £200,000. These are intended to help contractors to reduce construction waste and identify the by-products produced, then minimise them by using materials efficiently, using recycled products and ensuring waste is disposed of responsibly. On completion the performance is checked against targets and lessons learned are carried through to the next job so that individual contractors can build up a portfolio of improvements. There is, however, ongoing debate with regard to the depth behind some of these green initiatives, and the reality of recycling materials to a plant that may be some distance from the site.

The Climate Change Bill (draft)

This was issued as a consultation document in March 2007. Consultation closed on 12 June 2007. The document discusses a clear, credible and long term framework for the UK to achieve its goals of reducing carbon dioxide emissions and also ensuring that steps are taken towards adapting to the impacts of climate change. The consultation document also discusses the thoughts behind the *Climate Change Bill*.

Measures coming into force which may affect UK legislation

❖ Floods Directive – this looks at the assessment and management of flood risks and may affect PPS25.

❖ Intelligent Energy Europe Programme – this looks at improving energy efficiency throughout the EU and increasing the number of renewables. Consultation will continue through to 2013.

❖ Energy Services and Energy Efficiency Directives – these require decreasing energy consumption by 1% in the member states. The first national efficiency action plans were to be submitted to the European Commission by June 2007. National efficiency action plans can be viewed at: www.ec.europa.eu/energy/demand/legislation/end_use_en.htm#efficiency

UK Government consultations on proposed legislation

Throughout the latter half of 2007, the UK Government issued a number of other consultation documents, with legislation likely to follow. These were:

- ❖ Permitted development rights for householder microgeneration – considers making it easier for homeowners to install microgeneration technology.
- ❖ Planning for a sustainable future – reforming of the planning system.
- ❖ Carbon emissions reduction target – obligation on utilities in response to carbon reduction schemes for consumers.
- ❖ Reform of the Renewable Obligations (Merton Rule).
- ❖ Waste Strategy for England 2007 – alternative for recycling by household – delivering housing and regeneration – the role of communities in England.

JCT Changes to contract

The Joint Contracts Tribunal (JCT) are meeting to consider changes to some of the clauses of the JCT suite of contracts, to enable greater controls on sustainable matters and selection of materials.

Landfill Directive

The Landfill Directive (EEC/1999/31/EC) came into force on 16 July 1999 and is implemented in the UK through the *Landfill (England and Wales) Regulations* 2002, and through equivalent legislation in Scotland and Northern Ireland.

It prohibits **all** businesses from sending non-hazardous waste to landfill without prior treatment. Landfills will no longer be able to accept untreated waste. The main changes are that liquid wastes will be banned from landfill and waste must be treated before it can be land filled (applicable from 30 October 2007). For more information see www.environment-agency.gov.uk/business/1745440/444663/landfill/?version=1&lang=_e

Maintenance management

Primary objectives of maintenance management

It is essential that property owners and managers allocate sufficient time and resources to maintenance. Managers need to be aware of the full extent of maintenance liabilities and how much money should be spent and when. Maintenance management requires a systematic approach to ensure high standards, value for money and management control.

Buildings comprise a number of elements. Their constituent materials and components have a range of life expectancies that in most cases will be shorter than the life of the building as a whole. Maintenance is therefore inevitable and arises from failure at this component level.

The primary objectives of maintenance are:

❖ **Protection of the investment to ensure high utilisation of the building and its long life:** Maintenance affects the profitability of a commercial organisation in a number of ways. First there are the direct costs of labour, plant, materials, and management. The second category is indirect where inadequate maintenance of buildings prevents the organisation from functioning properly.

❖ **Safeguarding the return on the investment:** Poorly maintained commercial buildings fare unfavourably in the market when compared with their well maintained equivalents. The run down of an investment from lack of maintenance will discourage tenants from wishing to remain in occupation. This will have an effect on rent levels and encourage assignments and vacations on termination of leases.

❖ **The control of costs:** Timely, planned maintenance enables efficient use of resources.

❖ **Establishing a safe working environment:** The safety of the building and establishing a safe working environment must be the first priority of the maintenance manager.

Maintenance closes the gap between the actual state of the building and the acceptable standard. The acceptable standard will be dependent upon a number of factors, which may include:

❖ statutory requirements (health and safety);

❖ tenant or occupant satisfaction;

❖ minimising loss of production;

❖ morale of users, employers and customers; and

❖ public image.

A systematic approach to maintenance management

A systematic approach to maintenance management has a number of elements.

Policy

A building may be an asset to an investor or a resource to the user. The maintenance policy defines the objectives that maintenance of the building sets out to achieve. It is a dynamic concept, subject to change, just as the plans and objectives of the user or organisation will change.

Standards have to be defined. The use of 'normal standard' is inadequate. The acceptable range of performance of any element of a building will depend upon the relationship between each of its functional requirements and the use of the building as a whole.

The policy must therefore contain objective criteria to define what constitutes failure or non-conformance in each category. The policy must identify those activities that are sensitive to the physical condition of the building and those building elements that play a significant role in providing the necessary conditions.

Once these components are identified, the acceptable delay time in correcting any failure can be assessed.

The statement of policy constitutes the brief for the maintenance manager. It should cover future requirements of the buildings, changes of use, statutory and legal conditions, maintenance cycles, required standards and acceptable response times for breakdown or failure.

The policy must be regularly reviewed and amended as necessary. Consideration of a maintenance policy often shows that there may be some conflict between parties with different interests, for example, between landlord and tenant.

Survey and data gathering

In order to measure how the buildings compare against the policy, and how to close the gap, it is essential to review all existing maintenance information and to undertake regular condition surveys. These identify the condition of the asset and record the status of the building at any one time. A condition survey has the specific purpose of:

- ❖ identifying maintenance needs;
- ❖ recording the priority of the need;
- ❖ recording proposed remedies and quantities of items requiring attention before the next survey; and
- ❖ predicting the scale of items requiring attention after the next survey.

Planning of work

Having agreed a policy for the organisation and identified work to be done, the first function of the maintenance manager is to formulate a maintenance plan. The objective of planning is to ensure that work is carried out with maximum economy. A key function of maintenance management is to achieve positive control over the work and to avoid overloading or inefficient utilisation of resources. Planned maintenance consists of preventive and corrective work.

- ❖ **Preventive maintenance:** That which is carried out at predetermined intervals and is intended to reduce the probability of failure.
- ❖ **Corrective maintenance:** That which is carried out after failure has occurred and is intended to restore an item to a state in which it can perform its required function.

Generally speaking, the most economic plan in direct cost terms would be the one that maximises preventive maintenance. However, by definition, this form of maintenance takes place before failure has occurred and some degree of useable life has been wasted. This wasted life has a value that can be costed and must be added to the direct cost of the maintenance resource used. The split of work between preventive and corrective maintenance is a management decision. The actual proportion of each will be determined by reference to the maintenance policy.

Plans must take into account practical considerations and the availability of resources. They are prepared with different time horizons for different purposes:

- ❖ Long term – for strategy, to establish general expenditure levels and to profile the maintenance demands of a property or portfolio over an extended time horizon.
- ❖ Medium term – addressing demands that are predicted within the next five years and to refine budgeting and the assessment of workload.
- ❖ Annual – for work and resource allocations.

Organising

The construction of an organisation and a control system capable of ensuring the implementation of the plan.

The main constituents of a maintenance organisation:

- ❖ Resources – i.e. labour, materials, plant and management. These may be either directly employed or obtained through contracts with outside contractors.
- ❖ Administration – a staff structure for coordinating and directing resources.
- ❖ Work planning and control – the system for work, budget, cost and condition control. At its heart lies a documentation procedure, an information base to support effective decision making.

  The documentation system will include a number of elements such as an asset register, a property information base, and preventive maintenance documentation together with a system for initiating and controlling works: works orders, work request forms, etc. These systems are generally computerised. There are a number of proprietary computer programs available. Such programs revolve around relational databases that can be tailored for strategic work, planning and budgeting right through to processing of day-to-day orders for reactive maintenance.

Procuring

A contract and procurement strategy must be established. The strategy will be driven by the nature of anticipated and known workloads and the need to achieve maximum efficiency of operation.

The workload may include the need to provide reactive maintenance cover for unforeseen or accidental repairs, 24-hour emergency call-out cover, planned maintenance contracts and small items of maintenance work packaged into cost-effective contracts.

The decision about which contract and procurement strategy to adopt will depend on a number of factors including the geographic spread of the portfolio in question; the preferred type of model arrangements to be implemented; and the number and type of resources available to the maintenance manager.

Monitoring

Monitoring and auditing is essential to ensure that the maintenance management system is functioning properly and achieving the requirements of the policy statement and if not, to record deficiencies and initiate corrective action.

The maintenance manager needs to monitor the system and organisation to ensure that quality and value for money is being achieved. The audit is a post examination of maintenance work and procedures, not dissimilar to a financial audit. The audit can be condition, technical, systems or design based or a combination of all these.

The condition audit involves the checking of planned maintenance schedules against the actual condition of the building.

The aim of the technical audit is to examine a sample of maintenance activities to investigate how each task has been approached and dealt with.

The systems audit will analyse maintenance management practices. It will establish the true nature and extent of the database being used and how this is stored and accessed. It will look at overall policy and whether or not there are realistic plans and programmes in existence, and at the method used for budget preparation, budget control, and for feedback of information to assist managers in future decision-making.

The design audit concentrates on the interaction between design and building performance. In most cases it is a question of lessons to be learned for the future.

'Best value' in local authorities

What is 'best value'?

The government has defined best value as:

> 'A duty to deliver services to clear standards – covering both cost and quality – by the most economic, efficient and effective means available.'

This clearly has a direct bearing on construction-related services provided by local authorities. The government will require local authorities to publish an annual best value performance plan (BVPP) covering the entire range of the authorities' services. This is intended to be a public document and will include an assessment of the authorities' past and current performance against nationally and locally defined standards.

The performance plan will be the main instrument by which local authorities will be held accountable to the local community for delivering best value.

How are best value studies carried out?

The Audit Commission appoint an external auditor to undertake an audit of the authorities' BVPP. In the case of construction related services this is likely to be a professional consultant in the relevant field. The audit will cover:

❖ compliance with legislation and guidance;

❖ performance information; and

❖ continuous improvement strategies (the 4 Cs – see below).

'The 4 Cs'

Authorities are required to carry out a Best Value Review as part of the BVPP this includes putting in place strategy for continuous improvement implementing the '4 Cs':

❖ **Challenge** – why and how the service is being provided.

❖ **Compare** – with others' performance (including organisations in the private sector) across a range of relevant indicators.

❖ **Consult** – with local taxpayers and service users with the view to setting new performance targets.

❖ **Compete** – as a means of securing efficient and effective services.

More detail regarding the methods of inspection can be seen on the Audit Commission website www.audit-commission.gov.uk

Continuous improvement for construction and property services

A Service Improvement Plan (SIP) is one which identifies areas of potential improvement from:

- ❖ those services already subjected to a Best Value Review;
- ❖ advice from the Audit Commission inspection service; or
- ❖ advice from an external consultant by way of a best value 'healthcheck' (commonly termed a 'critical friend').

Depending on the particular service, the following core issues will be included in the SIP:

- ❖ Description of action – to be taken to improve service.
- ❖ Target – either qualitative or quantitative.
- ❖ Target and timescales – timescale for achieving the improvement(s).
- ❖ Likely effect – impact of the improvement identified.

Other issues which are likely to be included in construction related services could be:

- ❖ current performance;
- ❖ national benchmarks;
- ❖ resource requirements; and
- ❖ monitoring and review strategies.

This overview of best value is intended to give some insight into government efforts in improving services to the taxpayer. When considering the detail of Service Improvement Plans for construction and property related services it is recommended that consultancy advice be sought.

Sources of information in maintenance management

BMI/BCIS – www.bcis.co.uk

Building Maintenance Price Book, published annually

SR 358 *The Economic Significance of Maintenance*, Feb 2007

SR 361 *Review of Maintenance Costs 2007*

SR 362 *Review of Occupancy Costs 2007*

BSRIA – www.bsria.co.uk

AG1/87.1 *Operating and Maintenance Manuals for Building Services Installations 1990*

AG4/89.2 *Maintenance Contracts for Building Engineering Services (2nd edition) 1992*

AG24/97 *Operation and Maintenance Audits 1997*

AG1/98 *Maintenance Programme Set-up 1998*

AG20/99 CD *Cost Benchmarks for the Installation of Building Services Parts 1–3 1999*

AG4/2000 *Condition Survey of Building Services 2000*

AG1/2003 *Condition-based Maintenance: Using Non-destructive Testing 2003*

AG5/2001 *Condition-based Maintenance – an evaluation guide for building services 2001*

BG2/2004 *Computer-based Operating and Maintenance Manuals – Options and Procurement Guidance 2004*

BG7/2004 *Business-focused Maintenance Toolkit 2005*

BG3/2004 *Business-focused Maintenance Sample Schedules 2004*

NJCC

Procedure Note 16, *Record Drawings and Operating and Maintenance Instructions and the health and safety file* (2nd edition), June 1996, RIBA Publications

Note: NJCC no longer in existence, but guidance notes still in general use.

RICS

Building Maintenance: Strategy, Planning and Procurement, RICS guidance note, 2000, RICS Books

Computerised Maintenance Management Systems, A Survey of Performance Requirements, May 1999, RICS Research Paper

Miscellaneous

Building Maintenance Management, B. Chanter, (2nd edition) August 2007, Blackwell Publishing

Lee's Building Maintenance Management, P. Wordsworth, (4th edition) November 2000, Blackwell Science

Strategic Maintenance Planning, A. Kelly, (1st edition) 2006, Butterworth-Heinemann

British Standards in maintenance management

BS 3811	Glossary of Terms in Terotechnology	1993
BS 3843	Guide to Terotechnology	1992
	Pt 2 Introduction to techniques and applications. Pt 3 Guide to the available techniques	1992
BS 6150	Code of Practice for Painting Buildings	2006
BS 6270	Code of Practice for Cleaning and Surface Repair of Buildings Pt 3 metals (cleaning)	1991
BS 7543	Guide to Durability of Buildings and Building Elements Products and Components	2003
BS ISO 15686	Buildings and constructed assets. Service life planning. General principles	2000
	Pt 2 Service Life Prediction Procedures	2001
	Pt 3 Performance Audits and Reviews	2002
	Pt 6 Procedures for considering environmental impacts	2004
	Pt 7 Performance evaluation for feedback of service life data from practice	2006
BS 8210	Guide to Building Maintenance Management	1986
BS 8221	Code of Practice for Cleaning and Surface Repair of Buildings	
	Pt 1 Cleaning of natural stones, brick, terracotta and concrete	2000
	Pt 2 Surface repair of natural stones, brick and terracotta	2000

APC student help

The RICS Assessment of Professional Competence

What is it?

The Assessment of Professional Competence (APC) is a route to professional membership of the Royal Institution of Chartered Surveyors (RICS). There are 21 APC pathways, which relate to land, property, construction and the environment. For example, Watts have a graduate training programme specifically for graduates following the Building Surveying, Quantity Surveying and Project Management pathways.

Successfully completing the APC entitles RICS members to practice as qualified chartered surveyors and put the letters MRICS after their names. There are a number of routes to membership and details of these, the APC pathways and specific requirements are set out on the RICS website.

What does it involve?

Candidates are required to be in suitable employment with a firm that has an RICS approved structured training agreement. They will complete a period of structured training, normally for a minimum of 24 months, although this depends upon the entry route. During this period they are allocated an APC Counsellor and Supervisor who will give them guidance on their training and day-to-day work.

The APC training is competency-based and candidates are required to demonstrate that they have the skills and abilities to satisfy specific competencies. Details of requirements for each pathway are set out in *RICS APC/ATC Requirements and competencies*, July 2006.

Assessment takes the form of a submission and professional interview. Candidates are required to make a presentation to a panel of RICS assessors and answer detailed questions relating to their work experience and wider issues.

In addition to achieving specific competency levels, candidates are required to demonstrate that they are:

- ❖ confident to work unsupervised;
- ❖ a good ambassador for the profession;
- ❖ aware of the professional and commercial implications of their work;
- ❖ able to understand their clients' and employer's objectives; and
- ❖ up to date with relevant technical and legal matters.

How do candidates enrol?

To apply for the APC candidates should contact RICS who will send them a résumé form to fill out and return. Once RICS has assessed their eligibility it will send candidates the relevant application form.

Ten APC tips

1. Choose your employer wisely – Attempt to gauge a firm's commitment to graduate training by enquiring about the level of support and training offered. It is also essential to gain the correct spread of work experience during your training period to satisfy relevant competency requirements.

2. Get organised – The timing of your APC application and other submissions can be critical. For example, a delay in your enrolment could hold up your final assessment by six months. Clarify requirements and diarise key dates and milestones.

3. Carefully consider competency choice – You should do some research and set about gaining good advice in relation to competency choices from your employer and colleagues who have recently undertaken their APC. It is essential to ensure that there is a 'fit' with the range and nature of work you will be undertaking.

4. Get out and about – There is no substitute for quality one-to-one on-the-job training; so try to ensure that you make the most of shadowing opportunities from the outset of your training period.

5. Take ownership of your training – Make time to administer your APC paperwork and proactively set about identifying and planning your own training needs and work experience requirements. Your Supervisor and Counsellor should help with this.

6. Network and get advice – Join in with company activities, speak to colleagues about their experience of the APC, consult with your local RICS APC Doctor, and get involved with RICS MATRICS, the organisation for young chartered surveyors, trainees and graduates. You will benefit from advice, broaden your perspective of the profession and, as importantly, have fun and make lifelong friendships.

7. Professional approach – Keeping abreast of current trends and hot topics is essential. Reading relevant property and industry magazines and keeping up to date with changes in legislation, etc. will help build your confidence as a rounded professional.

8. Personal development – You will need to develop personal skills during the course of your training period in preparation for the final assessment. Good time management, organisation and presentation skills are essential. These cannot be attained at the last minute.

9. Technical competence – Continually develop your technical ability. Be resourceful, grow interest in your subject area, attend seminars and undertake structured reading relevant to your workload.

10. Prepare for the final assessment – Ask experienced colleagues to conduct a mock final assessment interview. Receive feedback, refine your presentation and repeat as necessary.

Contact details

Royal Institution of Chartered Surveyors

RICS Contact Centre

Surveyor Court

Westwood Way

Coventry CV4 8JE

Website: www.rics.org and www.rics.org/matrics

Email: contactrics@rics.org

Telephone: +44 (0)870 333 1600

Graduate Recruitment

Watts Academy

Watts Group PLC

1 Great Tower Street

London EC3R 5AA

Website: www.watts-international.com

Email: helen.farrow@watts-int.com

Telephone: +44 (0)20 7280 8000

Useful references

These guides are all available to download free on the RICS website:

- ❖ *RICS APC/ATC Requirements and competencies*, July 2006
- ❖ *RICS APC Candidate's guide – graduate route to membership*, July 2006
- ❖ *RICS APC Guide for supervisors, counsellors and employers – graduate route to membership*, July 2006

Technical resources

Technical resources

Conversion factors

Within the lists below, to convert the units in column A into the equivalent in column B, multiply by the factor shown. To convert the units in column B into the equivalent in column A, divide by the factor shown.

Units in Column A	Factor	To give units in Column B
Atmospheres (atm)	0.007348	Ton/sq inch
atm	76.0	cm of mercury
atm	14.70	pounds/sq in.
atm	1,058	tons/sq ft
bars	10,200	kgm^{-2}
bars	2,089	pounds/sq ft
bars	14.50	pounds/sq in.
Btu	10.409	litre-atmosphere
Btu	1,054.8	joules
Btu	0.0002928	kWh
Btu/hr	0.2931	Watts (W)
cm	0.03281	feet
cm	0.3937	inches
cm	0.00001	km
cm	0.01	m
cm	10	mm
cm^2	0.001076	sq feet
cm^2	0.1550	sq inches
cm^2	0.0001	m^2
cm^2	100.0	mm^2
cm^2	0.0001196	sq yards
cm^3	0.0003531	cu feet
cm^3	0.06102	cu inches
cm^3	0.000001	m^3
cm^3	0.000001308	cu yards
cm^3	0.0002642	gallons (US liq.)
cm^3	0.001	litres
cm^3	0.002113	pints (US liq.)
cm^3	0.001057	quarts (US liq.)
cubic feet	28,320.0	cm^3
cubic feet	1,728.0	cu inches
cubic feet	0.02832	m^3
cubic feet	0.03704	cu yards
cubic feet	7.48052	gallons (US liq.)

Units in Column A	Factor	To give units in Column B
cubic feet	28.32	litres
cubic feet	59.84	pints (US liq.)
cubic feet	29.92	quarts (US liq.)
cubic inches	16.39	cm³
cubic inches	0.0005787	cu feet
cubic inches	0.00001639	m³
cubic inches	0.00002143	cu yards
cubic inches	0.004329	gallons (US liq.)
cubic inches	0.01639	litres
cubic inches	0.03463	pints (US liq.)
cubic inches	0.01732	quarts (US liq.)
cubic inches	28.38	bushels (dry)
m³	1,000,000	cm³
m³	35.31	cu feet
m³	61,023	cu inches
m³	1.308	cu yards
m³	264.2	gallons (US liq.)
m³	1,000	litres
m³	2,113	pints (US liq.)
m³	1,057	quarts (US liq.)
cubic yards	764,600	cm³
cubic yards	27	cu feet
cubic yards	46,656	cu inches
cubic yards	0.7646	m³
cubic yards	202	gallons (US liq.)
cubic yards	764.6	litres
cubic yards	1,615.9	pints (US liq.)
cubic yards	807.9	quarts (US liq.)
cubic yards/min	0.45	cubic ft/sec
cubic yards/min	3.367	gallons/sec
cubic yards/min	12.74	litres/sec
days	86,400	seconds
drams	1.7718	grammes
drams	0.0625	ounces
feet	30.48	cm
feet	0.0003048	km
feet	0.3048	m
feet	0.0001645	miles (naut.)
feet	0.0001984	miles (stat.)

Units in Column A	Factor	To give units in Column B
feet	304.8	mm
feet/sec	30.48	cm/sec
feet/sec	1.097	km/hr
feet/sec	0.5921	knots
feet/sec	18.29	m/min
feet/sec	0.6818	miles/hr
feet/sec	0.01136	miles/min
gallons	0.004951	cu yards
gallons	3.785	litres
gallons (liq. Br. Imp.)	1.20095	gallons (US liq.)
gallons (US liq.)	0.83267	gallons (Br. Imp.)
gallons of water	8.3453	pounds of water
gallons/min	0.0002228	cu ft/sec
gallons/min	0.06308	litres/sec
gallons/min	8.0208	cu ft/hr
grammes	0.001	kg
grammes	1,000	mg
grammes	0.03527	ounces (avdp)
grammes	0.03215	ounces (troy)
grammes	0.002205	pounds
horsepower	33,000	foot-lbs/min
horsepower	550	foot-lbs/sec
horsepower	10/68	kg-calories/min
horsepower	0.7457	Kilowatts (kW)
horsepower	745.7	watts
inches	2.540	cm
inches	0.002540	m
inches	25.40	mm
joules	0.0009480	Btu
kg	1,000	grammes
kg	9.807	joules/metre (newtons)
kg	2.205	pounds
kgm^{-2}	0.00009678	atmospheres
kgm^{-2}	0.00009807	bars
kgm^{-2}	0.003281	feet of water
kgm^{-2}	0.002896	inches of mercury
kgm^{-2}	0.2048	pounds/sq ft
km	3,281	feet
km	39,370	inches

Units in Column A	Factor	To give units in Column B
km	0.6214	miles
km/hr	27.78	cms/sec
km/hr	54.68	feet/min
km/hr	0.9113	feet/sec
km/hr	0.5396	knots
km/hr	16.67	m/min
km/hr	0.6214	miles/hr
kWh	3,413	Btu
kw	56.92	Btu/min
kw	1,000	watts
litres	1,000	cm³
litres	0.03531	cu feet
litres	61.02	cu inches
litres	0.001	m³
litres	0.001308	cu yards
litres	0.2642	gallons (US liq.)
litres	2.113	pints (US liq.)
litres	1.057	quarts (US liq.)
m	0.0005396	miles (naut.)
m	0.0006214	miles (stat.)
m	1,000	mm
m	1.094	yards
metres per min (m/min)	1.667	cm/sec
m/min	3.281	feet/min
m/min	0.05468	feet/sec
m/min	0.06	km/hr
m/min	0.03238	knots
m/min	0.03728	miles/hr
m/sec	196.8	feet/min
m/sec	3.281	feet/sec
m/sec	3.6	km/hr
m/sec	0.06	km/min
m/sec	2.237	miles/hr
m/sec	0.03728	miles/min
miles (statute)	5,280	feet
miles (statute)	63,360	inches
miles (statute)	1.609	km
miles (statute)	1,609	metres (m)
miles (statute)	0.868357	miles (nautical)

Units in Column A	Factor	To give units in Column B
miles (statute)	1,760	yards
miles/hr	44.70	cm/sec
miles/hr	88	feet/min
miles/hr	1.467	feet/sec
miles/hr	1.609	km/hr
miles/hr	0.02682	km/min
miles/hr	0.8684	knots
miles/hr	26.82	m/min
miles/hr	0.1667	miles/min
ml	0.001	litres
mm	0.1	cm
mm	0.003281	feet
mm	0.03937	inches
mm	0.000001	km
mm	0.001	m
ounces	0.0625	pounds
ounces	0.9115	ounces (troy)
pounds/cu ft	0.01602	grammes/cm^3
pounds/cu ft	16.02	kg/m^{-3}
pounds/sq in.	703.1	kgm^{-2}
pounds/sq in.	144	pounds/sq ft
quarts	0.9463	litres
square feet	0.00002296	acres
square feet	929.0	cm^2
square feet	144.0	sq inches
square feet	0.0929	m^2
square feet	0.1111	sq yards
watts	3.413	Btu/hr
watts	0.05688	Btu/min
watts	0.001341	horsepower
watts	0.001360	horsepower (metric)
watts	0.01433	kg-calories/min
watts	0.001	kilowatts

To convert temperature

°C = 5/9 (°F) − 32

°F = 9/5 (°C) + 32

Useful information sources

Agencies and Public Bodies
T: 020 7276 2040
Web: www.civilservice.gov.uk/other/agencies

Association for Project Management
T: 08454 581944 Web: www.apm.org.uk

Association of British Insurers
T: 020 7600 3333 Web: www.abi.org.uk

Association of Building Engineers
T: 0845 126 1058 Web: www.abe.org.uk

Association of Consultant Approved Inspectors
T: 020 7491 1914 Web: www.acai.org.uk

Barbour Expert-online to the built environment
T: 01344 899 280 Web: www.barbour-index.co.uk

Boundary Problems
T: 023 8036 1344 Web: www.boundary-problems.co.uk

BRE Certification Ltd
T: 01923 664100 Web: www.brecertification.co.uk

BREEAM
T: 01923 664462 Web: www.breeam.org

British Cement Association
T: 01276 608700 Web: www.cementindustry.co.uk

British Council for Offices
T: 020 7283 0125 Web: www.bco.org.uk

British Geological Survey
T: 0115 936 3143 Web: www.bgs.ac.uk

British Institute of Facilities Management
T: 0845 058 1356 Web: www.bifm.org.uk

British Property Federation
T: 020 7828 0111 Web: www.bpf.org.uk

British Standards Institution
T: 020 8996 9001 Web: www.bsi-global.com

Building
T: 020 7921 5000 Web: www.building.co.uk

Building Conservation
T: 01747 871717 Web: www.buildingconservation.com

Building Cost Information Service Ltd
T: 020 7695 1500 Web: www.bcis.co.uk

Building Maintenance Information
T: 020 7695 1500 Web: www.bcis.co.uk

Building Research Establishment
T: 01923 664000 Web: www.bre.co.uk

Building Services Research and Information Association
T: 01344 465600 Web: www.bsria.co.uk

Businessparks.net
T: 020 8658 8000 Web: www.businessparks.net

Centre for Accessible Environments
T: 020 7840 0125 Web: www.cae.org.uk

Centre for Window and Cladding Technology
T: 01225 386541 Web: www.cwct.co.uk

Chartered Institute of Arbitrators
T: 020 7421 7444 Web: www.arbitrators.org

Chartered Institute of Building
T: 01344 630700 Web: www.ciob.org.uk

Commission for Architecture and the Built Environment
T: 020 7070 6700 Web: www.cabe.org.uk

Compliance+
T: 020 7549 3300 Web: www.ciria.org/complianceplus/

Concrete Repair Association
T: 01252 357 835 Web: www.concreterepair.org.uk

Concrete Society
T: 01276 607140 Web: www.concrete.org.uk

Construction Best Practice Program
T: 0845 605 55 56 Web: www.constructingexcellence.org.uk

Construction Europe
T: 01892 784088 Web: www.khl.com

Construction Health and Safety Group
T: 01932 561871 Web: www.chsg.co.uk

Construction Industry Council
T: 020 7399 7400 Web: www.cic.org.uk

Construction Industry Research and Information Association (CIRIA)
T: 020 7549 3300 Web: www.ciria.org.uk

Construction Line
T: 0870 240 0152 Web: www.constructionline.co.uk

Construction Plus
T: 0906 326 3766 Web: www.constructionplus.co.uk

Construction Research and Innovation Strategy Panel (CRISP)
T: 020 7592 1100 Web: www.ncrisp.org.uk

Construct Sustainably
Web: www.constructsustainably.co.uk

Contamlinks
Web: www.contamlinks.co.uk

Corrosion Prevention Association
T: 01252 357 834 Web: www.corrosionprevention.org.uk

Countyweb
T: Freephone 0800 980 2425 or 01926 431552
Web: www.countyweb.co.uk

Court Service
Web: www.courtservice.gov.uk

DDA Tax Guidance
T: 0845 010 9000
Web: www.inlandrevenue.gov.uk/specialist/disability-act-guidance.htm

Department for Communities and Local Government
T: 020 7944 4400 Web: www.communities.gov

Department for Environment, Food and Rural Affairs (Defra)
T: 08459 335577 Web: www.defra.gov.uk

Design Council
T: 020 7420 5200 Web: www.designcouncil.org.uk

DfES Public Private Partnerships
Web: www.dfes.gov.uk/ppppfi

Disability Rights Commission
T: 08457 622633 Web: www.drc-gb.org

Energy Watch
T: 08459 06 07 08 Web: www.energywatch.org.uk

English Heritage
T: 08703 331181 Web: www.english-heritage.org.uk

Environment Agency
T: 08708 506506 Web: www.environment-agency.gov.uk

Environmental Organisation Web Directory
Web: www.webdirectory.com

European Forecasting Group for the Construction Industry
Web: www.euroconstruct.org

Fire Protection Association
T: 01608 812500 Web: www.thefpa.co.uk

Glass & Glazing Federation
T: 0870 0424255 Web: www.ggf.org.uk

Health and Safety Executive
T: 0845 345 0055 Web: www.hse.gov.uk

HM Land Registry
T: 020 7917 8888 Web: www.landreg.gov.uk

HM Treasury – PFI
T: 020 7270 4558 Web: www.hm-treasury.gov.uk

House Builders Federation
T: 020 7960 1600 Web: www.hbf.co.uk

Institution of Civil Engineering Surveyors
T: 0161 972 3100 Web: www.ices.org.uk

Institution of Structural Engineers
T: 020 7235 4535 Web: www.istructe.org.uk

isurv – surveyors' information centre
T: 020 7695 1777 Web: www.isurv.com

Joint Contracts Tribunal
T: 020 7637 8650 Web: www.jctltd.co.uk

Landlord Zone
T: 0845 260 4420 Web: www.landlordzone.co.uk

Lead Development Association
T: 020 7499 8422 Web: www.ldaint.org

Mastic Asphalt Council
T: 01424 814400 Web: www.masticasphaltcouncil.co.uk

National Green Specification
Web: www.greenspec.co.uk

National Trust
T: 01793 817400 Web: www.nationaltrust.org.uk

NetRegs
T: 0870 8506 506 Web: www.netregs.gov.uk

Official Journal of the European Union
T: 01224 636999 Web: www.ojec.com

PPP Forum
T: 020 7842 5610 Web: www.pppforum.com/

Public Private Finance
T: 020 7970 4827 Web: www.publicprivatefinance.com

Pyramus & Thisbe
T: 028 4063 2082 Web: www.partywalls.org.uk

Radiation Protection Division (part of the Centre for Radiation, Chemical
and Environmental Hazards)
T: 01235 831600 Web: www.hpa.org.uk/radiation/

Radon Centres Ltd
T: 01604 494118 Web: www.radon.co.uk

RIBA Bookshops
T: 020 7256 7222 Web: www.ribabookshops.com

RICS Books
T: 0870 333 1600 (option 3) Web: www.ricsbooks.com

Royal Forestry Society
T: 01442 822028 Web: www.rfs.org.uk

Royal Institute of British Architects
T: 020 7580 5533 Web: www.architecture.com

Royal Institution of Chartered Surveyors (RICS)
T: 0870 333 1600 Web: www.rics.org

Royal Institution of Chartered Surveyors in Scotland
T: 0131 225 7078 Web: www.rics.org

Service Charges Guide
Web: www.servicechargeguide.propertymall.com

SIMAP
Web: www.simap.eu.int/

Society of Construction Law
T: 01235 770606 Web: www.scl.org.uk

Society of Expert Witnesses
T: 0163 866 0684 Web: www.sew.org.uk

Society of Property Researchers
T: 01206 298205 Web: www.sprweb.co.uk

Stone Federation Great Britain
T: 01303 856123 Web: www.stone-federationgb.org.uk

Tenders Electronic Daily (TED)
Web: www.ted.europa.eu

The Stationery Office Bookshop
T: 0870 242 2345 Web: www.tsoshop.co.uk

The Survey Association
T: 0163 664 2840 Web: www.tsa-uk.org.uk

Timber Research and Development Association
T: 01494 569600 Web: www.trada.co.uk

Timber Trade Federation
T: 020 3205 0067 Web: www.ttf.co.uk

UK Online Government
Web: www.direct.gov.uk

UK Taxation Directory
Web: www.uktax.demon.co.uk

Whole Life Cost Forum
Web: www.wlcf.org.uk

Contributors to the Watts Pocket Handbook

External contributors

The scope of the Watts Pocket Handbook would not be possible without the cooperation of external professionals who have dedicated their expertise and valued time to produce specialist information for inclusion in the publication. For this help and support, Watts would like to express their sincere appreciation to the following:

Building and construction
Adjudication Under the Scheme for Construction Contracts – how to get started
Dispute resolution
Expert witness
The Provisions of Part II of the Housing Grants, Construction and Regeneration Act 1996

Suzanne Reeves
Wedlake Bell
52 Bedford Row
London WC1R 4LR
T: 020 7395 3168
E: sreeves@wedlakebell.com

Building and construction
Part L 2006 compliance

Arlo Mills
Gleeds
95 New Cavendish Street
London W1W 6XF
T: 020 7631 7000
E: arlo.mills@gleeds.co.uk

Building services design
Air-conditioning systems
Data installations
Lift terminology
Lighting design
Plant and equipment
Sustainability
Energy conservation
Renewable energy

Keith Crosby
Watkins Payne Partnership
51 Staines Road West
Sunbury-on-Thames
Middlesex TW16 7AH
T: 01932 781641
E: keithcrosby@ wppgroup.co.uk

Cost management
Capital allowances
Land remediation tax relief

Chris Doyle
Yewell Consulting LLP
1 Hall Road
Wallington
Surrey SM6 0RT
T: 020 8544 4810
E: chris.doyle@yewell.co.uk

Cost management
Rating revaluation 2005

David Shortall
Alexander Reece Thomson
11 Welbeck Street
London W1G 9XZ
T: 020 7486 1681
E: davidshortall@artbg.co.uk

Geomatics
Geomatics

Simon Barnes
Plowman Craven
141 Lower Luton Road
Harpenden
Hertfordshire AL5 5EQ
T: 01582 765566
E: sbarnes@plowman craven.co.uk

Legislation
Appeals and called-in applications
Development applications and fees
Development plans and monitoring
General Development Order and Use
  Classes Order

Alan Gunne-Jones
Tribal MJP
87–91 Newman Street
London W1T 3EY
T: 020 8289 1800
E: alan.gunne-jones@tribalmjp.co.uk

Watts' contributors

A basic introduction to structures	Trevor Rushton
A systematic approach to maintenance management	Steve Brewer
Access agreements	Paul Lovelock
Achieving excellence in construction	Spencer Carroll
Airtightness	Trevor Rushton
Alkali aggregate reactions	Trevor Rushton
Asbestos	Paul Winstone
Basic design data	Sarah Houlden, Michael Lee
BCO best practice for new offices and fitting out works	Michael Lee
Best practice in building surveys	Trevor Rushton
'Best value' in local authorities	Stuart Russell
Building Research Establishment Environmental Assessment Method	Mark Ratcliff
The Building Act 1984 and the Building (Amendment) Regulations 2004	Trevor Rushton
Building into the basement	Allen Gilham
Building Regulations and historic building conservation	Martin Shaw
Building types	Sarah Houlden, Michael Lee
Chemical and physical testing requirements	Trevor Rushton
Chlorides	Trevor Rushton
Collateral warranties and reliance letters	Paul Lovelock
Common defects in commercial and residential properties	Trevor Rushton
Compensation for flooding	Kelvin Naylor, Roger Stanton
Composite panels	Trevor Rushton
Condensation and toxic moulds	Allen Gilham
The Construction (Design and Management) Regulations 2007	Paul Winstone
The Construction (Health, Safety and Welfare) Regulations 1996	Paul Winstone
Construction management	John Watson
Construction noise and vibration	Paul Lovelock, Keith Martin
The contract administrator's role	John Edwards
Contract insurance	Jon Evans
Contractor appointment/tendering	Tim Brock
Conversion factors	Angela Dawson, Trevor Rushton
Corrosion of metals	Phil Kirby, Trevor Rushton
Cost management	Christopher Knott
Curtain walling systems	Jane Dalgliesh, Trevor Rushton
Daylight and sunlight amenity	Paul Lovelock
Defects in concrete	Trevor Rushton
Deleterious materials	Trevor Rushton
Development monitoring	Rebecca Jermy
Dilapidations	Jon Rowling
The Disability Discrimination Act and access for disabled people	Mark Ratcliff
Discovery of building defects – statutory time limits	Paul Lovelock
Employer's agent	Christopher Knott

Rising damp	Trevor Rushton
Rising groundwater	Trevor Rushton
Section 18 (1) of the Landlord and Tenant Act 1927	Jon Rowling
Site archaeology	Allen Gilham
Soil survey	Graeme Lees
Soils and foundation design	Trevor Rushton
Sources of information in maintenance management	Angela Dawson
Specification writing	Jon Evans
Specifications	Jon Evans
Spontaneous glass fracturing	Trevor Rushton
Standard form contracts	Robert Lane
Steel frame corrosion (Regent Street disease)	Trevor Rushton
Structural engineering	Graeme Lees
Subsidence	Trevor Rushton
The surveyor's role in flooding	Kelvin Naylor, Roger Stanton
Sustainable development	Robert Burke
Tenant fit out and licences to alter	Michael Kirkman
Tender prices and building cost indices	Prince Damankah, Tim French
Thin stone cladding	Trevor Rushton
Troublesome plant growth – Giant Hogweed	Trevor Rushton
Troublesome plant growth – Japanese Knotweed	Trevor Rushton
Types of specification	Jon Evans
Types of tendering route	John Edwards
Useful information sources	Angela Dawson
Value engineering	Christopher Knott
VAT in the construction industry – zero rating	Stuart Russell
Vendor surveys	Trevor Rushton
Watts' publications	Duncan Coombs, Samantha Rumens
The Work at Height Regulations 2005	Paul Winstone
The Workplace Regulations – Glazing	Trevor Rushton
The Workplace Regulations – Falls from height	Paul Winstone
The Workplace Regulations – Lighting	Paul Winstone, Neil Wotherspoon
The Workplace Regulations – Provision of sanitary facilities	Paul Winstone

Envest contributors

Contaminated land	Toby Andrews
Electromagnetic fields	Toby Andrews, Janette McCartney
Environmental impact assessments	Gordon Smith
Environmental Liability Directive	Janette McCartney
Forecasting floods	Toby Andrews, Joe Lawrence
Ground gas including radon	Toby Andrews
Ozone depleting substances	Toby Andrews, Tim Coffin
Water Framework Directive	Toby Andrews, Tim Coffin

ikon contributors

Code for Sustainable Homes	Chris Cheeseman
Urban regeneration	Nick Cook

Watts' publications

For further information on any of the following publications, please contact Samantha Rumens, Marketing Production Manager, Watts' Marketing Department. Tel: +44 (0)20 7280 8000. Email: marketing@watts-int.com

Watts website

watts-international.com

The Watts website gives an overview of the business and includes information about our staff, teams, news and history. It also houses all contact details, career information, service scope literature and case study examples.

Watts Review and Accounts

This annual report document, published in October, provides a flavour of the businesses' activities and an overview of the people, personality, values, financial performance and plans for our future.

Watts Review and Accounts 2006–2007 looks at Watts' successes and achievements over the last 12 months. It illustrates Watts' significant European expansion and outlines ambitious plans for the future. Hard copy and PDF versions are available on request from the Watts Marketing department.

Watts Bulletin

The Watts Bulletin is the technical companion to the *Watts Pocket Handbook*, keeping its readership abreast of industry news, every month. It covers a variety of topics, including environmental issues, health and safety, new materials and the latest techniques within the industry. It is distributed to selected clients and contacts in hard or digital copy. Subscription is complimentary and available on request from the Watts Marketing department. Back copies of the Bulletin are also available on the Watts website.

Practice Profile

The Profile provides a comprehensive overview of Watts' offices, services, performance and procedures, and is presented, as a matter of course, when tendering for new business. The Practice Profile is updated monthly and is available in a variety of languages, e.g. Dutch, Spanish, Swedish, French and German. All versions of the Profile are available on request from the Watts Marketing department and the English-language version is available on the website.

See also the RICS Books' publication pages for publications written by Watts' employees as authors and published by RICS Books.

RICS Books' publications

RICS Books publishes a range of authoritative, practical and essential books for surveyors. All books can be purchased by telephoning mail order on 0870 333 1600 (option 2) or by email at mailorder@rics.org

There is also an online bookshop www.ricsbooks.com with over 12,000 relevant publications, contracts and electronic services for property professionals.

Key titles include:

Investigating Hazardous and Deleterious Building Materials

Trevor Rushton

Price: £49.95

Item code: 9898

Written by Trevor Rushton, Partner at Watts, and published by RICS Books, this book provides a first point of reference and practical guidance to the identification and treatment of problems associated with some types of building materials. It brings together the essentials of a wide range of different materials and forms of construction over the years that:

- ❖ may have been found to be hazardous to persons or to the environment;
- ❖ may have been considered to be deleterious;
- ❖ might have been regarded as being problematical in some way; and
- ❖ would probably be labelled as deleterious if they had their chance again.

It gives advice on:

- ❖ the nature of the material;
- ❖ its normal use;
- ❖ problem areas;
- ❖ methods of diagnosis and analysis; and
- ❖ methods of repair.

Investigating Hazardous and Deleterious Building Materials also examines the history of the use of the materials in question and guidance to the ages and types of building most at risk.

It is essential reading for building surveyors, home inspectors, building engineers, architects, facilities managers, students and other built environment professionals.

About the author

Trevor Rushton FRICS FBEng has over 25 years' experience in commercial building surveying. A Partner at Watts since 1990, Trevor specialises in building engineering and technology and is a prolific writer and speaker on technical topics. He is editor-in-chief of the regular Watts Bulletin publication and has written the chapters on materials and defects for *isurv building surveying* for which he is also one of the consultant editors. Trevor is a Fellow of both the Royal Institution of Chartered Surveyors (RICS) and the Association of Building Engineers (ABE).

Surveying Buildings

Malcolm Hollis
Price: £60

Item code: 7859

Established as the leading surveying text and a must for all building surveyors and students. It is full of practical advice based on Malcolm Hollis' experience of thousands of real-life surveys. Written in a lively style and packed with colour photographs, diagrams and charts, an essential companion to any building inspection.

Pocket Surveying Buildings

Malcolm Hollis
Price: £22.50

Item code: 9114

The ideal on-site companion, this book is a handy pocket size and the ideal companion to the main work *Surveying Buildings* by the same author. Practical and user-friendly this book will be an essential companion on all your home inspections.

Diagnosing Damp

Ralph Burkinshaw and Mike Parrett
Price: £49.95

Item code: 6090

Diagnosing Damp provides you with the knowledge and tools to understand the causes of dampness in buildings and is packed full of features, diagrams and photographs to aid correct diagnosis.

Cracking and Building Movement – Book and CD ROM

Peter R. Dickinson and Nigel Thornton
Price: £49.95 (plus VAT on CD ROM)

Item code: 7273

This book provides practising building surveyors, structural engineers and construction professionals with a true one-stop guide to inspection, diagnosis, reporting and repair of cracking problems in buildings.

DDA and Access: a Surveyor's Handbook

Mark Ratcliff
Price: £39.95

Item code: 16546

Written by Mark Ratcliff, Associate with Watts, *Access and the DDA: A Surveyor's Handbook* is a practical aid to interpreting, understanding and applying the requirements of the *Disability Discrimination Act* 1995 (as amended by the *Special Educational Needs and Disability Act* 2001 and the *Disability Discrimination Act* 2005).

Access and inclusive design is a complex topic area, which is constantly evolving. This handbook will get you up to date and cut through the confusion by providing a comprehensive, definitive guide to the last 11 years of the DDA legislation in its application to property. There are also practical sections, including design guidance, standards and best practice to assist in both audit and design work, in addition to including useful advice to assist in advising clients.

isurv has evolved ... evolve with us

isurv is an online database of best practice guidance. It has over 120 contributors (including a number from Watts) providing expert commentary on surveying issues, and contains RICS guidance notes, model letters, forms and a case-law database. It is updated twice a month and is an ideal reference resource for surveyors.

For more information on *isurv* and to take out a free trial, please go to www.isurv.com or email isurv@rics.org